ALRA
www.alra.co.uk

HYMNS
ANCIENT & MODERN
REVISED

HYMNS
ANCIENT & MODERN
REVISED

ORGAN EDITION

HYMNS ANCIENT & MODERN LIMITED

ISBN 0 907547 09 5

Hymns Ancient & Modern Ltd.
St. Mary's Works, St. Mary's Plain
Norwich, Norfolk NR3 3BH

New Imprint

First Impression	July 1981
Second Impression	February 1983
Third Impression	June 1984
Fourth Impression	November 1986

Printed and bound in Great Britain by
Anchor Brendon Ltd
Tiptree, Essex

INDEX TO
PRELIMINARY MATTER

PREFACE

HYMNS ANCIENT AND MODERN was first published (in a form complete with music) in 1861. It was an attempt to consolidate the hymn-books, Anglican and others, which had appeared in the previous hundred years or more and had now become very numerous. It soon became something of a national institution. The Proprietors, a body of Church of England clergymen, found themselves almost embarrassed by the success of their undertaking. An appendix was added in 1868. A revised edition appeared in 1875, to which a Supplement was added in 1889. A new edition, published in 1904, did not succeed in replacing the old book, which with a Second Supplement (1916) has continued to be the most widely used Hymnal of the Church of England. The Standard Edition dates from 1922, when it was reset and many improvements were introduced.

The Proprietors, five in number, were appointed under a Trust Deed. They nominated Assessors to aid them. After certain deductions authorized by the Trust Deed, the whole of the profits on the book was paid to a body of Trustees who distributed them to charities in accordance with the instructions of the Proprietors. It was the custom of the Proprietors to make a donation to the Central Board of Finance of the Church of England a first charge on the sum available for charitable donations. The Rev. Sir Henry Baker was the first Chairman of the Proprietors. Among his successors, Bishop W. H. Frere and Sir Sydney Nicholson may be specially mentioned.

The Musical Editors have been as follows: Dr. W. H. Monk (helped by the Rev. Sir F. A. Gore-Ouseley) from 1861 to 1889; then Dr. C. Steggall for the 1889 Supplement. The music of the 1904 edition was edited by Mr. B. Luard Selby, the Supplement of 1916 by Sir Sydney Nicholson, who continued to be Musical Editor until his death in 1947. In the preparation of the edition now published Sir Sydney was assisted by Mr. G. H. Knight and Dr. J. Dykes Bower.

The shaping of *Hymns Ancient and Modern Revised* has been a task of much labour, and the Proprietors had a good hope that it would be welcomed by the large public for whom it was designed, as preserving the general tone and character which the book has always had and at the same time making it more serviceable both by what it adds and by what it omits.

Preface

The cumbrous device of two Supplements was inconvenient in itself and had made the book too large. It will be seen that the hymns are now arranged in one series of not much over 600 in all. In order to effect this reduction and to make room for new matter the Editors were obliged to leave out a good number of hymns. These fell into two distinct classes. The first was of those which had never really found favour. It was easy to cut them out, but there were not enough of them to meet the whole of the necessary reduction. The second class was of those which the Editors felt could well be spared, yet undoubtedly they were endeared to quite a number of congregations. Most of these had to go on the assumption that they were not likely to last much longer. They were bound in the end to be discarded, the Editors thought, and by a justifiable anticipation might be discarded now. Sometimes a favourite hymn may therefore seem to be missing, but the Editors believe that prevailing tendencies would have swept it away before long. They have tried to respect the strong power of association which operates in the minds of hymn-singers by preserving, where possible, the old numbers in the earlier part of the book. A few hymns which have recently become popular are absent owing to copyright difficulties.

Of the hymns to be found in this book which have not appeared in previous editions of *Hymns Ancient and Modern*, the greater number are old hymns which have been successfully resuscitated in one place or another and have won a wide acceptance and so have become such as no hymn-book could well omit. The Editors have brought in a certain number of new hymns, mainly to satisfy a particular need or occasion, or to match a good tune with fitting words.

The book does not always adhere to the original text of the hymns. The Editors of the earlier editions made alterations to meet the requirements of a hymn-singing congregation, and the present Editors see no reason to go back upon the practice of their predecessors. Many of the great Charles Wesley's hymns have hardly ever been sung as he originally wrote them. Not a few authors, including Dr. Neale, have agreed that for the purpose of a hymn-book the versions of their hymns in *Hymns Ancient and Modern* were, on the whole, improvements. The case for alteration has been considered on its merits, and in many hymns the author's text has been restored. In others, however, the emended text has been retained as more convenient and having the sanction of long usage.

The provision of hymns to be sung in Procession has been very much increased and made more methodical. On the other hand, from some hymns which seemed over-long for ordinary use one or more verses have been omitted where this appeared not to spoil the effect as a whole.

Preface

In concluding what has been the labour of many years, the Proprietors expressed a hope that in this new book the Church will find the same endearing and enduring qualities as in the old, the same heartfelt yet sober tone, so much in keeping with English-speaking Christianity. At the same time they believed that what is new in sense and sound will commend itself as a real augmentation of the rich treasury of hymns and hymn-tunes which are now employed in the divine praises and catholic teaching of the Christian Church. The new book does not aim at breaking fresh ground or exploiting novel ideas. The hope is that it may prove to be, as it was before, a consolidation of all that has been gained over many a long year since the wholesome practice of hymn-singing won an accepted place in Church, School and Home.

The old or Standard edition will continue to be printed so long as the demand for it continues.

MUSICAL PREFACE

THE COMPILER of tunes for a modern hymn-book has at his disposal a great wealth of tunes which have come into existence over a period of some sixteen centuries. So great is this wealth that the problem of selection is not always easy, and is bound to be influenced not only by the personal taste of the compiler, but even more by the need of providing music suited to the capabilities of congregations and choirs. No hymn-book designed to meet popular requirements can be an anthology of perfect hymn-tunes any more than it can be an anthology of fine poetry: it must cater for a variety of occasions and for all sorts and conditions of men.

Ever since it was first published in 1861, *Hymns Ancient and Modern* has always included plainsong tunes. In addition, *A Plainsong Hymnbook* published in 1932, under the inspired guidance of the late Bishop Frere, contained 163 of the best plainsong tunes which could be found, and the Compilers of *Hymns Ancient and Modern Revised* have drawn largely on that collection.

The German Chorale also finds a place. Perhaps it may be well to state that, in deciding on the exact form of the melody and the harmony, the Musical Editors have been concerned to provide a setting which should be not too elaborate to be rendered by a congregation supported by a choir of average ability, rather than to include a setting which, although perhaps even more beautiful, would not fulfil this condition.

English, Scottish and Genevan psalm tunes, together with ecclesiastical and folksong melodies of other countries (some of which have not appeared in previous editions of *Hymns Ancient and Modern*), are well represented here. Inasmuch as controversy has often centred upon the form of individual tunes, it should be understood that the Musical Editors have not felt obliged in every case to adopt the earliest existing form of the tune, for the extreme ornateness of some of the products of the eighteenth century often makes simplification desirable to meet the capacity of the ordinary congregation of today. In this matter the Compilers have followed the practice of many other hymnals.

The best of English hymn-tunes, from those of the Tudor period to the compositions of living musicians, occupy an important place in this book. It may fairly be claimed that the book is rightly named *Hymns Ancient and Modern*. In a few cases only have copyright difficulties prevented the use of tunes which might otherwise have been included.

NOTES ON THE MUSIC

I. PLAINSONG

1. *Notation*

The quaver has been adopted as the unit note though, owing to the varying length of syllables in the English language, quavers can be only approximately equal in duration.

Three kinds of bar-line are used:—

    (i) The double-bar, which is used only at the end of a stanza.

    (ii) The full bar, indicating a break equal to a crotchet rest.

    (iii) The half bar, which allows a short break, but may be disregarded where the verbal sense would be thereby improved.

2. *Method of Singing*

The melodies should be sung lightly and rather quietly; excessive accents are to be avoided, yet the rhythm must be clear. Groups of notes (neums) should be sung smoothly and without hurry, quavers being approximately equal in length and the first note of the neum being slightly stressed. When two crochets occur at the end of a line of a hymn, the second should be sung rather more softly than the first.

Although office-hymns were " meant to be sung full " (Bishop Frere), it is now quite customary for the verses to be shared between different groups of singers—boys, men, a cantor intoning the first line of the first verse. Sequences were " designed to follow an antiphonal plan," and provision has been made for this (e.g. Nos. 138, 466).

3. *Accompaniment*

When there is an accompaniment to plainsong melodies, it is essential that it should be of the right kind if the singing is not to be hampered or the character of the melodies destroyed. The following points should be borne in mind:—

    (*a*) The accompanist should not attempt to " lead " the singers as in a modern hymn tune by playing more loudly or by playing *staccato*.

Notes on the Music

(*b*) The accompaniment should provide a background to the singing and should move with, not in front of or behind, the singers. The frequent use of 16-foot stops on manuals or pedals is, therefore, generally inadvisable.

(*c*) Variety may be obtained by omitting the melody from the accompaniment from time to time. If additional accompaniments are improvised, the modal character of the melodies as well as their rhythm should be scrupulously respected.

II. MODERN

1. *Notation*

In order that the exact length of all notes as observed in actual performance may be evident, all pause marks have been eliminated and a note of the appropriate time value has been printed instead.

With the same object in view, a longer note has been printed at the ends of certain lines in some tunes of the Psalm-tune type. For an example, see *Winchester New*, hymn 2, second tune.

2. *Verbal Sense*

In order that the verbal sense may be clearly shown, the sign ‿, first used in the Shortened Music Edition of *Hymns Ancient and Modern*, has been included in this edition. It indicates that breath is not to be taken, nor break made between the two lines in which it occurs, e.g. hymn 4, verse 4, lines 3 and 4:

> Room to deny ourselves, a road‿
> To bring us daily nearer God.

3. *Variety*

By way of encouraging some variety in the singing of hymns, suggestions are inserted that certain verses in some of the hymns should be sung by Treble voices, by Men, or in Unison. In the case of a few tunes faux-bourdons are provided (some of which have appeared in previous editions), and certain hymns are supplied with simple descants.

ACKNOWLEDGEMENTS

THANKS ARE DUE to those who have given permission for the use of their copyright hymns. The present owners so far as they can be ascertained, are:

Mr. Barclay Baron 500 — Mrs. Bourflower 404 — Miss M. Cropper 450 — J. Curwen & Sons Ltd. 172, 292, 431, 629 — Girls' Friendly Society (and Miss Cropper) 434 — Lord Gorell 428 — The Mothers' Union 498 — A. R. Mowbray & Co. Ltd. 302, 436, 594 — Novello & Co. Ltd. 604 — The Royal School of Church Music 297 — St. Christopher's College, Blackheath 438, 495 — Mr. C. R. Sedgwick 406 — The S.P.C.K. 155, 426, 430, 440, 455, 460, 461, 492, 499, 501, 585 — The Universities Mission to Central Africa 469 — Mr. E. M. S. Wood 408.

Also to the personal representatives of the authors for these:
150, 315, 380, 403, 496, 534, 560.

The following belong to *Hymns Ancient and Modern Limited:*
10, 37, 84, 85, 100, 115, 121, 145, 174, 260, 270, 340, 388, 391, 422, 423, 427, 465, 476, 493, 494, 497, 511, 512, 519, 520, 522, 537, 538, 542, 547, 551, 556, 562, 564, 574, 583, 586, 596, 598, 599, 600, 603, 608, 612, 618, 622, 627, 633.

Thanks are also due to those who have given permission for the use of copyright tunes and arrangements. The present owners, so far as they can be ascertained, are:

The Abbot of Downside 185*b* — Mr. H. A. Bate 180 — Mr. L. J. Blake 36 (arrangement) — The Cambridge University Press (descants) 167*a* and *b*, 190*a* 506 — The Proprietors of the *Church and School Hymnal* 449 — J. Curwen & Sons Ltd. 182, 269, 442*a*, 495 — The English Hymnal Co. Ltd. 65*a*, 326, 380, 416, 589 — The Faith Press Ltd. 385*b*, 547 — Mr. K. G. Finlay 33*a*, 433*a*, 494, 583 — Sir William H. Harris 235, 528*a*, 614 — A. R. Mowbray & Co. Ltd. 594 — Novello & Co. Ltd. 36, 304*b*, 606*b* — The Oxford University Press, 21, 120, 224*a*, 257*a*, 298*a*, 299*a*, 332*a*, 341, 450, 456, 500, 550, — The Royal School of Church Music 79 (arrangement and descant), 143, 171 (arrangement and descant), 190*b*, 223*a* 244, 245 (descant), 297, 319*b* 332*b*, 441, 445*a*, 575, 576, 584*a*, 623, 627 — Schott & Co. Ltd. 312, 429 — The S.P.C.K. 492 — Stainer & Bell Ltd. 162, 283, 527*a*.

Acknowledgements

Also to the personal representatives of the composers for these:
    65*b*, 67, 102, 131*a*, 174, 230*b*, 247, 256, 271, 296*b*, 331, 339, 375, 386*b*, 417, 489, 496, 522, 555, 579.

The following tunes belong to *Hymns Ancient and Modern Limited:*
    9*a* and *b*, 46, 72*a*, 133, 155, 215, 237, 270, 302, 307*a*, 308*a*, 315, 324*a* 359, 369, 381, 392, 396*a*, 404, 407*b*, 421, 446, 453, 455, 497, 532, 534, 562, 585, 607, 610,616, 622, 633.

Also these arrangements:
    1*a*, 2*a* 10*a* and *b*, 14, 15*a*, 26*a*, 45*a*, 70, 96*a*, 97*a* and *b*, 105*a*, 129*b* 138, 145*a*, 151*a*, 157, 158*a* and *b*, 164*a*, 188*a*, 211, 213*a*, 228, 239, 253*a*, 268, 277, 294, 304*a*, 319*a*, 337, 383*a* and *b*, 385*a*, 386*a*, 387*a*, 388*a*, 390, 391, 407*a*, 409*a*, 410, 423, 425, 428, 430, 448, 466, 474*a*, 477*a*, 479, 501, 504*a*, 505, 507*a*, 512*a* and *b*, 514, 516*b*, 519 520, 523, 525, 538, 551*a*, 554, 558*a* and *b*, 564*b*, 567, 581, 586, 587, 588, 591 (alternative version), 598, 601, 602 (alternative version), 605, 608, 609, 612, 618. And (from the *Plainsong Hymn Book*) 16, 37, 74*a*, 82*a*, 84*a*, 95*a*, 129*a*, 145*a*, 384*a*, 503*a*, 516*a*, 564*a*, 600.

Also these descants:
    3, 24*b*, 59, 108, 147*a* 161, 165, 197, 222, 292*b*, 371, 593.

Apologies are offered to any authors or composers whose names have been omitted from the above lists through inadvertence or inability to trace: mistakes will be rectified as soon as possible.

June 1984

COPYRIGHT AND GRANTS

TABLE OF CONTENTS

Table of Contents

INDEX OF FIRST LINES

Index of First Lines

Index of First Lines

Index of First Lines

METRICAL INDEX OF TUNES

INDEX OF TUNES

INDEX OF AUTHORS AND TRANSLATORS

(A single date denotes the first appearance of a hymn, when birth and death years are unobtainable. Square brackets indicate a translation)

INDEX OF COMPOSERS AND SOURCES

(A single date denotes the first appearance of a tune, when birth and death dates are unobtainable)

EXPLANATION OF MARKS

† signifies a slight alteration of the author's original;
‡ a more extensive alteration; * indicates that these
verses may be omitted if so desired; ⌣ (phrasing sign)
indicates that there should be no break between the end
of a line and that which follows it.

MORNING

FIRST TUNE

Jam lucis orto sidere — L.M.

Mode viii

SECOND TUNE

Illsley (*or* Bishop) — L.M.

J. Bishop, 1665–1737

A higher setting of this tune will be found at Hymn 503

(*Prime*)

Jam lucis orto sidere

Now that the daylight fills the sky,
We lift our hearts to God on high,
That he, in all we do or say,
Would keep us free from harm to-day:

2
Would guard our hearts and tongues
from strife;
From anger's din would hide our life:
From all ill sights would turn our eyes,
Would close our ears from vanities:

3
Would keep our inmost conscience pure;
Our souls from folly would secure;

Would bid us check the pride of sense
With due and holy abstinence.

4
So we, when this new day is gone,
And night in turn is drawing on,
With conscience by the world unstained
Shall praise his name for victory gained.

[UNISON] 5
All laud to God the Father be;
All praise, eternal Son, to thee;
All glory, as is ever meet,
To God the holy Paraclete.

Tr. J. M. NEALE

1

HYMN **2**

FIRST TUNE

Splendor paternae gloriae — L.M.

Mode i

SECOND TUNE

Winchester New — L.M.

Musikalisch Handbuch (Hamburg, 1690)

A higher setting of this tune will be found at Hymn 50

Splendor paternae gloriae

O splendour of God's glory bright,
Who bringest forth the light from Light;
O Light, of light the fountain-spring;
O Day, our days illumining;

2
Come, very Sun of truth and love,
Come in thy radiance from above,
And shed the Holy Spirit's ray
On all we think or do to-day.

3
Teach us to work with all our might;
Put Satan's fierce assaults to flight;

Turn all to good that seems most ill;
Help us our calling to fulfil.

4
O joyful be the livelong day,
Our thoughts as pure as morning ray,
Our faith like noonday's glowing height,
Our souls undimmed by shades of night.

[UNISON]   5
All praise to God the Father be,
All praise, eternal Son, to thee,
Whom with the Spirit we adore
For ever and for evermore.

ST. AMBROSE   *Tr.* Compilers† (1904)

Morning

The Descant may be sung by Trebles for the Doxology, the main melody being sung in Unison

PART 1

Awake, my soul, and with the sun
Thy daily stage of duty run;
Shake off dull sloth, and joyful rise
To pay thy morning sacrifice.

2
Redeem thy mis-spent time that's past,
And live this day as if thy last;
Improve thy talent with due care;
For the great day thyself prepare.

3
Let all thy converse be sincere,
Thy conscience as the noon-day clear;
Think how all-seeing God thy ways
And all thy secret thoughts surveys.

4
Wake, and lift up thyself, my heart,
And with the angels bear thy part,
Who all night long unwearied sing
High praise to the eternal King.

PART 2

5
Glory to thee, who safe hast kept
And hast refreshed me whilst I slept;
Grant, Lord, when I from death shall wake,
I may of endless light partake.

6
Lord, I my vows to thee renew;
Disperse my sins as morning dew;
Guard my first springs of thought and will,
And with thyself my spirit fill.

7
Direct, control, suggest, this day,
All I design or do or say;
That all my powers, with all their might,
In thy sole glory may unite.

The following Doxology may be sung at the end of either Part:

[UNISON]
Praise God, from whom all blessings flow,
Praise him, all creatures here below,
Praise him above, angelic host,
Praise Father, Son, and Holy Ghost.

BISHOP T. KEN†

3

Morning

New every morning is the love
Our wakening and uprising prove;
Through sleep and darkness safely brought,
Restored to life and power and thought.

2
New mercies, each returning day,
Hover around us while we pray;
New perils past, new sins forgiven,
New thoughts of God, new hopes of heaven.

3
If on our daily course our mind⏝
Be set to hallow all we find,
New treasures still, of countless price,
God will provide for sacrifice.

4
The trivial round, the common task,
Will furnish all we need to ask,
Room to deny ourselves, a road⏝
To bring us daily nearer God.

5
Only, O Lord, in thy dear love
Fit us for perfect rest above;
And help us, this and every day,
To live more nearly as we pray.

J. Keble†

4

Morning

HYMN **5**   St. Timothy — C.M.   Sir H. W. Baker, 1821–77

A higher setting of this tune will be found at Hymn 234

My Father, for another night
　Of quiet sleep and rest,
For all the joy of morning light,
　Thy holy name be blest.

2
Now with the new-born day I give
　Myself anew to thee,
That as thou willest I may live,
　And what thou willest be.

3
Whate'er I do, things great or small,
　Whate'er I speak or frame,
Thy glory may I seek in all,
　Do all in Jesus' name.

4
My Father, for his sake, I pray,
　Thy child accept and bless;
And lead me by thy grace to-day
　In paths of righteousness.

SIR H. W. BAKER

5

Morning

mf At thy feet, O Christ, we lay⌣
    Thine own gift of this new day;
    Doubt of what it holds in store
    Makes us crave thine aid the more;
    Lest it prove a time of loss,
    Mark it, Saviour, with thy Cross.

2

    If it flow on calm and bright,
    Be thyself our chief delight;
p If it bring unknown distress,
    Good is all that thou canst bless;
    Only, while its hours begin,
    Pray we, keep them clear of sin.

3

mf We in part our weakness know,
    And in part discern our foe;
    Well for us, before thine eyes⌣
    All our danger open lies;
    Turn not from us, while we plead⌣
    Thy compassions and our need.

4

    Fain would we thy word embrace,
    Live each moment on thy grace,
    All our selves to thee consign,
    Fold up all our wills in thine,
    Think and speak and do and be⌣
    Simply that which pleases thee.

5

    Hear us, Lord, and that right soon;
    Hear, and grant the choicest boon⌣
    That thy love can e'er impart,
    Loyal singleness of heart:
f So shall this and all our days,
    Christ our God, show forth thy praise.

W. Bright

6

Morning

  f   Christ, whose glory fills the skies,
        Christ, the true, the only Light,
     Sun of Righteousness, arise,
        Triumph o'er the shades of night;
     Dayspring from on high, be near;
     Daystar, in my heart appear.

2

  p   Dark and cheerless is the morn
        Unaccompanied by thee;
     Joyless is the day's return,
        Till thy mercy's beams I see,
     Till they inward light impart,
     Glad my eyes, and warm my heart.

3

  mf   Visit then this soul of mine,
        Pierce the gloom of sin and grief;
     Fill me, radiancy divine,
        Scatter all my unbelief;
  f   More and more thyself display,
     Shining to the perfect day.

                     C. WESLEY

HYMN **8** Hilderstone — L.M. P. Hart (*c.* 1713)

God of the morning, at whose voice⌣
  The cheerful sun makes haste to rise,
And like a giant doth rejoice
  To run his journey through the skies;
    2
O, like the sun, may I fulfil⌣
  The appointed duties of the day,

With ready mind and active will
  March on, and keep my heavenly way.
    3
Give me thy counsel for my guide,
  And then receive me to thy bliss:
All my desires and hopes beside
  Are faint and cold, compared with this.
                    I. WATTS

Alternative Tune, Truro, 220

HYMN **9** FIRST TUNE

Veryan — 6 6 8 6. 11 11 G. H. Knight

Morning

SECOND TUNE

Gerrans — 6 6 8 6. 11 11   A. H. Brown, 1830–1926

ἐξεγερθέντες τοῦ ὕπνου

mf   Awaked from sleep we fall
    Before thee, God of love,
    And chant the praise the angels raise,
      O God of might, above :
  Holy, Holy, Holy! Thou art God adored!
p   In thy pitying mercy show us mercy, Lord.

2

mf   As at thy call I rise,
    Shine on this mind and heart,
    And touch my tongue, that I among
      Thy choir may take my part :
  Holy, Holy, Holy! Trinity adored!
p   In thy pitying mercy show me mercy, Lord.

3

mf   The Judge will come with speed,
    And each man's deeds be known;
    Our trembling cry shall rise on high
      At midnight to thy throne :
  Holy, Holy, Holy! King of Saints adored!
p   In the hour of judgement show us mercy, Lord.

Tr. R. M. MOORSOM

Morning

HYMN **10**

FIRST TUNE

Nocte surgentes — II II II 5

Mode vi

Nocte surgentes

1 Let hearts a - wa - ken, now the night is end - ed,
2 So, with the an - thems of the blest u - ni - ting,
3 Grant this, O Fa - ther, Son, and Ho - ly Spi - rit,

1 And raise their morn - ing psalm of ad - o - ra - tion,
2 May we find grace to win the courts ce - les - tial,
3 Tri - ni - ty bles - sèd, who one God - head shar - est:

1 In sweet-est con-cert the Cre - a - tor's glo - ry Joy-ful - ly sing-ing.
2 And hymn the praise of heaven's high King e - ter - nal Through life un - end-ing.
3 Thine be the glo - ry through the whole cre-a - tion Now and for ev - er.

10

HYMN **10**   SECOND TUNE

Christe sanctorum — 11 11 11 5   La Feillée, *Méthode*, 1782

May be sung in Unison

Nocte surgentes

Let hearts awaken, now the night is ended,
And raise their morning psalm of adoration,
In sweetest concert the Creator's glory
    Joyfully singing.

2
So, with the anthems of the blest uniting,
May we find grace to win the courts celestial,
And hymn the praise of heaven's high King eternal
    Through life unending.

3
Grant this, O Father, Son, and Holy Spirit,
Trinity blessèd, who one Godhead sharest:
Thine be the glory through the whole creation
    Now and for ever.

Tr. C. S. PHILLIPS

11

Morning

FIRST TUNE

Jam lucis — L.M.

G. Guidetti, *Directorium Chori*, 1582

SECOND TUNE

Warrington — L.M.

R. Harrison, 1748–1810

Morning

(Terce)

Nunc Sancte nobis Spiritus

Come, Holy Ghost, who ' ever One
Art with the ' Father and the Son,
Come, Holy Ghost, our ' souls possess
With thy full ' flood of holiness.

2

In will and deed, by ' heart and tongue,
With all our ' powers, thy praise be sung;
And love light up our ' mortal frame,
Till others ' catch the living flame.

3

Almighty Father, ' hear our cry
Through Jesus ' Christ our Lord most high,
Who with the Holy ' Ghost and thee
Doth live and ' reign eternally.

? St. Ambrose
Tr. Cardinal J. H. Newman‡

MID-DAY

(Sext)

Rector potens, verax Deus

O God of truth, O ' Lord of might,
Who orderest ' time and change aright,
Arraying morn with ' joyful gleams,
And kindling ' noonday's fiery beams;

2

Quench thou on earth the ' flames of strife;
From passion's ' heat preserve our life;
Our bodies keep from ' perils free,
And grant our ' souls true peace in thee.

3

Almighty Father, ' hear our cry
Through Jesus ' Christ our Lord most high,
Who with the Holy ' Ghost and thee
Doth live and ' reign eternally.

St. Ambrose
Tr. Compilers

Mid-day

Suitable for Unison singing. A higher setting of this tune will be found at Hymn 192

Behold us, Lord, a little space
From daily tasks set free,
And met within thy holy place
To rest awhile with thee.

2
Around us rolls the ceaseless tide
Of business, toil, and care;
And scarcely can we turn aside
For one brief hour of prayer.

3
Yet these are not the only walls
Wherein thou may'st be sought:
On homeliest work thy blessing falls,
In truth and patience wrought.

4
Thine is the loom, the forge, the mart,
The wealth of land and sea;
The worlds of science and of art,
Revealed and ruled by thee.

5
Then let us prove our heavenly birth
In all we do and know;
And claim the kingdom of the earth
For thee, and not thy foe.

6
Work shall be prayer, if all be wrought
As thou wouldst have it done;
And prayer, by thee inspired and taught,
Itself with work be one.

J. ELLERTON

14

EVENING

HYMN **14** Optatus votis — L.M.   *Barking Hymnal*, Mode iv

(*None*)

Rerum Deus tenax vigor

1 O God, the world's sus - tain - ing force, Thy - self un -
2 O grant us light at ev - en - tide, That life may
3 Al - migh - ty Fa - ther, hear our cry Through Je - sus

1 moved, all mo - tion's source, Who, from the morn till
2 un - im - paired a - bide, And that a ho - ly
3 Christ our Lord most high, Who with the Ho - ly

1 eve - ning's ray, Dost through its chang - es guide the day;
2 death may be The door of im - mor - ta - li - ty.
3 Ghost and thee Doth live and reign e - ter - nal - ly.

? ST. AMBROSE *Tr.* J. M. Neale and Compilers (1904)

Alternative Tune, Illsley, 1

15

HYMN **15**   FIRST TUNE

O Lux beata Trinitas — L.M.   Mode viii

O Lux beata Trinitas

1 O Tri - ni - ty, most bles - sèd Light, O Un - -
2 To thee our morn - ing song of praise, To thee
3 All praise to God the Fa - ther be, All praise,

1 i - ty of sove - reign might, As now the fie - ry
2 our eve - ning prayer we raise; Thee may our souls for
3 e - ter - nal Son, to thee, Whom with the Spi - rit

1 sun de - parts, Shed thou thy beams with - in our hearts.
2 ev - er - more In low - ly rev - er - ence a - dore.
3 we a - dore, For ev - er and for ev - er - more.

HYMN 15

Westminster — L.M.   B. Cooke, 1734-93

O Lux beata Trinitas

O Trinity, most blessèd Light,
O Unity of sovereign might,
As now the fiery sun departs,
Shed thou thy beams within our hearts.

2

To thee our morning song of praise,
To thee our evening prayer we raise;
Thee may our souls for evermore
In lowly reverence adore.

[UNISON]   **3**

All praise to God the Father be,
All praise, eternal Son, to thee,
Whom with the Spirit we adore,
For ever and for evermore.

? ST. AMBROSE
Tr. J. M. Neale and Compilers

Evening

(*Compline*)

Te lucis ante terminum

Before the ending of the day,
Creator of the world, we pray,
That with thy wonted favour thou⏝
Wouldst be our guard and keeper now.

2
From all ill dreams defend our eyes,
From nightly fears and fantasies;
Tread under foot our ghostly foe,
That no pollution we may know.

3
O Father, that we ask be done,
Through Jesus Christ thine only Son:
Who, with the Holy Ghost and thee,
Doth live and reign eternally.

Tr. J. M. NEALE

Alternative Tune, St. Gregory, 83

HYMN **17**   FIRST TUNE

Genevan Psalm xii — 11 10 11 10   L. Bourgeois, *Genevan Psalter*, 1551

Evening

SECOND TUNE

Strength and Stay — 11 10 11 10

J. B. Dykes, 1823–76
(Original harmonies slightly altered)

Rerum Deus tenax vigor

mf O strength and stay upholding all creation,
Who ever dost thyself unmoved abide,
Yet day by day the light in due gradation
From hour to hour through all its changes guide;

2

p Grant to life's day a calm unclouded ending,
An eve untouched by shadows of decay,
The brightness of a holy death-bed blending
With dawning glories of the eternal day.

3

mf Hear us, O Father, gracious and forgiving,
Through Jesus Christ thy co-eternal Word,
Who with the Holy Ghost by all things living
Now and to endless ages art adored.

? St. Ambrose
Tr. J. Ellerton and F. J. A. Hort

19

HYMN **18** Sebaste — Irregular   Sir J. Stainer, 1840–1901

φῶς ἱλαρὸν ἁγίας δόξης

Hail, gladdening Light, of his pure glo - ry poured

Who is the immortal Fa - ther, heaven - ly, blest,

Ho - li - est of Ho - lies, Je - sus Christ our Lord!

Now we are come to the sun's hour of rest,

The lights of eve - ning round us shine, We hymn the Fa - ther,

Evening

Son, and Ho - ly Spi - rit di - vine.

Worthiest art thou at all times to be sung With un - de - fil - èd tongue, Son of our God, gi - ver of life, a - lone: There-fore in all the world thy glo - ries, Lord, they own.

3rd cent. or earlier
Tr. J. KEBLE

21

HYMN **19**   St. Gabriel — 8 8 8 4   Sir F. A. G. Ouseley, 1825–89

mf The radiant morn hath passed away,
And spent too soon her golden store;
The shadows of departing day ⌣
          Creep on once more.

2
Our life is but an autumn day,
Its glorious noon how quickly past!
Lead us, O Christ, thou living Way,
          Safe home at last.

3
O by thy soul-inspiring grace
Uplift our hearts to realms on high;
Help us to look to that bright place ⌣
          Beyond the sky,

4
Where light and life and joy and peace
In undivided empire reign,
And thronging angels never cease ⌣
          Their deathless strain;

5
Where saints are clothed in spotless white,
And evening shadows never fall,
Where thou, eternal Light of Light,
          Art Lord of all.

G. THRING

HYMN **20** Angelus — L.M. G. Joseph (1657)

mf At even, ere the sun was set,
 The sick, O Lord, around thee lay;
 O in what divers pains they met!
 O with what joy they went away!

2
 Once more 'tis eventide, and we
 Oppressed with various ills draw near;
 What if thy form we cannot see?
 We know and feel that thou art here.

3
 O Saviour Christ, our woes dispel;
 For some are sick, and some are sad,
 And some have never loved thee well,
 And some have lost the love they had;

4
 And some have found the world is vain,
 Yet from the world they break not free;
 And some have friends who give them pain,
 Yet have not sought a friend in thee;

5
 And none, O Lord, have perfect rest,
 For none are wholly free from sin;
 And they who fain would serve thee best
 Are conscious most of wrong within.

6
 O Saviour Christ, thou too art Man;
 Thou hast been troubled, tempted, tried;
 Thy kind but searching glance can scan
 The very wounds that shame would hide;

[UNISON]   7
f Thy touch has still its ancient power;
 No word from thee can fruitless fall:
mf Hear, in this solemn evening hour,
 And in thy mercy heal us all.

H. TWELLS

23

Evening

HYMN 21   St. Anatolius — 7 6 7 6. 8 8   A. H. Brown, 1830–1926

τὴν ἡμέραν διελθών

The day is past and over;
All thanks, O Lord, to thee;
I pray thee now that sinless
The hours of dark may be:
O Jesu, keep me in thy sight,
And guard me through the coming night.

2
The joys of day are over;
I lift my heart to thee,
And ask thee that offenceless
The hours of dark may be:
O Jesu, keep me in thy sight,
And guard me through the coming night.

3
The toils of day are over;
I raise the hymn to thee,
And ask that free from peril
The hours of dark may be:
O Jesu, keep me in thy sight,
And guard me through the coming night.

4
Be thou my soul's preserver,
For thou alone dost know
How many are the perils
Through which I have to go:
O loving Jesu, hear my call,
And guard and save me from them all.

Tr. J. M. NEALE‡

HYMN 22   Vesper — 7 7 7 5   Sir J. Stainer, 1840–1901

Evening

mf Holy Father, cheer our way
With thy love's perpetual ray;
Grant us every closing day
Light at evening time.

2
Holy Saviour, calm our fears
When earth's brightness disappears;
Grant us in our latter years
Light at evening time.

3
p Holy Spirit, be thou nigh
When in mortal pains we lie;
Grant us, as we come to die,
Light at evening time.

4
f Holy, blessèd Trinity,
Darkness is not dark with thee;
Those thou keepest always see
Light at evening time.

R. H. ROBINSON

Alternative Tune, Capetown, 163

HYMN **23**   Canon — L.M.
T. Tallis, *c.* 1505-85
As shortened by T. Ravenscroft (1621)

f Glory to thee, my God, this night
For all the blessings of the light;
Keep me, O keep me, King of Kings,
Beneath thy own almighty wings.

2
mf Forgive me, Lord, for thy dear Son,
The ill that I this day have done,
That with the world, myself, and
thee,
I, ere I sleep, at peace may be.

3
Teach me to live, that I may dread
The grave as little as my bed;
Teach me to die, that so I may
Rise glorious at the awful day.

4
O may my soul on thee repose, [close,
And may sweet sleep mine eyelids
Sleep that may me more vigorous make
To serve my God when I awake.

5
When in the night I sleepless lie,
My soul with heavenly thoughts
supply;
Let no ill dreams disturb my rest,
No powers of darkness me molest.

[UNISON] 6
f Praise God, from whom all blessings
flow,
Praise him, all creatures here below,
Praise him above, angelic host,
Praise Father, Son, and Holy Ghost.

BISHOP T. KEN

Evening

FIRST TUNE

Abends — L.M. Sir H. S. Oakeley, 1830–1903

SECOND TUNE

Hursley — L.M. *Katholisches Gesangbuch, c.* **1775**

The Descant may be sung by Trebles for verse 6, the main melody being sung in Unison

26

mf Sun of my soul, thou Saviour dear,
It is not night if thou be near:
O may no earth-born cloud arise
To hide thee from thy servant's eyes.

2

p When the soft dews of kindly sleep
My wearied eyelids gently steep,
Be my last thought, how sweet to rest
For ever on my Saviour's breast.

3

mf Abide with me from morn till eve,
For without thee I cannot live;
Abide with me when night is nigh,
For without thee I dare not die.

4

If some poor wandering child of thine
Have spurned to-day the voice divine,

Now, Lord, the gracious work begin;
Let him no more lie down in sin.

5

Watch by the sick; enrich the poor
With blessings from thy boundless store;
Be every mourner's sleep to-night
Like infant's slumbers, pure and light.

[UNISON] 6

f Come near and bless us when we wake,
Ere through the world our way we take;
Till in the ocean of thy love
We lose ourselves in heaven above.

J. KEBLE

HYMN 25   Dretzel — 8 7. 8 7. 7 7   C. H. Dretzel, 1698–1775

Through the day thy love has spared us;
Now we lay us down to rest;
Through the silent watches guard us,
Let no foe our peace molest:
Jesus, thou our guardian be;
Sweet it is to trust in thee.

2

Pilgrims here on earth and strangers,
Dwelling in the midst of foes,
Us and ours preserve from dangers;
In thine arms may we repose,
And, when life's sad day is past,
Rest with thee in heaven at last.

T. KELLY

Evening

FIRST TUNE

All through the night — 8 4 8 4. 8 8 8 4

Welsh Traditional Melody

SECOND TUNE

Nutfield — 8 4 8 4. 8 8 8 4

W. H. Monk, 1823–89

Evening

God, that madest earth and heaven,
    Darkness and light;
Who the day for toil hast given,
    For rest the night;
May thine angel-guards defend us,
Slumber sweet thy mercy send us,
Holy dreams and hopes attend us,
    This livelong night.

2
Guard us waking, guard us sleeping,
    And, when we die,
May we in thy mighty keeping
    All peaceful lie:
When the last dread call shall wake us,
Do not thou our God forsake us,
But to reign in glory take us
    With thee on high.

1 Bishop R. Heber
2 Archbishop R. Whately

29

Evening

mf Abide with me; fast falls the eventide:
The darkness deepens; Lord, with me abide:
When other helpers fail, and comforts flee,
Help of the helpless, O abide with me.

2
p Swift to its close ebbs out life's little day;
Earth's joys grow dim, its glories pass away;
Change and decay in all around I see:
O thou who changest not, abide with me.

3
mf I need thy presence every passing hour;
What but thy grace can foil the tempter's power?
Who like thyself my guide and stay can be?
Through cloud and sunshine, Lord, abide with me.

[UNISON]   4
f I fear no foe with thee at hand to bless;
Ills have no weight, and tears no bitterness.
Where is death's sting? Where, grave, thy victory?
I triumph still, if thou abide with me.

5
p Hold thou thy Cross before my closing eyes;
Shine through the gloom, and point me to the skies:
f Heaven's morning breaks, and earth's vain shadows flee;
In life, in death, O Lord, abide with me.

H. F. LYTE

Evening

A higher setting of this tune will be found at Hymn 203

mf Sweet Saviour, bless us ere we go;
　　Thy word into our minds instil,
　　And make our lukewarm hearts to
　　　glow
　　With lowly love and fervent will.
f　Through life's long day and death's
　　　dark night,
　　O gentle Jesus, be our Light.

2
p　The day is done, its hours have run,
　　And thou hast taken count of all,
　　The scanty triumphs grace hath won,
　　The broken vow, the frequent fall.
f　Through life's long day, etc.

3
mf Grant us, dear Lord, from evil
　　　ways‿
　　True absolution and release;
　　And bless us, more than in past
　　　days,
　　With purity and inward peace.
f　Through life's long day, etc.

4
mf Do more than pardon; give us
　　　joy,
　　Sweet fear, and sober liberty,
　　And loving hearts without alloy
　　That only long to be like thee.
f　Through life's long day, etc.

5
p　For all we love, the poor, the sad,
　　The sinful, unto thee we call;
mf　O let thy mercy make us glad:
　　Thou art our Jesus, and our all
f　Through life's long day, etc.

F. W. FABER

Alternative Tune, Stella, 203

HYMN **29**   St. Columba — C.M.   Traditional Irish Melody

Labente jam solis rota

p   As now the sun's declining rays
  At eventide descend,
So life's brief day is sinking down
  To its appointed end.

2

Lord, on the Cross thine arms were stretched
  To draw thy people nigh :
O grant us then that Cross to love,
  And in those arms to die.

[UNISON]   3
f   All glory to the Father be,
  All glory to the Son,
All glory, Holy Ghost, to thee,
  While endless ages run.

C. COFFIN   *Tr.* J. Chandler‡

Alternative Tune, St. Peter, 13

Hymn **30**   St. Columba — 6 4 6 6   H. S. Irons, 1834–1905

Sol praeceps rapitur

p   The sun is sinking fast,
    The daylight dies;
    Let love awake, and pay‿
      Her evening sacrifice.

2
As Christ upon the Cross
    His head inclined,
And to his Father's hands
    His parting soul resigned,

3
mf   So now herself my soul
    Would wholly give‿
    Into his sacred charge,
    In whom all spirits live;

4
So now beneath his eye
    Would calmly rest,
Without a wish or thought
    Abiding in the breast,

5
Save that his will be done,
    Whate'er betide,
Dead to herself, and dead‿
    In him to all beside.

6
f   Thus would I live; yet now‿
    Not I, but he,
In all his power and love
    Henceforth alive in me.

7
One sacred Trinity!
    One Lord divine!
May I be ever his,
    And he for ever mine.

c. 18th cent. *Tr.* E. Caswall†

Evening

FIRST TUNE

Ellers — 10 10 10 10   E. J. Hopkins, 1818–1901

SECOND TUNE

Pax Dei — 10 10 10 10   J. B. Dykes, 1823–76

Evening

(At the end of Service)

mf Saviour, again to thy dear name we raise
With one accord our parting hymn of praise;
We stand to bless thee ere our worship cease;
p   Then, lowly kneeling, wait thy word of peace.

2
Grant us thy peace upon our homeward way;
With thee began, with thee shall end, the day:
Guard thou the lips from sin, the hearts from shame,
That in this house have called upon thy name.

3
Grant us thy peace, Lord, through the coming night;
f   Turn thou for us its darkness into light;
From harm and danger keep thy children free,
For dark and light are both alike to thee.

4
mf Grant us thy peace throughout our earthly life,
Our balm in sorrow, and our stay in strife;
p   Then, when thy voice shall bid our conflict cease,
Call us, O Lord, to thine eternal peace.

J. ELLERTON

Evening

A higher setting of this tune will be found at Hymn 285

(At the end of Service)

mf And now the wants are told, that
brought⌣
Thy children to thy knee;
Here lingering still, we ask for
nought,
But simply worship thee.

2

The hope of heaven's eternal days
Absorbs not all the heart
That gives thee glory, love, and
praise,
For being what thou art.

3

For thou art God, the One, the
Same,
O'er all things high and bright;
And round us, when we speak thy
name,
There spreads a heaven of light.

4

p O wondrous peace, in thought to
dwell⌣
On excellence divine;
To know that nought in man can tell
How fair thy beauties shine!

5

mf O thou, above all blessing blest,
O'er thanks exalted far,
Thy very greatness is a rest
To weaklings as we are;

6

For when we feel the praise of thee
A task beyond our powers,
We say, 'A perfect God is he,
And he is fully ours.'

[UNISON] 7

f All glory to the Father be,
All glory to the Son,
All glory, Holy Ghost, to thee,
While endless ages run.

W. Bright

36

Evening

FIRST TUNE

Ardgowan — 9 8 9 8

K. G. Finlay

mf The day thou gavest, Lord, is ended,
　　The darkness falls at thy behest;
　　To thee our morning hymns ascended,
　　Thy praise shall sanctify our rest.

2
We thank thee that thy Church unsleeping,
　While earth rolls onward into light,
Through all the world her watch is keeping,
　And rests not now by day or night.

3
As o'er each continent and island
　The dawn leads on another day,
The voice of prayer is never silent,
　Nor dies the strain of praise away.

4
The sun that bids us rest is waking⌣
　Our brethren 'neath the western sky,
And hour by hour fresh lips are making⌣
　Thy wondrous doings heard on high.

[UNISON]　5
f　So be it, Lord; thy throne shall never,
　　Like earth's proud empires, pass away;
　　Thy Kingdom stands, and grows for ever,
　　Till all thy creatures own thy sway.

J. ELLERTON

Evening

St. Clement — 9 8 9 8   C. C. Scholefield, 1839–1904

mf The day thou gavest, Lord, is ended,
The darkness falls at thy behest;
To thee our morning hymns ascended,
Thy praise shall sanctify our rest

2
We thank thee that thy Church unsleeping,
While earth rolls onward into light,
Through all the world her watch is keeping,
And rests not now by day or night.

3
As o'er each continent and island
The dawn leads on another day,
The voice of prayer is never silent,
Nor dies the strain of praise away.

4
The sun that bids us rest is waking ⌣
Our brethren 'neath the western sky,
And hour by hour fresh lips are making ⌣
Thy wondrous doings heard on high.

[UNISON]   5
f So be it, Lord; thy throne shall never,
Like earth's proud empires, pass away;
Thy Kingdom stands, and grows for ever,
Till all thy creatures own thy sway.

J. ELLERTON

Evening

mf The duteous day now closeth,
Each flower and tree reposeth,
  Shade creeps o'er wild and wood:
Let us, as night is falling,
On God our Maker calling,
  Give thanks to him, the giver good.

2
Now all the heavenly splendour
Breaks forth in starlight tender
  From myriad worlds unknown;
And man, the marvel seeing,
Forgets his selfish being,
  For joy of beauty not his own.

3
His care he drowneth yonder,
Lost in the abyss of wonder;
  To heaven his soul doth steal:
This life he disesteemeth,
The day it is that dreameth,
  That doth from truth his vision seal.

4
p Awhile his mortal blindness
May miss God's loving-kindness,
  And grope in faithless strife:
cr But when life's day is over
Shall death's fair night discover
  The fields of everlasting life.

Yattendon Hymnal Based on
Nun ruhen alle Wälder, P. GERHARDT

Hymn **35** Thuringia — 5 5. 8 8. 5 5   A. Drese, 1620–1701
Harmonized by F. Layriz (1844)

mf   Round me falls the night;
       Saviour, be my light:
     Through the hours in darkness shrouded
     Let me see thy face unclouded;
       Let thy glory shine
       In this heart of mine.

2

p   Earthly work is done,
       Earthly sounds are none;
     Rest in sleep and silence seeking,
     Let me hear thee softly speaking;
       In my spirit's ear
       Whisper, 'I am near.'

3

mf   Blessèd, heavenly Light,
       Shining through earth's night;
     Voice, that oft of love hast told me;
     Arms, so strong to clasp and hold me;
       Thou thy watch wilt keep,
       Saviour, o'er my sleep.

W. Romanis

HYMN **36** Twyford — C.M.   L. J. Blake

By permission of Novello & Co., Ltd.

mf And now another day is gone,
      I'll sing my Maker's praise,
      My comforts every hour make known,
      His providence and grace.

2

p I lay my body down to sleep;
     May angels guard my head,
     And through the hours of darkness keep‿
     Their watch around my bed.

3

f With cheerful heart I close my eyes,
     Since thou wilt not remove;
     And in the morning let me rise
     Rejoicing in thy love.

I. WATTS

Evening

Sol praeceps rapitur

1 Fast sinks the sun to rest, Fast fall the shades of night;
2 E'en as the Cru - ci - fied, Calm in the hour of death,
3 Meek - ly be - neath his hand Li - eth my help - less - ness,
4 Be it not I who live But God who lives in me,

1 Fain would the wea - ry heart Keep love's frail flame a - light,
2 In - to his Fa - ther's hands Yield - ed his la - test breath,
3 Think - ing and car - ing naught Save what he pur - po - ses,
4 Reign - ing and tri - umph - ing In love's sweet ma - jes - ty;

1 End the day that fa - ding dies With an off - ering of sa - cri - fice.
2 So my spi - rit would re - pose Safe in God's migh - ty keep - ing close.
3 And in ut - ter calm a - bides, Dead to self and to all be - sides.
4 May he mine for ev - er be, God who One is in Trin - i - ty.

c. 18th cent. *Tr.* C. S. Phillips

Evening

(For Festivals)

mf   Our day of praise is done;
      The evening shadows fall;
    But pass not from us with the sun,
    True Light that lightenest all.

2

f   Around the throne on high,
     Where night can never be,
   The white-robed harpers of the sky
   Bring ceaseless hymns to thee.

3

p   Too faint our anthems here;
    Too soon of praise we tire:
mf But O the strains how full and clear
    Of that eternal choir!

4

Yet, Lord, to thy dear will
If thou attune the heart,
We in thine angels' music still
May bear our lower part.

5

'Tis thine each soul to calm,
Each wayward thought reclaim,
And make our life a daily psalm
Of glory to thy name.

6

f   A little while, and then
   Shall come the glorious end;
 And songs of angels and of men
  In perfect praise shall blend.

J. ELLERTON

Alternative Tune, Carlisle, 374

43

SUNDAY

(*Morning*)

Die parente temporum

f On this day, the first of days,
God the Father's name we praise,
Who, creation's Lord and spring,
Did the world from darkness bring.

2
On this day the eternal Son
Over death his triumph won;
On this day the Spirit came
With his gifts of living flame.

3
O that fervent love to-day
May in every heart have sway,
Teaching us to praise aright
God the source of life and light!

4
mf Father, who didst fashion me
Image of thyself to be,
Fill me with thy love divine,
Let my every thought be thine.

5
Holy Jesus, may I be
Dead and risen here with thee,
And upon love's fire arise
Unto thee a sacrifice.

6
Thou who dost all gifts impart,
Shine, good Spirit, in my heart;
Best of gifts, thyself bestow;
Make me burn thy love to know.

7
God, the one God of my heart,
I am thine, and mine thou art;
Take me, blessèd One in Three,
Here I give myself to thee.

18th cent. *Tr.* Sir H. W. Baker‡

44

Sunday

En dies est dominica

Again the Lord's own day is here,
The day to Christian people dear,
As, week by week, it bids them tell
How Jesus rose from death and hell.

2
For by his flock their Lord declared
His Resurrection should be shared;
And we who trust in him to save
With him are risen from the grave.

3
We, one and all, of him possessed,
Are with exceeding treasures blessed;
For all he did, and all he bare,
He gives us as our own to share.

4
Eternal glory, rest on high,
A blessèd immortality,
True peace and gladness, and a throne,
Are all his gifts, and all our own.

5
And therefore unto thee we sing,
O Lord of peace, eternal King;
Thy love we praise, thy name adore,
Both on this day and evermore.

Ascribed to THOMAS À KEMPIS
Tr. J. M. Neale and Compilers

45

Sunday

Hymn **41** Wordsworth — 7 6 7 6. D W. H. Monk, 1823–89

3*

O day of rest and gladness,
    O day of joy and light,
O balm of care and sadness,
    Most beautiful, most bright;
On thee the high and lowly
    Before the eternal throne
Sing Holy, Holy, Holy,
    To the great Three in One.

To-day on weary nations
    The heavenly manna falls,
To holy convocations
    The silver trumpet calls,
Where Gospel-light is glowing
    With pure and radiant beams,
And living water flowing
    With soul-refreshing streams.

2

On thee, at the creation,
    The light first had its birth;
On thee for our salvation
    Christ rose from depths of earth;
On thee our Lord victorious
    The Spirit sent from heaven;
And thus on thee most glorious
    A triple light was given.

4

New graces ever gaining
    From this our day of rest,
We reach the rest remaining
    To spirits of the blest:
To Holy Ghost be praises,
    To Father, and to Son;
The Church her voice upraises
    To thee, blest Three in One.

BISHOP CHR. WORDSWORTH†

Alternative Tune, Offertorium, 176

HYMN **42** Dominica — S.M.   Sir H. S. Oakeley, 1830–1903

> *f*   This is the day of light:
>   Let there be light to-day;
>   O Dayspring, rise upon our night,
>   And chase its gloom away.

> 2
> *mf*   This is the day of rest:
>   Our failing strength renew;
>   On weary brain and troubled breast
>   Shed thou thy freshening dew.

> 3
>   This is the day of peace:
>   Thy peace our spirits fill;
>   Bid thou the blasts of discord cease,
>   The waves of strife be still.

> 4
>   This is the day of prayer:
>   Let earth to heaven draw near;
>   Lift up our hearts to seek thee there,
>   Come down to meet us here.

> 5
> *f*   This is the first of days:
>   Send forth thy quickening breath,
>   And wake dead souls to love and praise,
>   O vanquisher of death.

> J. ELLERTON

Sunday

f This is the day the Lord hath made,
     He calls the hours his own;
    Let heaven rejoice, let earth be glad,
     And praise surround the throne.

2
To-day he rose and left the dead,
   And Satan's empire fell;
To-day the saints his triumphs spread,
   And all his wonders tell.

3
Hosanna to the anointed King,
   To David's holy Son!
O help us, Lord, descend and bring
   Salvation from thy throne.

4
mf Blest be the Lord, who comes to men
     With messages of grace;
    Who comes, in God his Father's name,
     To save our sinful race.

[UNISON] 5
f Hosanna in the highest strains
     The Church on earth can raise;
    The highest heavens in which he reigns
     Shall give him nobler praise.

                        I. WATTS†

HYMN **44**   Vienna — 7 7 7 7   J. H. Knecht, 1752–1817

(*Evening*)

Lucis Creator optime

mf Blest Creator of the light,
Making day with radiance bright,
Thou didst o'er the forming earth
Give the golden light its birth.

2
Shade of eve with morning ray
Took from thee the name of day;
Darkness now is drawing nigh;
Listen to our humble cry.

3
p May we ne'er by guilt depressed
Lose the way to endless rest;
Nor with idle thoughts and vain
Bind our souls to earth again.

4
mf Rather may we heavenward rise
Where eternal treasure lies;
Purified by grace within,
Hating every deed of sin.

5
Holy Father, hear our cry
Through thy Son our Lord most high,
f Whom our thankful hearts adore
With the Spirit evermore.

Tr. COMPILERS

ADVENT

FIRST TUNE

Conditor alme — L.M.

Mode iv

SECOND TUNE

Brockham — L.M.

J. Clarke, *c.* 1659–1707

A lower setting of this tune will be found at Hymn 420

Conditor alme siderum

Creator of the starry height,
Thy people's everlasting Light,
Jesu, Redeemer of us all,
Hear thou thy servants when they call.

2

Thou, sorrowing at the helpless cry
Of all creation doomed to die,
Didst come to save our fallen race
By healing gifts of heavenly grace.

3
When earth was near its evening hour,
Thou didst, in love's redeeming power,
Like bridegroom from his chamber,
    come,
Forth from a Virgin-mother's womb.

4
At thy great name, exalted now,
All knees in lowly homage bow;
All things in heaven and earth adore,
And own thee King for evermore.

5
To thee, O Holy One, we pray,
Our Judge in that tremendous day,
Ward off, while yet we dwell below,
The weapons of our crafty foe.

[UNISON] **6**
To God the Father, God the Son,
And God the Spirit, Three in One,
Praise, honour, might, and glory be
From age to age eternally.

Tr. J. M. Neale and Compilers

Hymn **46**   Geronimo — 8 8 8. 8 8 6   Sir C. V. Stanford, 1852–1924

ἰδοὺ ὁ Νυμφίος

f 'Behold, the Bridegroom draweth
    nigh!'
    Hear ye the oft-repeated cry?
    Go forth into the midnight dim;
mf For blest are they whom he shall
    find
    With ready heart and watchful mind;
    Go forth, my soul, to him.

2
f 'Behold, the Bridegroom cometh by!'
    The call is echoed from the sky:
    Go forth, ye servants, watch and
    wait;
mf The slothful cannot join his train;
    No careless one may entrance gain:
    Awake, my soul, 'tis late.

3
p The wise will plead with one accord,
    'O Holy, Holy, Holy Lord,
    On us thy quickening grace bestow,
    That none may reach the door too
    late,
    When thou shalt enter at the gate
    And to thy Kingdom go.'

4
f 'Behold, the Bridegroom draweth
    near!'
    The warning falls on every ear:
    That night of dread shall come to
    all:
    Behold, my soul, thy lamp so dim,
    Rise, rise the smoking flax to trim;
    Soon shalt thou hear his call.

Tr. R. M. Moorsom

Advent

Vox clara ecce intonat

f Hark! a thrilling voice is sounding;
  'Christ is nigh,' it seems to say;
  'Cast away the dreams of darkness,
  O ye children of the day!'

2
Wakened by the solemn warning,
  Let the earth-bound soul arise;
Christ, her Sun, all ill dispelling,
  Shines upon the morning skies.

3
mf Lo, the Lamb, so long expected,
  Comes with pardon down from
    heaven;
  Let us haste, with tears of sorrow,
  One and all to be forgiven;

4
That when next he comes with glory,
  And the world is wrapped in fear,
With his mercy he may shield us,
  And with words of love draw near.

5
f   Honour, glory, might, and blessing
      To the Father and the Son,
    With the everlasting Spirit,
      While eternal ages run.

Tr. E. CASWALL‡

HYMN **48**   FIRST TUNE

St. Thomas — S.M.   Adapted from A. Williams (1765)

SECOND TUNE

Franconia — S.M.   *Harmonischer Liederschatz*, 1738

Instantis adventum Dei

The advent of our King
Our prayers must now employ,
And we must hymns of welcome sing
In strains of holy joy.

2
The everlasting Son
Incarnate deigns to be;
Himself a servant's form puts on,
To set his servants free.

3
Daughter of Sion, rise⌣
To meet thy lowly King;
Nor let thy faithless heart despise⌣
The peace he comes to bring.

4
As Judge, on clouds of light,
He soon will come again,
And his true members all unite
With him in heaven to reign.

[UNISON]   5
All glory to the Son
Who comes to set us free,
With Father, Spirit, ever One,
Through all eternity.

C. COFFIN
Tr. J. Chandler and Compilers

53

HYMN **49**   Veni Emmanuel — 8 8. 8 8. 8 8   *Hymnal Noted* (from a
French Missal)

To be sung in Unison

Re-joice! Re-joice! Em-man - u - el Shall come to thee, O Is - ra - el.

Veni, veni Emmanuel

O come, O come, Emmanuel,
And ransom captive Israel,
That mourns in lonely exile here,
Until the Son of God appear.
　　Rejoice! Rejoice! Emmanuel
　　Shall come to thee, O Israel.

2
O come, thou Rod of Jesse, free
Thine own from Satan's tyranny;
From depths of hell thy people save,
And give them victory o'er the grave.
　　Rejoice, etc.

3
O come, thou Dayspring, come and
　　cheer
Our spirits by thine advent here;
Disperse the gloomy clouds of night,
And death's dark shadows put to flight.
　　Rejoice, etc.

4
O come, thou Key of David, come,
And open wide our heavenly home;
Make safe the way that leads on high,
And close the path to misery.
　　Rejoice, etc.

5
O come, O come, thou Lord of Might,
Who to thy tribes, on Sinai's height,
In ancient times didst give the law
In cloud and majesty and awe.
　　Rejoice, etc.

Tr. J. M. NEALE and Compilers

54

HYMN **50**   Winchester New — L.M.

Musikalisch Handbuch
(Hamburg, 1690)

A lower setting of this tune will be found at Hymn 2

Jordanis oras praevia

On Jordan's bank the Baptist's cry
Announces that the Lord is nigh;
Awake, and hearken, for he brings
Glad tidings of the King of Kings.

2
Then cleansed be every breast from sin;
Make straight the way for God within;
Prepare we in our hearts a home,
Where such a mighty guest may come.

3
For thou art our salvation, Lord,
Our refuge, and our great reward;
Without thy grace we waste away,
Like flowers that wither and decay.

4
To heal the sick stretch out thine hand,
And bid the fallen sinner stand;
Shine forth, and let thy light restore
Earth's own true loveliness once more.

[UNISON]   5
All praise, eternal Son, to thee
Whose advent doth thy people free,
Whom with the Father we adore
And Holy Ghost for evermore.

C. COFFIN
Tr. J. Chandler and Compilers

55

HYMN **51**   Helmsley — 8 7. 8 7. 8 7   T. Olivers, 1725–99

3

f Lo, he comes with clouds descend-
     ing,
   Once for favoured sinners slain;
   Thousand thousand saints attending
   Swell the triumph of his train :
       Alleluia!
   Christ appears on earth to reign.

mf Those dear tokens of his Passion
    Still his dazzling body bears,
    Cause of endless exultation
    To his ransomed worshippers :
        With what rapture
    Gaze we on those glorious scars !

2

p Every eye shall now behold him
   Robed in dreadful majesty; [him,
   Those who set at naught and sold
   Pierced and nailed him to the Tree,
       Deeply wailing,
   Shall the true Messiah see.

[UNISON]   4

f Yea, Amen, let all adore thee,
   High on thine eternal throne;
   Saviour, take the power and glory,
   Claim the kingdom for thine own :
       Alleluia!
   Thou shalt reign, and thou alone.

C. WESLEY and J. CENNICK

HYMN **52**   St. Stephen — C.M.   W. Jones, 1726–1800

A lower setting of this tune will be found at Hymn 424

[UNISON]
The Lord will come and not be slow,
  His footsteps cannot err;
Before him righteousness shall go,
  His royal harbinger.

2
Truth from the earth, like to a flower,
  Shall bud and blossom then;
And justice, from her heavenly bower,
  Look down on mortal men.

[UNISON]   3
Rise, God, judge thou the earth in might,
  This wicked earth redress;
For thou art he who shalt by right
  The nations all possess.

4
The nations all whom thou hast made
  Shall come, and all shall frame
To bow them low before thee, Lord,
  And glorify thy name.

[UNISON]   5
For great thou art, and wonders great
  By thy strong hand are done:
Thou in thy everlasting seat
  Remainest God alone.

JOHN MILTON

HYMN **53**   Bristol — C.M.   T. Ravenscroft, *Psalms*, 1621

ALTERNATIVE VERSION

(Melody in the Tenor part)

Harmonized by T. Ravenscroft (1621)

The Alternative Version may be used for verses 2 and 4

f   Hark the glad sound! the Saviour comes,
      The Saviour promised long:
      Let every heart prepare a throne,
      And every voice a song.

2

He comes, the prisoners to release
In Satan's bondage held;
The gates of brass before him burst,
The iron fetters yield.

3

mf He comes, the broken heart to bind,
The bleeding soul to cure,
And with the treasures of his grace
To bless the humble poor.

4

f Our glad Hosannas, Prince of Peace,
Thy welcome shall proclaim;
And heaven's eternal arches ring
With thy belovèd name.

P. DODDRIDGE†

HYMN **54**   Cross of Jesus — 8 7 8 7   Sir J. Stainer, 1840–1901

mf Come, thou long-expected Jesus,
Born to set thy people free;
From our fears and sins release us;
Let us find our rest in thee.

2

Israel's strength and consolation,
Hope of all the earth thou art;
Dear Desire of every nation,
Joy of every longing heart.

3

f Born thy people to deliver;
Born a Child and yet a King;
Born to reign in us for ever;
Now thy gracious kingdom bring.

4

mf By thy own eternal Spirit,
Rule in all our hearts alone:
By thy all-sufficient merit,
Raise us to thy glorious throne.

C. WESLEY

Alternative Tune, Halton Holgate, 186

59

Advent

HYMN 55   Sleepers, wake — 8 9 8. 8 9 8. 6 6 4 4 4 8   P. Nicolai, 1556–1608

Harmony from J. S. Bach, 1685–1750

Advent

Wachet auf

Sleepers, wake! the watch-cry pealeth,
While slumber deep each eyelid sealeth:
Awake, Jerusalem, awake!
Midnight's solemn hour is tolling,
And seraph-notes are onward rolling;
They call on us our part to take.
   Come forth, ye virgins wise :
   The Bridegroom comes, arise!
     Alleluia!
   Each lamp be bright
   With ready light
To grace the marriage feast to-night

2

Zion hears the voice that singeth,
With sudden joy her glad heart springeth,
At once she wakes, she stands arrayed :
Her Light is come, her Star ascending,
Lo, girt with truth, with mercy blending,
Her Bridegroom there, so long delayed
   All hail! God's glorious Son,
   All hail! our joy and crown,
     Alleluia!
   The joyful call
   We answer all,
And follow to the bridal hall.

3

Praise to him who goes before us!
Let men and angels join in chorus,
Let harp and cymbal add their sound.
Twelve the gates, a pearl each portal—
We haste to join the choir immortal
Within the Holy City's bound.
   Ear ne'er heard aught like this,
   Nor heart conceived such bliss.
     Alleluia!
   We raise the song,
   We swell the throng,
To praise thee ages all along.

P. Nicolai
Tr. Frances E. Cox†

Advent

When came in flesh the incarnate Word,
The heedless world slept on,
And only simple shepherds heard
That God had sent his Son.

2
When comes the Saviour at the last,
From east to west shall shine͜
The aweful pomp, and earth aghast
Shall tremble at the sign.

3
Lord, who could dare see thee descend͜
In state, unless he knew
Thou art the sorrowing sinner's friend,
The gracious and the true?

4
Dwell in our hearts, O Saviour blest:
So shall thine advent's dawn
'Twixt us and thee, our bosom-guest,
Be but the veil withdrawn.

J. ANSTICE

The following hymns are suitable for this season:

227   O quickly come, dread Judge of all.
228   That day of wrath, that dreadful day.
229   Ye servants of the Lord.
262 Thy Kingdom come, O God.
263   Thy Kingdom come! on bended knee.

CHRISTMAS

FIRST TUNE

Sedulius — L.M. *Nürnbergisches Gesangbuch,* 1676

A solis ortus cardine

f From east to west, from shore to
  shore,
  Let every heart awake and sing,
  The holy Child whom Mary bore,
  The Christ, the everlasting King.

2
mf Behold, the world's Creator wears
  The form and fashion of a slave;
  Our very flesh our Maker shares,
  His fallen creature, man, to save.

3
For this how wondrously he wrought!
A maiden, in her lowly place,
Became, in ways beyond all thought,
The chosen vessel of his grace.

4
She bowed her to the angel's word
Declaring what the Father willed,
And suddenly the promised Lord
That pure and hallowed temple filled.

5
p He shrank not from the oxen's stall,
  He lay within the manger bed,
  And he whose bounty feedeth all
  At Mary's breast himself was fed.

6
mf And while the angels in the sky
  Sang praise above the silent field,
  To shepherds poor the Lord most high,
  The one great Shepherd, was revealed.

[UNISON] 7
f All glory for this blessèd morn
  To God the Father ever be;
  All praise to thee, O Virgin-born,
  All praise, O Holy Ghost, to thee.

SEDULIUS *Tr.* J. Ellerton

Christmas

Trinity College — L.M.   J. B. Dykes, 1823–76

A solis ortus cardine

f From east to west, from shore to
    shore,
    Let every heart awake and sing⌣
The holy Child whom Mary bore,
    The Christ, the everlasting King.

2
mf Behold, the world's Creator wears⌣
    The form and fashion of a slave;
Our very flesh our Maker shares,
    His fallen creature, man, to save.

3
For this how wondrously he wrought!
    A maiden, in her lowly place,
Became, in ways beyond all thought,
    The chosen vessel of his grace.

4
She bowed her to the angel's word
    Declaring what the Father willed,
And suddenly the promised Lord
    That pure and hallowed temple filled.

5
p He shrank not from the oxen's stall,
    He lay within the manger bed,
And he whose bounty feedeth all
    At Mary's breast himself was fed.

6
mf And while the angels in the sky
    Sang praise above the silent field,
To shepherds poor the Lord most high,
    The one great Shepherd, was revealed.

[UNISON]   7
f All glory for this blessèd morn
    To God the Father ever be;
All praise to thee, O Virgin-born,
    All praise, O Holy Ghost, to thee.

SEDULIUS *Tr.* J. Ellerton

Alternative Tune, Erfurt, 151

HYMN **58** Divinum mysterium — 8 7 8 7. 8 7 7   Nyland, *Piæ Cantiones*, 1582

UNISON

Corde natus ex Parentis

mf Of the Father's love begotten
    Ere the worlds began to be,
He is Alpha and Omega,
    He the source, the ending he,
Of the things that are, that have been,
    And that future years shall see,
        Evermore and evermore.

2
O that birth for ever blessèd!
    When the Virgin, full of grace,
By the Holy Ghost conceiving,
    Bare the Saviour of our race,

And the Babe, the world's Redeemer,
    First revealed his sacred face,
        Evermore and evermore.

3
f O ye heights of heaven, adore him;
    Angel hosts, his praises sing;
Powers, dominions bow before him,
    And extol our God and King;
Let no tongue on earth be silent,
    Every voice in concert ring,
        Evermore and evermore.

PRUDENTIUS *Tr.* J. M. Neale‡

NOTE. *A longer version of this hymn will be found in the 'Processional' section* (**591**)

Christmas

Probably by J. F. Wade,
c. 1711–86

Adeste fideles

DESCANT

Yea, Lord, we greet thee, Born this hap-py

1 O   come, all ye   faith - ful, Joy-ful and tri -
2 God   of ....   God, ...   Light .... of ....
3 Sing, choirs of an - gels, Sing in ex - ul -
4 [UNISON] Yea, Lord, we   greet thee, Born this hap-py

morn - ing;   Je - su, to   thee   be

1 um - phant, O   come   ye, O   come   ye to
2 Light, ...   Lo,   he ab - hors .. not the
3 ta - tion,   Sing, all ye · ci - ti - zens of
4 morn - ing;   Je - su, to   thee .. be ....

glo - ry given;   Word   of the   Fa - ther,

1 Beth - le - hem; Come and be - hold him‿
2 Vir - gin's womb; Ve - ry .... God, Be -
3 heaven a - bove: 'Glo - ry to   God ....
4 glo - ry given;   Word of the   Fa - ther,

66

Now in flesh ap - pear - ing: O come,

1 Born, the King of An - gels:
2 got - ten, not cre - a - ted: O come, let us a -
3 In .... the .... high - est:' O come, let us a -
4 Now in flesh ap - pear - ing:

O come,

dore him, O come, let us a - dore him, O

come, let us a - dore him, Christ the Lord.

come, let us a - dore him, Christ the Lord.

18th cent. *Tr.* F. OAKELEY‡

The Descant may be sung by Trebles for verse 4, the main melody being sung in Unison

NOTE. *A longer version of this hymn will be found in the 'Processional' section* (593)

HYMN 60 Mendelssohn — 7 7 7 7. 7 7 7 7. 7 7   F. Mendelssohn-Bartholdy,
1809–47

Christmas

Hark! the herald-angels sing
Glory to the new-born King,
Peace on earth, and mercy mild,
God and sinners reconciled.
Joyful, all ye nations, rise,
Join the triumph of the skies;
With the angelic host proclaim,
'Christ is born in Bethlehem.'
 Hark! the herald-angels sing
 Glory to the new-born King.

2

Christ, by highest heaven adored,
Christ, the everlasting Lord,
Late in time behold him come,
Offspring of a Virgin's womb.
Veiled in flesh the Godhead see!
Hail, the incarnate Deity!
Pleased as Man with man to dwell,
Jesus, our Emmanuel.
 Hark! the herald-angels sing
 Glory to the new-born King.

3

Hail, the heaven-born Prince of Peace!
Hail, the Sun of Righteousness!
Light and life to all he brings,
Risen with healing in his wings.
Mild he lays his glory by,
Born that man no more may die,
Born to raise the sons of earth,
Born to give them second birth.
 Hark! the herald-angels sing
 Glory to the new-born King.

C. WESLEY and others

HYMN **61** Yorkshire — 10 10. 10 10. 10 10 J. Wainwright, 1723–68

Christmas

f   Christians, awake! salute the happy morn,
Whereon the Saviour of the world was born;
Rise to adore the mystery of love,
Which hosts of angels chanted from above:
With them the joyful tidings first begun
Of God incarnate and the Virgin's Son.

2

Then to the watchful shepherds it was told,
Who heard the angelic herald's voice, 'Behold,
I bring good tidings of a Saviour's birth
To you and all the nations upon earth:
This day hath God fulfilled his promised word,
This day is born a Saviour, Christ the Lord.'

3

He spake; and straightway the celestial choir
In hymns of joy, unknown before, conspire;
The praises of redeeming love they sang,
And heaven's whole orb with Alleluias rang:
God's highest glory was their anthem still,
Peace upon earth, and unto men good will.

4

To Bethlehem straight the enlightened shepherds ran,
To see the wonder God had wrought for man,
And found, with Joseph and the blessèd Maid,
Her Son, the Saviour, in a manger laid:
Then to their flocks, still praising God, return,
And their glad hearts with holy rapture burn.

PART 2

5

mf   O may we keep and ponder in our mind
God's wondrous love in saving lost mankind;
Trace we the Babe, who hath retrieved our loss,
From his poor manger to his bitter Cross;
Tread in his steps, assisted by his grace,
Till man's first heavenly state again takes place.

6

f   Then may we hope, the angelic hosts among,
To sing, redeemed, a glad triumphal song:
He that was born upon this joyful day
Around us all his glory shall display;
Saved by his love, incessant we shall sing
Eternal praise to heaven's almighty King.

J. BYROM‡

71

HYMN **62**   Winchester Old — C.M.   Este, *Psalms,* 1592

ALTERNATIVE VERSION

(Melody in the Tenor part)

Harmonized by T. Ravenscroft (1621)

The Alternative Version may be used for verses 2, 3, and 4

Christmas

mf While shepherds watched their flocks by night,
All seated on the ground,
The angel of the Lord came down,
And glory shone around.

2

'Fear not,' said he (for mighty dread
Had seized their troubled mind);
'Glad tidings of great joy I bring
To you and all mankind.

3

'To you in David's town this day
Is born of David's line
A Saviour, who is Christ the Lord;
And this shall be the sign:

4

'The heavenly Babe you there shall find
To human view displayed,
All meanly wrapped in swathing bands,
And in a manger laid.'

5

Thus spake the seraph; and forthwith
Appeared a shining throng
Of angels praising God, who thus
Addressed their joyful song:

6

f 'All glory be to God on high,
And to the earth be peace;
Good will henceforth from heaven to men
Begin and never cease.'

N. TATE

Christmas

Jam desinant suspiria

f God from on high hath heard!
　Let sighs and sorrows cease!
Lo, from the opening heaven descends⌣
　To man the promised peace.

2
Hark! through the silent night
　Angelic voices swell;
Their joyful songs proclaim that God⌣
　Is born on earth to dwell.

3
mf See how the shepherd-band
　Speed on with eager feet;
Come to the hallowed cave with them
　The holy Babe to greet.

4
p But O what sight appears
　Within that lowly door!
A manger, stall, and swaddling clothes,
　A child, and mother poor!

5
mf　Art thou the Christ? the Son?
　　The Father's Image bright?
　And see we him whose arm upholds⌣
　　Earth and the starry height?

6
f　Yea, faith can pierce the cloud
　　Which veils thy glory now;
　We hail thee God, before whose throne⌣
　　The angels prostrate bow.

7
mf　Our sinful pride to cure
　　With that pure love of thine,
　O be thou born within our hearts,
　　Most holy Child divine.

C. COFFIN
Tr. Bp. J. R. Woodford and Compilers

74

Christmas

mf Angels, from the realms of glory,
    Wing your flight o'er all the earth;
    Ye who sang creation's story,
    Now proclaim Messiah's birth:
f   Come and worship,
    Worship Christ, the new-born King.

2
mf Shepherds, in the field abiding,
    Watching o'er your flocks by night,
    God with man is now residing,
    Yonder shines the infant Light:
f   Come and worship, etc.

3
mf Sages, leave your contemplations;
    Brighter visions beam afar:
    Seek the great Desire of Nations;
    Ye have seen his natal star:
f   Come and worship, etc.

4
mf Saints before the altar bending,
    Watching long in hope and fear,
    Suddenly the Lord, descending,
    In his temple shall appear:
f   Come and worship, etc.

5
mf Though an infant now we view him,
    He shall fill his Father's throne,
    Gather all the nations to him;
    Every knee shall then bow down:
f   Come and worship, etc.

J. Montgomery

Christmas

FIRST TUNE

Forest Green — D.C.M.

English Traditional Melody

By permission of the English Hymnal Company, Ltd.

SECOND TUNE

Wengen — D.C.M.

Sir H. Walford Davies, 1869–1941

To be sung in Unison except verse 3

Christmas

The last line of each verse is repeated in Second Tune

p O little town of Bethlehem,
　How still we see thee lie!
Above thy deep and dreamless sleep
　The silent stars go by:
mf Yet in thy dark streets shineth
　The everlasting Light;
f The hopes and fears of all the years
　Are met in thee to-night.

2
For Christ is born of Mary;
　And, gathered all above,
p While mortals sleep, the angels keep
　Their watch of wondering love.
f O morning stars, together
　Proclaim the holy birth,
And praises sing to God the King,
　And peace to men on earth.

3
p How silently, how silently,
　The wondrous gift is given!
So God imparts to human hearts
　The blessings of his heaven.
No ear may hear his coming;
　But in this world of sin,　[still
Where meek souls will receive him,
　The dear Christ enters in.

4
mf O holy Child of Bethlehem,
　Descend to us, we pray;
Cast out our sin, and enter in:
　Be born in us to-day.
f We hear the Christmas angels
　The great glad tidings tell:
O come to us, abide with us,
　Our Lord Emmanuel.

BISHOP PHILLIPS BROOKS

77

Christmas

Traditional Air, adapted by
Sir A. Sullivan, 1842–1900

mf It came upon the midnight clear,
  That glorious song of old,
From angels bending near the earth
  To touch their harps of gold :
'Peace on the earth, good will to
    men,
  From heaven's all-gracious King!'
The world in solemn stillness lay
  To hear the angels sing.

2
Still through the cloven skies they
    come,
  With peaceful wings unfurled ;
And still their heavenly music floats
  O'er all the weary world :
Above its sad and lowly plains
  They bend on hovering wing ;
And ever o'er its Babel-sounds
  The blessèd angels sing.

3
p Yet with the woes of sin and strife
  The world has suffered long ;
Beneath the angel-strain have rolled
  Two thousand years of wrong ;

And man, at war with man, hears
    not‿
  The love-song which they bring :
O hush the noise, ye men of strife,
  And hear the angels sing.

4*
And ye, beneath life's crushing load,
  Whose forms are bending low,
Who toil along the climbing way
  With painful steps and slow,
Look, now! for glad and golden
    hours‿
  Come swiftly on the wing ;
O rest beside the weary road,
  And hear the angels sing.

5
mf For lo, the days are hastening on,
  By prophet-bards foretold,
When, with the ever-circling years,
  Comes round the age of gold ;
f When peace shall over all the earth
  Its ancient splendours fling,
And the whole world give back the
  Which now the angels sing. [song

E. H. SEARS

78

Christmas

1 In the bleak mid - win - ter Fros - ty wind made moan,
2 Our God, heaven can - not hold him Nor . . . earth sus - tain;
3 E - nough for him, whom cher-u-bim Wor-ship night and day, A
4 An - gels and arch - an - gels May have ga - thered there,
5 What . . . can I give him, Poor . . . as I am?

1 Earth stood hard as i - ron, Wa - ter like a stone:
2 Heaven and earth shall flee a - way When he comes to reign:
3 breast - ful of milk, And a man - ger - ful of hay: E -
4 Cher - u - bim and ser - a - phim Throng - ed the air— But
5 If I were a shep - herd I would bring a lamb;

1 Snow had fall - en, snow on snow, Snow . . . on . . . snow,
2 In the bleak mid - win - ter A sta - ble - place suf - ficed The
3 nough for him, whom an - gels Fall . . . down be - fore, The
4 on - ly his . . . . mo - ther In her mai - den bliss
5 If I were a wise man I would do my part; Yet

1 In the bleak mid - win - ter, Long a - go.
2 Lord . . . God Al - migh - ty, Je - sus . . . Christ.
3 ox and ass and ca - mel Which a - dore.
4 Wor-shipped the Be - lov - èd With a . . . . kiss.
5 what I can I give him— Give my . . . heart.

CHRISTINA ROSSETTI

HYMN **68**   Es ist ein' Ros' — 7 6 7 6. 6 7 6   Old German

Harmonies based on M. Praetorius, 1571–1621

μέγα καὶ παράδοξον θαῦμα

mf A great and mighty wonder,
A full and holy cure!
The Virgin bears the Infant
With virgin-honour pure:
f   Repeat the hymn again!
'To God on high be glory,
And peace on earth to men.'

2

mf The Word becomes incarnate,
And yet remains on high;
And cherubim sing anthems
To shepherds from the sky:
f   Repeat, etc.

3
While thus they sing your Monarch,
Those bright angelic bands,
Rejoice, ye vales and mountains,
Ye oceans, clap your hands:
Repeat, etc.

4
mf Since all he comes to ransom,
By all be he adored,
The infant born in Bethlem,
The Saviour and the Lord:
f   Repeat, etc.

ST. GERMANUS *Tr.* J. M. Neale†

HYMN **69** Kilmarnock — C.M. N. Dougall, 1776–1862

Behold, the great Creator makes
  Himself a house of clay,
A robe of virgin flesh he takes
  Which he will wear for ay.

2
Hark, hark! the wise eternal Word
  Like a weak infant cries;
In form of servant is the Lord,
  And God in cradle lies.

3
This wonder struck the world amazed,
  It shook the starry frame;
Squadrons of spirits stood and gazed,
  Then down in troops they came.

4
Glad shepherds ran to view this sight;
  A choir of angels sings,
And eastern sages with delight
  Adore this King of Kings.

5
Join then, all hearts that are not stone,
  And all our voices prove,
To celebrate this Holy One,
  The God of peace and love.

T. PESTEL

HYMN **70** Ach Herr — 8 8 7. 8 8 7 Melody from M. Praetorius, 1571–1621

I sing the birth was born to-night,
The Author both of life and light :
　The angels so did sound it ;
And like the ravished shepherds said,
Who saw the light and were afraid,
　Yet searched, and true they found it.

3
The Father's wisdom willed it so,
The Son's obedience knew no 'No,'
　Both wills were in one stature ;
And, as that wisdom hath decreed,
The Word was now made flesh indeed,
　And took on him our nature.

2
The Son of God, the eternal King,
That did us all salvation bring,
　And freed the world from danger,
He whom the whole world could not
　　take,　　　　　　　[make,
The Lord which heaven and earth did
Was now laid in a manger.

4
What comfort by him do we win,
Who made himself the price of sin,
　To make us heirs of glory !
To see this Babe, all innocence,
A martyr born in our defence—
　Can man forget this story ?

BEN JONSON

82

HYMN **71**   Devonshire — L.M.   J. F. Lampe, 1703–51

To us a Child of royal birth,
    Heir of the promises, is given ;
The invisible appears on earth,
    The Son of Man, the God of heaven.

2
A Saviour born, in love supreme,
    He comes our fallen souls to raise,
He comes his people to redeem,
    With all the fulness of his grace.

3
The Christ, by raptured seers foretold,
    Filled with the eternal Spirit's power,
Prophet, and Priest, and King behold,
    And Lord of all the worlds adore.

4
The Lord of Hosts, the God most high,
    Who quits his throne on earth to live,
With joy we welcome from the sky,
    With faith into our hearts receive.

C. WESLEY†

NEW YEAR

HYMN 72　　　　　　　FIRST TUNE

Perranporth — 7 5 7 5. D　　　　　　　A. W. Wilson

SECOND TUNE

Father, let me dedicate — 7 5 7 5. D　　　Sir G. A. Macfarren, 1813–87

84

New Year

mf Father, let me dedicate⌣
 All this year to thee,
In whatever worldly state⌣
 Thou wilt have me be :
Not from sorrow, pain, or care
 Freedom dare I claim;
This alone shall be my prayer,
 'Glorify thy name.'

2
Can a child presume to choose
 Where or how to live?
Can a Father's love refuse
 All the best to give?
More thou givest every day
 Than the best can claim,
Nor withholdest aught that may⌣
 Glorify thy name.

3
p If thou callest to the cross,
 And its shadow come,
Turning all my gain to loss,
 Shrouding heart and home;
mf Let me think how thy dear Son⌣
 To his glory came,
And in deepest woe pray on,
 'Glorify thy name.'

4
If in mercy thou wilt spare⌣
 Joys that yet are mine;
If on life, serene and fair,
 Brighter rays may shine;
f Let my glad heart, while it sings,
 Thee in all proclaim,
And, whate'er the future brings,
 Glorify thy name.

L. TUTTIETT

HYMN **73** Culbach — 7 7 7 7 J. Scheffler, *Heilige Seelenlust*, 1657

mf For thy mercy and thy grace,
 Faithful through another year,
Hear our song of thankfulness;
 Jesu, our Redeemer, hear.

2
In our weakness and distress,
 Rock of strength, be thou our stay;
In the pathless wilderness
 Be our true and living Way.

3
p Who of us death's awful road
 In the coming year shall tread,

With thy rod and staff, O God,
 Comfort thou his dying bed.

4
mf Keep us faithful, keep us pure,
 Keep us evermore thine own,
Help, O help us to endure,
 Fit us for thy promised crown.

5
f So within thy palace gate
 We shall praise on golden strings
Thee the only potentate,
 Lord of Lords and King of Kings.

H. DOWNTON†

EPIPHANY

FIRST TUNE

Hostis Herodes impie — L.M.

Mode iii

Hostis Herodes impie

1 How vain the cru - el He - rod's fear,
2 The east - ern sa - ges saw from far
3 With - in the Jor - dan's sa - cred flood
4 And O what mi - ra - cle di - vine,
5 All glo - ry, Je - su, be to thee

1 When told that Christ the King is near! He takes not earth - ly
2 And fol - lowed on his guid - ing star; By light their way to
3 The heaven - ly Lamb in meek - ness stood; That he who knew no
4 When wa - ter red - dened in - to wine! He spake the word, and
5 For this thy glad E - piph - an - y; Whom with the Fa - ther

1 realms a - way, Who gives the realms that ne'er de - cay.
2 Light they trod, And by their gifts con - fessed their God.
3 sin that day, His peo - ple's sin might wash a - way.
4 forth it flowed In streams that na - ture ne'er be - stowed.
5 we a - dore And Ho - ly Ghost for ev - er - more.

HYMN **74**

SECOND TUNE

Ely — L.M.

Bishop T. Turton, 1780–1864

Hostis Herodes impie

mf How vain the cruel Herod's fear,
When told that Christ the King is near!
He takes not earthly realms away,
Who gives the realms that ne'er decay.

2
The eastern sages saw from far
And followed on his guiding star;
By light their way to Light they trod,
And by their gifts confessed their God.

3
Within the Jordan's sacred flood
The heavenly Lamb in meekness stood;
That he who knew no sin that day
His people's sin might wash away.

4
And O what miracle divine,
When water reddened into wine!
He spake the word, and forth it flowed
In streams that nature ne'er bestowed.

{UNISON} 5
f All glory, Jesu, be to thee
For this thy glad Epiphany;
Whom with the Father we adore
And Holy Ghost for evermore.

SEDULIUS *Tr.* Compilers

87

Epiphany

FIRST TUNE

Bede — 11 10 11 10

Adapted from Handel's *Athalia* by
Sir J. Goss, 1800–80

SECOND TUNE

Epiphany — 11 10 11 10

E. J. Hopkins, 1818–1901

f Brightest and best of the sons of the morning,
Dawn on our darkness, and lend us thine aid;
Star of the east, the horizon adorning,
Guide where our infant Redeemer is laid

Epiphany

2

mf Cold on his cradle the dew-drops are shining;
 Low lies his head with the beasts of the stall;
 Angels adore him in slumber reclining,
 Maker and Monarch and Saviour of all.

3

Say, shall we yield him, in costly devotion,
 Odours of Edom, and offerings divine,
 Gems of the mountain, and pearls of the ocean,
 Myrrh from the forest, or gold from the mine?

4

Vainly we offer each ample oblation,
 Vainly with gifts would his favour secure:
 Richer by far is the heart's adoration,
 Dearer to God are the prayers of the poor.

BISHOP R. HEBER

The first verse may be repeated at the end

HYMN **76**   Stuttgart — 8 7 8 7   C. F. Witt, 1660–1716

O sola magnarum urbium

mf Earth has many a noble city;
 Bethlem, thou dost all excel:
 Out of thee the Lord from heaven
 Came to rule his Israel.

2

Fairer than the sun at morning
 Was the star that told his birth,
 To the world its God announcing
 Seen in fleshly form on earth.

3

Eastern sages at his cradle
 Make oblations rich and rare;

See them give in deep devotion
 Gold and frankincense and myrrh.

4

Sacred gifts of mystic meaning:
 Incense doth their God disclose,
 Gold the King of Kings proclaimeth,
 Myrrh his sepulchre foreshows.

5

f Jesu, whom the Gentiles worshipped
 At thy glad Epiphany,
 Unto thee with God the Father
 And the Spirit glory be.

PRUDENTIUS
Tr. E. Caswall and Compilers

89

HYMN **77**   Was lebet — 13 10 13 10   *Rheinhardt MS.*, Üttingen, 1754

* *For first verse only*

O worship the Lord in the beauty of holiness!
  Bow down before him, his glory proclaim;
With gold of obedience, and incense of lowliness,
  Kneel and adore him: the Lord is his name.

2
Low at his feet lay thy burden of carefulness:
  High on his heart he will bear it for thee,
Comfort thy sorrows, and answer thy prayerfulness,
  Guiding thy steps as may best for thee be.

3
Fear not to enter his courts in the slenderness
  Of the poor wealth thou wouldst reckon as thine:
Truth in its beauty, and love in its tenderness,
  These are the offerings to lay on his shrine.

4
These, though we bring them in trembling and fearfulness,
  He will accept for the name that is dear;
Mornings of joy give for evenings of tearfulness,
  Trust for our trembling and hope for our fear.

                                        J. S. B. MONSELL

The first verse may be repeated at the end

HYMN **78**   Tallis — C.M.   T. Tallis, *c.* 1505–85

A lower setting of this tune will be found at Hymn 231

Divine crescebas puer

mf The heavenly Child in stature grows,
    And, growing, learns to die;
    And still his early training shows⌣
    His coming agony.

2
The Son of God his glory hides
    To dwell with parents poor;
And he who made the heavens abides⌣
    In dwelling-place obscure.

3
Those mighty hands that rule the sky
    No earthly toil refuse;
The Maker of the stars on high
    An humble trade pursues.

4
He whom the choirs of angels praise,
    Bearing each dread decree,
His earthly parents now obeys
    In glad humility.

[UNISON]   5
f For this thy lowliness revealed,
    Jesu, we thee adore,
And praise to God the Father yield
    And Spirit evermore.

J. B. DE SANTEUIL
Tr. J. Chandler and Compilers

Epiphany

C. Kocher, 1786–1872

DESCANT

If preferred, the harmonies for lines 1 and 2 may be repeated
for lines 3 and 4

The Descant may be sung by Trebles for verses 3 and 5, the main melody being sung in Unison.
In this case the above harmonies should be played on the organ

Epiphany

f   As with gladness men of old
Did the guiding star behold,
As with joy they hailed its light,
Leading onward, beaming bright;
So, most gracious Lord, may we
Evermore be led to thee.

2

mf As with joyful steps they sped,
Saviour, to thy lowly bed,
There to bend the knee before
Thee whom heaven and earth adore;
So may we with willing feet
Ever seek thy mercy-seat.

3

As they offered gifts most rare
At thy cradle rude and bare,
So may we with holy joy,
Pure and free from sin's alloy,
All our costliest treasures bring,
Christ, to thee our heavenly King.

4

p   Holy Jesus, every day
Keep us in the narrow way,
mf And, when earthly things are past,
Bring our ransomed souls at last
f   Where they need no star to guide,
Where no clouds thy glory hide.

5

In the heavenly country bright
Need they no created light;
Thou its light, its joy, its crown,
Thou its sun which goes not down;
There for ever may we sing
Alleluias to our King.

W. CHATTERTON DIX

93

HYMN **80** Dundee — C.M. *Psalms* (Edinburgh, 1615)

A lower setting of this tune will be found at Hymn 272

ALTERNATIVE VERSION

(Melody in the Tenor part)

Harmonized by T. Ravenscroft (1621)

The Alternative Version may be used for verses 3 and 6

mf The people that in darkness sat
 A glorious light have seen;
The light has shined on them who long⌣
 In shades of death have been.

2
To hail thee, Sun of Righteousness,
 The gathering nations come;
They joy as when the reapers bear⌣
 Their harvest treasures home.

3
For thou their burden dost remove,
 And break the tyrant's rod,
As in the day when Midian fell
 Before the sword of God.

4
f For unto us a Child is born,
 To us a Son is given,
And on his shoulder ever rests⌣
 All power in earth and heaven.

5
His name shall be the Prince of Peace,
 The everlasting Lord,
The Wonderful, the Counsellor,
 The God by all adored.

6
His righteous government and power⌣
 Shall over all extend;
On judgement and on justice based,
 His reign shall have no end.

7
mf Lord Jesus, reign in us, we pray,
 And make us thine alone,
Who with the Father ever art
 And Holy Spirit One.

J. Morrison and Compileis

HYMN **81**   St. Edmund — 7 7 7 7. D   C. Steggall, 1826–1905

mf   Songs of thankfulness and praise,
     Jesu, Lord, to thee we raise,
     Manifested by the star
     To the sages from afar ;
     Branch of royal David's stem
     In thy birth at Bethlehem :
 f   Anthems be to thee addrest,
     God in Man made manifest.

2

mf   Manifest at Jordan's stream,
     Prophet, Priest, and King supreme ;
     And at Cana wedding-guest
     In thy Godhead manifest ;
     Manifest in power divine,
     Changing water into wine :
 f   Anthems be to thee addrest,
     God in Man made manifest.

96

Epiphany

3

mf Manifest in making whole
Palsied limbs and fainting soul;
Manifest in valiant fight,
Quelling all the devil's might;
Manifest in gracious will,
Ever bringing good from ill:
f Anthems be to thee addrest,
God in Man made manifest.

4*

mf Sun and moon shall darkened be,
Stars shall fall, the heavens shall flee;
f Christ will then like lightning shine,
All will see his glorious sign;
All will then the trumpet hear,
All will see the Judge appear:
Thou by all wilt be confest,
God in Man made manifest.

5

mf Grant us grace to see thee, Lord,
Mirrored in thy holy word;
May we imitate thee now,
And be pure, as pure art thou;
That we like to thee may be
At thy great Epiphany;
f And may praise thee, ever blest,
God in Man made manifest.

BISHOP CHR. WORDSWORTH

The following hymns are suitable for this season:

219 Hail to the Lord's Anointed.
220 Jesus shall reign where'er the sun.
264 God of mercy, God of grace.
265 From Greenland's icy mountains.
266 Thou, whose almighty word.
267 Lord, her watch thy Church is keeping.
268 Fling out the banner! let it float.
269 Hills of the north, rejoice.
270 Trumpet of God, sound high.
271 God is working his purpose out.

THE WEEK BEFORE SEPTUAGESIMA

HYMN 82 FIRST TUNE

Alleluia, dulce carmen — 8 7. 8 7. 8 7

Melody from La Feillée
Méthode de Plain Chant, 1808

Alleluia, dulce carmen

1 Al - le - lu - ia, song of sweet-ness, Voice of joy that can - not die;
2 Al - le - lu - ia thou re - sound-est, True Je - ru - sa - lem and free;
3 Al - le - lu - ia can - not al - ways Be our song while here be - low;
4 There-fore in our hymns we pray thee, Grant us, bless - èd Tri - ni - ty,

1 Al - le - lu - ia is the an - them Ev - er dear to choirs on high:
2 Al - le - lu - ia, joy - ful mo - ther, All thy chil - dren sing with thee;
3 Al - le - lu - ia our trans - gres - sions Make us for a while for - go;
4 At the last to keep thine Eas - ter In our home be - yond the sky,

1 In the house of God a - bi - ding Thus they sing e - ter - nal - ly.
2 But by Bab - y - lon's sad wa - ters Mourn - ing ex - iles now are we.
3 For the so - lemn time is com - ing When our tears for sin must flow.
4 There to thee for ev - er sing - ing Al - le - lu - ia joy - ful - ly.

The Week before Septuagesima

Alleluia, dulce carmen — 8 7. 8 7. 8 7

Essay on the Church Plain Chant, 1782

A higher setting of this tune will be found at Hymn 568

Alleluia, dulce carmen

f Alleluia, song of sweetness,
  Voice of joy that cannot die;
Alleluia is the anthem
  Ever dear to choirs on high:
In the house of God abiding
  Thus they sing eternally.

2
Alleluia thou resoundest,
  True Jerusalem and free;
Alleluia, joyful mother,
  All thy children sing with thee;
p But by Babylon's sad waters
  Mourning exiles now are we.

3
Alleluia cannot always ‿
  Be our song while here below;
Alleluia our transgressions ‿
  Make us for awhile forgo;
For the solemn time is coming
  When our tears for sin must flow.

4
mf Therefore in our hymns we pray thee,
  Grant us, blessèd Trinity,
At the last to keep thine Easter
  In our home beyond the sky,
f There to thee for ever singing
  Alleluia joyfully.

Tr. J. M. NEALE and Compilers

SEPTUAGESIMA

HYMN **83**   St. Gregory — L.M.   *Darmstadt Gesangbuch,* 1698

Te laeta, mundi Conditor

mf   Creator of the world, to thee
       An endless rest of joy belongs;
       And heavenly choirs are ever free
       To sing on high their festal songs.

2

p   But we are fallen creatures here,
       Where pain and sorrow daily come;
       And how can we in exile drear
       Sing out, as they, sweet songs of home?

3

mf   O Father, who dost promise still
       That they who mourn shall blessèd be,
p   Help us to grieve for deeds of ill
       That banish us so long from thee:

4

       And, while we grieve, give faith to rest
       In hope upon thy loving care;
mf   Till thou restore us, with the blest,
       Their songs of praise in heaven to share.

C. COFFIN *Tr.* Compilers

*From Septuagesima Sunday to Lent the following
hymns are suitable:*

For Septuagesima:	For Sexagesima:
168 There is a book, who runs may read.	**185** Praise to the Holiest in the height.
170 The spacious firmament on high.	
172 All creatures of our God and King.	
173 I praised the earth in beauty seen.	*For Quinquagesima:*
174 Lord of beauty, thine the splendour.	**233** Gracious Spirit, Holy Ghost.
442 All things bright and beautiful.	**316** Great mover of all hearts, whose hand.

LENT

Audi, benigne Conditor — L.M. Mode ii

Audi, benigne Conditor

1 O Ma - ker of the world, give ear; In pi - tying
2 All hearts are o - pen un - to thee; Thou know - est
3 Help us to grow in self - con - trol, To make the

1 love vouch - safe to hear The prayers our con - trite
2 each in - fir - mi - ty; Now, as we turn to
3 bo - dy serve the soul: So may thy lov - ing -

1 spi - rits raise In this our fast of for - ty days.
2 seek thy face, Pour down on us thy par - doning grace.
3 kind - ness bless Our fast with fruits of ho - li - ness.

HYMN 84   SECOND TUNE

Cannons — L.M.   G. F. Handel, 1685–1759

Audi, benigne Conditor

O Maker of the world, give ear;
In pitying love vouchsafe to hear
The prayers our contrite spirits raise
In this our fast of forty days.

2

All hearts are open unto thee;
Thou knowest each infirmity;
Now, as we turn to seek thy face,
Pour down on us thy pardoning grace.

3

Help us to grow in self-control,
To make the body serve the soul:
So may thy loving-kindness bless
Our fast with fruits of holiness.

Tr. COMPILERS

HYMN 85 Keble — L.M.   J. B. Dykes, 1823–76

Jesu quadragenariae

Jesu, who this our Lenten-tide
Of abstinence hast sanctified,
Be with thy Church in saving power
In this her penitential hour.

2
And, as thou dost forgive the past,
Thy sheltering arms around us cast,
That we may in thy grace remain
And fall not back to sins again.

3
Make, Lord, this Lenten discipline
An expiation for our sin;
And through these days ourselves prepare
The joys of Eastertide to share.

Tr. BISHOP W. H. FRERE

Alternative Plainsong Tune, Audi, benigne Conditor, 84

103

HYMN **86**   Aberystwyth — 7 7 7 7. D   J. Parry, 1841–1903

<p> Saviour, when in dust to thee
Low we bow the adoring knee;
When, repentant, to the skies
Scarce we lift our weeping eyes;
O by all thy pains and woe
Suffered once for man below,
Bending from thy throne on high,
Hear our solemn litany.

2

mf By thy helpless infant years,
By thy life of want and tears,
By thy days of sore distress
In the savage wilderness;

By the dread mysterious hour
Of the insulting tempter's power:
Turn, O turn a favouring eye,
p   Hear our solemn litany.

3*

mf By the sacred griefs that wept
O'er the grave where Lazarus slept;
By the boding tears that flowed
Over Salem's loved abode;
By the mournful word that told
Treachery lurked within thy fold:
From thy seat above the sky
p   Hear our solemn litany.

Lent

4

By thine hour of dire despair;
By thine agony of prayer;
By the Cross, the nail, the thorn,
Piercing spear, and torturing scorn;
By the gloom that veiled the skies
O'er the dreadful Sacrifice:
Listen to our humble cry,
Hear our solemn litany.

5

By thy deep expiring groan;
By the sad sepulchral stone;
By the vault whose dark abode
Held in vain the rising God:
f O, from earth to heaven restored,
Mighty, re-ascended Lord,
mf Listen, listen to the cry
p Of our solemn litany.

SIR R. GRANT†

HYMN **87**   Tunbridge — 7 7 7 7   J. Clarke, *c.* 1659–1707

p Sinful, sighing to be blest;
　Bound, and longing to be free;
　Weary, waiting for my rest:
　　God, be merciful to me.

2

Goodness I have none to plead,
　Sinfulness in all I see,
I can only bring my need:
　　God, be merciful to me.

3*

Broken heart and downcast eyes
　Dare not lift themselves to thee;
Yet thou canst interpret sighs:
　　God, be merciful to me.

4

From this sinful heart of mine
　To thy bosom I would flee;
I am not my own, but thine:
　　God, be merciful to me.

5

f There is One beside the throne,
　And my only hope and plea
Are in him, and him alone:
mf　　God, be merciful to me.

6

He my cause will undertake,
　My interpreter will be;
He's my all; and for his sake,
　　God, be merciful to me.

J. S. B. MONSELL

Lent

p When wounded sore the stricken heart
　　Lies bleeding and unbound,
　One only hand, a piercèd hand,
　　Can salve the sinner's wound.

2
　When sorrow swells the laden breast,
　　And tears of anguish flow,
　One only heart, a broken heart,
　　Can feel the sinner's woe.

3
　When penitential grief has wept
　　Over some foul dark spot,
　One only stream, a stream of Blood,
　　Can wash away the blot.

4
mf 'Tis Jesus' Blood that washes white,
　　His hand that brings relief;
　His heart is touched with all our joys,
　　And feels for all our grief.

5
　Lift up thy bleeding hand, O Lord,
　　Unseal that cleansing tide :
　We have no shelter from our sin
　　But in thy wounded side.

MRS. C. F. ALEXANDER

Alternative Tune, St. Bernard, 104

A higher setting of this tune will be found at Hymn 413

Lent

My spirit longs for thee
Within my troubled breast,
Though I unworthy be
Of so divine a guest.

2
Of so divine a guest
Unworthy though I be,
Yet has my heart no rest
Unless it come from thee.

3
Unless it come from thee,
In vain I look around;
In all that I can see
No rest is to be found.

4
No rest is to be found
But in thy blessèd love:
O let my wish be crowned,
And send it from above!

J. BYROM

HYMN 90   Colchester — 8 8. 8 8. 8 8   S. S. Wesley, 1810–76

Still nigh me, O my Saviour, stand,
    And guard in fierce temptation's hour;
Hide in the hollow of thy hand,
    Show forth in me thy saving power;
Still be thine arm my sure defence:
Nor earth nor hell shall pluck me
    thence.

2
Still let thy love point out my way:
    How wondrous things thy love hath
    wrought!

Still lead me, lest I go astray;
    Direct my work, inspire my thought;
And, if I fall, soon may I hear
Thy voice, and know that Love is near.

3
In suffering be thy love my peace,
    In weakness be thy love my power;
And when the storms of life shall cease,
    Jesus, in that tremendous hour,
In death as life be thou my guide,
And save me, who for me hast died.

C. WESLEY†

107

Lent

St. Andrew of Crete — 6 5 6 5. D   J. B. Dykes, 1823–76

UNISON IN VERSES 1, 2, 3   HARMONY

SECOND TUNE

Gute Bäume bringen — 6 5 6 5. D   P. Sohren, *d. c.* 1692

Lent

p Christian, dost thou see them
    On the holy ground,
How the troops of Midian‿
    Prowl and prowl around?
f Christian, up and smite them,
    Counting gain but loss;
Smite them by the merit‿
    Of the holy Cross.

2
p Christian, dost thou feel them,
    How they work within,
Striving, tempting, luring,
    Goading into sin?
f Christian, never tremble;
    Never be down-cast;
Smite them by the virtue‿
    Of the Lenten fast.

3
p   Christian, dost thou hear them,
      How they speak thee fair?
   'Always fast and vigil?
   Always watch and prayer?'
f   Christian, answer boldly,
      'While I breathe I pray:'
   Peace shall follow battle,
   Night shall end in day.

4
mf 'Well I know thy trouble,
      O my servant true;
   Thou art very weary,
   I was weary too;
f   But that toil shall make thee‿
      Some day all mine own,
   And the end of sorrow‿
   Shall be near my throne.'

J. M. NEALE†

Lent

mf Forty days and forty nights
   Thou wast fasting in the wild;
Forty days and forty nights
   Tempted, and yet undefiled:

2
Sunbeams scorching all the day;
   Chilly dew-drops nightly shed;
Prowling beasts about thy way;
   Stones thy pillow, earth thy bed.

3
Shall not we thy sorrows share,
   And from earthly joys abstain,
Fasting with unceasing prayer,
   Glad with thee to suffer pain?

4
And if Satan, vexing sore,
   Flesh or spirit should assail,
Thou, his vanquisher before,
   Grant we may not faint nor fail.

5
p So shall we have peace divine;
   Holier gladness ours shall be;
Round us too shall angels shine,
   Such as ministered to thee.

6
mf Keep, O keep us, Saviour dear,
   Ever constant by thy side;
f That with thee we may appear
   At the eternal Eastertide.

G. H. SMYTTAN and F. POTT

Lent

O Lord, turn not thy face from me,
Who lie in woeful state,
Lamenting all my sinful life
Before thy mercy-gate:

2
A gate which opens wide to those⌣
That do lament their sin;
Shut not that gate against me, Lord,
But let me enter in.

3
And call me not to strict account
How I have sojourned here;
For then my guilty conscience knows
How vile I shall appear.

4
Mercy, good Lord, mercy I ask:
This is my humble prayer;
For mercy, Lord, is all my suit:
O let thy mercy spare.

J. MARCKANT‡
(Form in *Supplement to the New Version*, 1708)

W. H. Monk, 1823–89

Lord, in this thy mercy's day,
Ere it pass for ay away,
On our knees we fall and pray.

2
Holy Jesu, grant us tears,
Fill us with heart-searching fears,
Ere that awful doom appears.

3
Lord, on us thy Spirit pour
Kneeling lowly at the door,
Ere it close for evermore.

4
By thy night of agony,
By thy supplicating cry,
By thy willingness to die;

5
By thy tears of bitter woe
For Jerusalem below,
Let us not thy love forgo.

6
Grant us 'neath thy wings a place,
Lest we lose this day of grace
Ere we shall behold thy face.

I. WILLIAMS

Lent

FIRST TUNE

Christe, qui lux — L.M.

Mode ii

Christe, qui lux es et dies

1 O Christ, who art the Light and Day,
2 All - ho - ly Lord, in hum - ble prayer
3 A - sleep though wea - ried eyes may be,
4* Be - hold, O God our shield, and quell
5 All praise to God the Fa - ther be,

1 Thou driv - est night and gloom a - way; O Light of Light, whose
2 We ask to - night thy watch - ful care; O grant us calm re -
3 Still keep the heart a - wake to thee; Let thy right hand out -
4* The crafts and sub - tle - ties of hell; Di - rect thy ser - vants
5 All praise, e - ter - nal Son, to thee, Whom with the Spi - rit

1 word doth show The light of heav'n to us be - low.
2 pose in thee, A qui - et night from per - ils free.
3 stretched a - bove Guard those who serve the Lord they love.
4* in all good, Whom thou hast pur - chased with thy Blood.
5 we a - dore, For ev - er and for ev - er - more.

Lent

Alfreton — L.M.   *Supplement to the New Version,* 1708

A higher setting of this tune will be found at Hymn 252

(*Evening*)

Christe, qui lux es et dies

mf O Christ, who art the Light and Day,
Thou drivest night and gloom away;
O Light of Light, whose word doth
    show⌣
The light of heaven to us below.

2
All-holy Lord, in humble prayer
We ask to-night thy watchful care;
O grant us calm repose in thee,
A quiet night from perils free.

3
Asleep though wearied eyes may be,
Still keep the heart awake to thee;

Let thy right hand outstretched above
Guard those who serve the Lord they
    love.

4*
Behold, O God our Shield, and quell⌣
The crafts and subtleties of hell;
Direct thy servants in all good,
Whom thou hast purchased with thy
    Blood.

[UNISON]   5
f All praise to God the Father be,
All praise, eternal Son, to thee,
Whom with the Spirit we adore,
For ever and for evermore.

Tr. COMPILERS (1904)

*The following hymns, and some of the hymns for Passiontide,
are suitable for this season:*

HYMN **96** FIRST TUNE

Vexilla Regis — L.M. Mode i

Vexilla Regis prodeunt

1 The roy - al ban - ners for - ward go, The Cross shines
2 There whilst he hung, his sa - cred side By sol - dier's
3 Ful - filled is now what Da - vid told In true pro -
4 O Tree of glo - ry, Tree most fair, Or - dained those
5 Up - on its arms, like bal - ance true, He weighed the
6 To thee, e - ter - nal Three in One, Let hom - age

1 forth in mys - tic glow; Where he in flesh, our
2 spear was o - pened wide, To cleanse us in the
3 phe - tic song of old, How God the hea - then's
4 ho - ly limbs to bear, How bright in pur - ple
5 price for sin - ners due, The price which none but
6 meet by all be done: As by the Cross thou

1 flesh who made, Our sen - tence bore, our ran - som paid.
2 pre - cious flood Of wa - ter min - gled with his blood.
3 King should be; For God is reign - ing from the Tree.
4 robe it stood, The pur - ple of a Sa - viour's blood!
5 he could pay, And spoiled the spoil - er of his prey.
6 dost re - store, So rule and guide us ev - er - more.

114

Passiontide

St. Cecilia — L.M.   J. Hampton, 1834–1921

(*Passion Sunday to Wednesday before Easter*)

Vexilla Regis prodeunt

f The royal banners forward go,
  The Cross shines forth in mystic
      glow;   [made,
  Where he in flesh, our flesh who
  Our sentence bore, our ransom paid.

2
mf There whilst he hung, his sacred side͜
  By soldier's spear was opened wide,
  To cleanse us in the precious flood͜
  Of water mingled with his blood.

3
f Fulfilled is now what David told
  In true prophetic song of old,
  How God the heathen's King should
      be;
  For God is reigning from the Tree.

4
mf O Tree of glory, Tree most fair,
  Ordained those holy limbs to bear,
  How bright in purple robe it stood,
  The purple of a Saviour's blood!

5
  Upon its arms, like balance true,
  He weighed the price for sinners due,
  The price which none but he could pay,
f   And spoiled the spoiler of his prey.

[UNISON]   6
  To thee, eternal Three in One,
  Let homage meet by all be done:
  As by the Cross thou dost restore,
  So rule and guide us evermore.

BISHOP VENANTIUS FORTUNATUS
Tr. J. M. Neale and Compilers

115

Passiontide

FIRST TUNE

Pange lingua — 8 7. 8 7. 8 7

Mode iii

Pange lingua gloriosi praelium certaminis

Sing, my tongue, the glo-rious bat-tle, Sing the last, the dread af - fray;

O'er the Cross, the Vic-tor's tro-phy, Sound the high tri-um-phal lay,

How, the pains of death en-dur-ing, Earth's Re-deem-er won the day.

This hymn may be sung to the Mechlin Version of this tune to be found at Hymn 383 or to St. Thomas, 388

Passiontide

(Passion Sunday to Wednesday before Easter)

Pange lingua gloriosi praelium certaminis

PART 1

Sing, my tongue, the glorious battle,
  Sing the last, the dread affray;
O'er the Cross, the Victor's trophy,
  Sound the high triumphal lay,
How, the pains of death enduring,
  Earth's Redeemer won the day.

2
When at length the appointed fulness
  Of the sacred time was come,
He was sent, the world's Creator,
  From the Father's heavenly home,
And was found in human fashion,
  Offspring of the Virgin's womb.

3
Now the thirty years are ended
  Which on earth he willed to see,
Willingly he meets his Passion,
  Born to set his people free;
On the Cross the Lamb is lifted,
  There the Sacrifice to be.

4
There the nails and spear he suffers,
  Vinegar and gall and reed;
From his sacred body piercèd
  Blood and water both proceed:
Precious flood, which all creation
  From the stain of sin hath freed.

PART 2

5
Faithful Cross, above all other,
  One and only noble Tree,
None in foliage, none in blossom,
  None in fruit thy peer may be;
Sweet the wood, and sweet the iron,
  And thy load, most sweet is he.

6
Bend, O lofty Tree, thy branches,
  Thy too rigid sinews bend;
And awhile the stubborn hardness,
  Which thy birth bestowed, suspend;
And the limbs of heaven's high Monarch
  Gently on thine arms extend.

7
Thou alone wast counted worthy
  This world's Ransom to sustain,
That a shipwrecked race for ever
  Might a port of refuge gain,
With the sacred Blood anointed
  Of the Lamb for sinners slain.

The following Doxology may be sung at the end of either Part:

Praise and honour to the Father,
  Praise and honour to the Son,
Praise and honour to the Spirit,
  Ever Three and ever One:
One in might, and One in glory,
  While eternal ages run.

BISHOP VENANTIUS FORTUNATUS
Tr. J. M. Neale and Compilers

117

Passiontide

HYMN **97**   SECOND TUNE

French Carol — 8 7. 8 7. 8 7   Traditional French Carol

HARMONIZED VERSION FOR UNACCOMPANIED SINGING
(VERSES 3, 5, 7)

118

Passiontide

(Passion Sunday to Wednesday before Easter)

Pange lingua gloriosi praelium certaminis

PART 1

[UNISON]

Sing, my tongue, the glorious battle,
  Sing the last, the dread affray;
O'er the Cross, the Victor's trophy,
  Sound the high triumphal lay,
How, the pains of death enduring,
  Earth's Redeemer won the day.

[UNISON] 2

When at length the appointed fulness
  Of the sacred time was come,
He was sent, the world's Creator,
  From the Father's heavenly home,
And was found in human fashion,
  Offspring of the Virgin's womb.

[HARMONY] 3

Now the thirty years are ended
  Which on earth he willed to see,
Willingly he meets his Passion,
  Born to set his people free;
On the Cross the Lamb is lifted,
  There the Sacrifice to be.

[UNISON] 4

There the nails and spear he suffers,
  Vinegar and gall and reed;
From his sacred body piercèd
  Blood and water both proceed:
Precious flood, which all creation
  From the stain of sin hath freed.

PART 2

[HARMONY] 5

Faithful Cross, above all other,
  One and only noble Tree,
None in foliage, none in blossom,
  None in fruit thy peer may be;
Sweet the wood, and sweet the iron,
  And thy load, most sweet is he.

[UNISON] 6

Bend, O lofty Tree, thy branches,
  Thy too rigid sinews bend;
And awhile the stubborn hardness,
  Which thy birth bestowed, suspend;
And the limbs of heaven's high Monarch
  Gently on thine arms extend.

[HARMONY] 7

Thou alone wast counted worthy
  This world's Ransom to sustain,
That a shipwrecked race for ever
  Might a port of refuge gain,
With the sacred Blood anointed
  Of the Lamb for sinners slain.

The following Doxology may be sung at the end of either Part:

[UNISON]

Praise and honour to the Father,
  Praise and honour to the Son,
Praise and honour to the Spirit,
  Ever Three and ever One:
One in might, and One in glory,
  While eternal ages run.

BISHOP VENANTIUS FORTUNATUS
Tr. J. M. Neale and Compilers

119

Passiontide

Fine.

D.C.

(*Palm Sunday*)

Gloria, laus et honor

ƒ All glory, laud, and honour
   To thee, Redeemer, King,
   To whom the lips of children
   Made sweet Hosannas ring.

2

mf Thou art the King of Israel,
   Thou David's royal Son,
   Who in the Lord's name comest
   The King and blessèd one.
   ƒ All glory, etc.

3

mf The company of angels
   Are praising thee on high,
   And mortal men and all things
   Created make reply.
   ƒ All glory, etc.

4

mf The people of the Hebrews
   With palms before thee went:
   Our praise and prayer and anthems
   Before thee we present.
   ƒ All glory, etc.

120

Passiontide

5
mf To thee before thy Passion
   They sang their hymns of praise :
   To thee now high exalted
   Our melody we raise.
  f All glory, etc.

6
mf Thou didst accept their praises :
   Accept the prayers we bring,
   Who in all good delightest,
   Thou good and gracious King.
  f All glory, etc.

ST. THEODULPH OF ORLEANS
Tr. J. M. Neale‡

NOTE. *A longer version of this hymn will be found in the
'Processional' section* (**597**)

HYMN **99** St. Drostane — L.M.   J. B. Dykes, 1823–76

(*Palm Sunday*)

Ride on ! ride on in majesty !
Hark ! all the tribes Hosanna cry !
O Saviour meek, pursue thy road
With palms and scattered garments
   strowed.

2
Ride on ! ride on in majesty !
In lowly pomp ride on to die :
O Christ, thy triumphs now begin
O'er captive death and conquered sin.

3
Ride on ! ride on in majesty !
The wingèd squadrons of the sky

Look down with sad and wondering eyes
To see the approaching Sacrifice.

4
Ride on ! ride on in majesty !
The last and fiercest strife is nigh :
The Father on his sapphire throne
Awaits his own anointed Son.

5
Ride on ! ride on in majesty !
In lowly pomp ride on to die ;
Bow thy meek head to mortal pain,
Then take, O God, thy power, and reign.

H. H. MILMAN‡

Alternative Tune, Winchester New, **50**

121

HYMN **100**   Genevan Psalm cx — 11 10 11 10   L. Bourgeois, *c.* 1500–61

(*Holy Week*)

mf Lord, through this Holy Week of our salvation,
      Which thou hast won for us who went astray,
In all the conflict of thy sore temptation
      We would continue with thee day by day.

2

We would not leave thee, though our weak endurance⌣
      Make us unworthy here to take our part;
Yet give us strength to trust the sweet assurance
      That thou, O Lord, art greater than our heart.

3

Thou didst forgive thine own who slept for sorrow,
      Thou didst have pity: O have pity now,
And let us watch through each sad eve and morrow⌣
      With thee, in holy prayer and solemn vow.

4

p Along that sacred way where thou art leading,
      Which thou didst take to save our souls from loss,
Let us go also, till we see thee pleading
      In all-prevailing prayer upon thy Cross;

122

Passiontide

5

mf Until thou see thy bitter travail's ending,
The world redeemed, the will of God complete,
And, to thy Father's hands thy soul commending,
Thou lay the work he gave thee at his feet.

W. H. Draper

Alternative Tune, Strength and Stay, 17

HYMN **101** Nun komm — 7 7 7 7 German Medieval Melody

1

See the destined day arise!
See, a willing sacrifice,
Jesus, to redeem our loss,
Hangs upon the shameful Cross!

3

Who but thou had dared to drain,
Steeped in gall, that cup of pain,
And with tender body bear
Thorns and nails and piercing spear?

2

Jesu, who but thou had borne,
Lifted on that Tree of scorn,
Every pang and bitter throe,
Finishing thy life of woe?

4

Thence the cleansing water flowed,
Mingled from thy side with blood:
Sign to all attesting eyes
Of the finished Sacrifice.

5

Holy Jesu, grant us grace
In that Sacrifice to place
All our trust for life renewed,
Pardoned sin, and promised good.

Bishop R. Mant

123

HYMN **102**   Love Unknown — 6 6 6 6. 4 4 4 4   John Ireland

[UNISON]
My song is love unknown,
　My Saviour's love to me,
Love to the loveless shown,
　That they might lovely be.
　　O who am I,
　　　That for my sake
　　My Lord should take‿
　Frail flesh, and die?

[HARMONY]   2
He came from his blest throne,
　Salvation to bestow;
But men made strange, and none‿
　The longed-for Christ would know.
　　But O, my Friend,
　　　My Friend indeed,
　　Who at my need‿
　His life did spend!

Passiontide

3

Sometimes they strew his way,
    And his sweet praises sing;
Resounding all the day
    Hosannas to their King.
        Then 'Crucify!'⌣
            Is all their breath,
            And for his death⌣
        They thirst and cry.

[HARMONY]   **4***

Why, what hath my Lord done?
    What makes this rage and spite?
He made the lame to run,
    He gave the blind their sight.
        Sweet injuries!
            Yet they at these⌣
            Themselves displease,
        And 'gainst him rise.

5

They rise, and needs will have⌣
    My dear Lord made away;
A murderer they save,
    The Prince of Life they slay.
        Yet cheerful he⌣
            To suffering goes,
            That he his foes⌣
        From thence might free.

6*

In life, no house, no home
    My Lord on earth might have;
In death, no friendly tomb
    But what a stranger gave.
        What may I say?
            Heaven was his home;
            But mine the tomb⌣
        Wherein he lay.

[UNISON]   **7**

Here might I stay and sing.
    No story so divine;
Never was love, dear King,
    Never was grief like thine!
        This is my Friend,
            In whose sweet praise
            I all my days⌣
        Could gladly spend.

S. CROSSMAN

125

Passiontide

FIRST TUNE

Genevan Psalm xii — 11 10 11 10   L. Bourgeois, *c.* 1500–61

SECOND TUNE

St. Winifred — 11 10 11 10   J. B. Dykes, 1823–76

Passiontide

Est-ce vous que je vois?

mf My Lord, my Master, at thy feet adoring,
     I see thee bowed beneath thy load of woe;
    For me, a sinner, is thy life-blood pouring:
     For thee, my Saviour, scarce my tears will flow.

2
Thine own disciple to the Jews has sold thee,
   With friendship's kiss and loyal word he came;
How oft of faithful love my lips have told thee,
   While thou hast seen my falsehood and my shame!

3
With taunts and scoffs they mock what seems thy weakness,
   With blows and outrage adding pain to pain;
Thou art unmoved and steadfast in thy meekness:
   When I am wronged how quickly I complain!

4
p My Lord, my Saviour, when I see thee wearing
    Upon thy bleeding brow the crown of thorn,
  Shall I for pleasure live, or shrink from bearing
    Whate'er my lot may be of pain or scorn?

5
mf O Victim of thy love! O pangs most healing!
    O saving Death! O wounds that I adore!
  O shame most glorious! Christ, before thee kneeling,
    I pray thee keep me thine for evermore.

J. BRIDAINE
Tr. T. B. Pollock

127

HYMN **104**   St. Bernard — C.M.   *Tochter Sion* (Cologne, 1741)

Quicumque certum quaeritis

All ye who seek for sure relief
In trouble and distress,
Whatever sorrow vex the mind,
Or guilt the soul oppress,

2
Jesus, who gave himself for you
Upon the Cross to die,
Opens to you his sacred heart:
O to that heart draw nigh.

3
Ye hear how kindly he invites;
Ye hear his words so blest:
'All ye that labour come to me,
And I will give you rest.'

4
O Jesus, joy of saints on high,
Thou hope of sinners here,
Attracted by those loving words
To thee we lift our prayer.

5
Wash thou our wounds in that dear Blood
Which from thy heart doth flow;
A new and contrite heart on all‿
Who cry to thee bestow.

18th cent. *Tr.* E. CASWALL‡

HYMN **105**   FIRST TUNE

Song 13 — 7 7 7 7   Orlando Gibbons, 1583–1625

Passiontide

St. Prisca — 7 7 7 7   R. Redhead, 1820–1901

In passione Domini

p In the Lord's atoning grief
Be our rest and sweet relief;
Store we deep in heart's recess
All the shame and bitterness:

2
Thorns and cross and nails and lance,
Wounds, our rich inheritance,
Vinegar and gall and reed,
And the cry his soul that freed.

3
mf May these all our spirits fill,
And with love's devotion thrill;
In our souls plant virtue's root,
And mature its glorious fruit.

4
Crucified, we thee adore;
Thee with all our hearts implore,
Us with all thy saints unite
In the realms of heavenly light.

5
Christ, by coward hands betrayed,
Christ, for us a captive made,
Christ, upon the bitter Tree
Slain for man, be praise to thee.

St. Bonaventura
Tr. F. Oakeley‡

129

HYMN 106   FIRST TUNE

First Mode Melody — D.C.M.   T. Tallis, *c.* 1505–85

SECOND TUNE

St. Francis Xavier — C.M.   Sir J. Stainer, 1840–1901

Passiontide

O Deus, ego amo te

mf My God, I love thee; not because
    I hope for heaven thereby,
    Nor yet because who love thee not
    Are lost eternally.

2
Thou, O my Jesus, thou didst me
    Upon the Cross embrace;
    For me didst bear the nails and spear,
    And manifold disgrace,

3
p And griefs and torments numberless,
    And sweat of agony;
    Yea, death itself—and all for me
    Who was thine enemy.

4
mf Then why, O blessèd Jesu Christ,
    Should I not love thee well?
    Not for the sake of winning heaven,
    Nor of escaping hell;

5
Not from the hope of gaining aught,
    Not seeking a reward;
    But as thyself hast lovèd me,
    O ever-loving Lord.

6
f So would I love thee, dearest Lord,
    And in thy praise will sing;
    Solely because thou art my God,
    And my most loving King.

17th cent. *Tr.* E. CASWALL†

HYMN 107 Caswall — 6 5 6 5   F. Filitz, 1804–76

Viva! Viva! Gesù

f Glory be to Jesus,
    Who, in bitter pains,
    Poured for me the life-blood
    From his sacred veins.

2
mf Grace and life eternal
    In that Blood I find;
    Blest be his compassion
    Infinitely kind.

3
Blest through endless ages
    Be the precious stream,
    Which from endless torments
    Did the world redeem.

4
Abel's blood for vengeance
    Pleaded to the skies;
    But the Blood of Jesus
    For our pardon cries.

5
Oft as it is sprinkled
    On our guilty hearts,
    Satan in confusion
    Terror-struck departs;

6
f Oft as earth exulting
    Wafts its praise on high,
    Angel-hosts rejoicing
    Make their glad reply.

7
Lift ye then your voices;
    Swell the mighty flood;
    Louder still and louder
    Praise the precious Blood.

18th cent. *Tr.* E. CASWALL†

HYMN **108**   Rockingham — L.M.   Adapted by E. Miller, 1731–1807

A lower setting of this tune will be found at Hymn 490

mf When I survey the wondrous Cross
       On which the Prince of Glory died,
       My richest gain I count but loss,
       And pour contempt on all my pride.

2
Forbid it, Lord, that I should boast
Save in the Cross of Christ my God;
All the vain things that charm me most,
I sacrifice them to his Blood.

3
p   See from his head, his hands, his feet,
       Sorrow and love flow mingling down;
       Did e'er such love and sorrow meet,
       Or thorns compose so rich a crown?

[UNISON]   4
f   Were the whole realm of nature mine,
       That were an offering far too small;
       Love so amazing, so divine,
       Demands my soul, my life, my all.

I. WATTS‡

Passiontide

Were the whole realm of na - ture mine, That were an

offer - ing far too small, Love so a - maz - ing,

so di - vine, De - mands my soul, my life, my all.

133

Passiontide

Lord Jesu, when we stand afar,
  And gaze upon thy holy Cross,
In love of thee and scorn of self,
  O may we count the world as loss!

2

When we behold thy bleeding wounds,
  And the rough way that thou hast
Make us to hate the load of sin   [trod,
  That lay so heavy on our God.

3

O holy Lord, uplifted high,   [woe,
  With outstretched arms, in mortal
Embracing in thy wondrous love
  The sinful world that lies below,

4

Give us an ever-living faith,
  To gaze beyond the things we see;
And in the mystery of thy Death
  Draw us and all men unto thee.

BISHOP W. WALSHAM HOW

Hymn **110**   FIRST TUNE

The Good Shepherd — 7 7. 7 7. 7 7   P. Heinlein, 1626–86

Passiontide

Gethsemane — 7 7. 7 7. 7 7

W. H. Monk, 1823–89
From C. Tye (1553)

Go to dark Gethsemane,
  Ye that feel the tempter's power,
Your Redeemer's conflict see,
  Watch with him one bitter hour;
Turn not from his griefs away:
Learn of Jesus Christ to pray.

2

Follow to the judgement-hall,
  View the Lord of Life arraigned;
O the wormwood and the gall!
  O the pangs his soul sustained!
Shun not suffering, shame, or loss:
Learn of him to bear the cross.

3

Calvary's mournful mountain climb;
  There, adoring at his feet,
Mark that miracle of time,
  God's own Sacrifice complete;
'It is finished!' hear him cry:
Learn of Jesus Christ to die.

J. Montgomery

135

Hymn **111**   Passion Chorale — 7 6 7 6. D   H. L. Hassler, 1564–1612

Harmony from J. S. Bach, 1685–1750

O Haupt voll Blut und Wunden

mf O sacred head, surrounded
By crown of piercing thorn!
O bleeding head, so wounded,
So shamed and put to scorn!
Death's pallid hue comes o'er thee,
The glow of life decays;
Yet angel-hosts adore thee,
And tremble as they gaze.

2

p Thy comeliness and vigour
Is withered up and gone,
And in thy wasted figure
I see death drawing on.

O agony and dying!
O love to sinners free!
Jesu, all grace supplying,
Turn thou thy face on me.

3

mf In this thy bitter Passion,
Good Shepherd, think of me
With thy most sweet compassion,
Unworthy though I be:
Beneath thy Cross abiding
For ever would I rest,
In thy dear love confiding,
And with thy presence blest.

P. Gerhardt Based on *Salve caput cruentatum*
Tr. Sir H. W. Baker‡

HYMN **112**   Ades Pater supreme — 7 7 7 7   *Melodiae Prudentianae,* 1533

(*Evening*)

Ades Pater supreme

mf Father most high, be with us,
　Unseen, thy goodness showing,
　And Christ the Word incarnate,
　And Spirit grace bestowing.

2
f O Trinity, O Oneness
　Of light and power exceeding;
　O God of God eternal,
　O God, from Both proceeding!

3
mf While daylight hours are passing,
　We live and work before thee;
　Now, ere we rest in slumber,
　We gather to adore thee.

4
Our Christian name and calling
　Of our new birth remind us;
　The Spirit's gifts and sealing
　To firm obedience bind us.

[UNISON]　5
f Begone, ye powers of evil
　With snares and wiles unholy!
　Disturb not with your temptings
　The spirits of the lowly.

[UNISON]　6
Depart! for Christ is present,
　Beside us, yea, within us;
　Away! his sign (ye know it)
　The victory shall win us.

7
p Awhile the body resteth;
　The spirit, wakeful ever,
　Abideth in communion‿
　With Christ, who sleepeth never.

[UNISON]　8
f To God, the eternal Father,
　To Christ our sure salvation,
　To God, the Holy Spirit,
　Be endless adoration.

PRUDENTIUS *Tr.* Compilers (1889)

The following hymns are suitable:

212 Behold the Lamb of God.
213 Jesu, meek and lowly.

214 There is a green hill far away.
215 We sing the praise of him who died.

MAUNDY THURSDAY

The following hymns are suitable:

110 Go to dark Gethsemane.
383 Now, my tongue, the mystery telling.

384 The heavenly Word, proceeding forth.
402 O thou, who at thy Eucharist didst
　　　pray.

GOOD FRIDAY

J. B. Dykes, 1823–76

p O come and mourn with me awhile;
O come ye to the Saviour's side;
O come, together let us mourn:
Jesus, our Lord, is crucified.

2
Have we no tears to shed for him,
While soldiers scoff and Jews deride?
Ah, look how patiently he hangs:
Jesus, our Lord, is crucified.

3
How fast his hands and feet are nailed;
His throat with parching thirst is dried;
His failing eyes are dimmed with blood:
Jesus, our Lord, is crucified.

4
Seven times he spake, seven words of love; [cried⌣
And all three hours his silence cried
For mercy on the souls of men:
Jesus, our Lord, is crucified.

5
mf O love of God! O sin of man!
In this dread act your strength is tried;
And victory remains with love:
Jesus, our Lord, is crucified.

F. W. FABER‡

HYMN **114**   FIRST TUNE

Vulpius — 7 6 7 6   M. Vulpius, *c.* 1560–1616

138

Good Friday

SECOND TUNE

St. Margaret — 7 6 7 6   W. Statham, 1832–98

THE FIRST WORD FROM THE CROSS

'Father, forgive them, for they know not what they do'

'Forgive them, O my Father,
  They know not what they do:'
The Saviour spake in anguish,
  As the sharp nails went through.

2
No word of anger spake he
  To them that shed his blood,
But prayer and tenderest pity
  Large as the love of God.

3
For me was that compassion,
  For me that tender care;
I need his wide forgiveness
  As much as any there.

4
It was my pride and hardness
  That hung him on the Tree;
Those cruel nails, O Saviour,
  Were driven in by me.

5
And often I have slighted
  Thy gentle voice that chid:
Forgive me too, Lord Jesus;
  I knew not what I did.

6
O depth of sweet compassion!
  O love divine and true!
Save thou the souls that slight thee,
  And know not what they do.

Mrs. C. F. Alexander†

139

Good Friday

p   O word of pity, for our pardon pleading,
     Breathed in the hour of loneliness and pain;
mf   O voice, which through the ages interceding
     Calls us to fellowship with God again!

2

p   O word of comfort, through the silence stealing,
     As the dread act of sacrifice began;
     O infinite compassion, still revealing
     The infinite forgiveness won for man!

3

mf   O word of hope to raise us nearer heaven,
     When courage fails us and when faith is dim!
     The souls for whom Christ prays to Christ are given,
     To find their pardon and their joy in him.

4

     O Intercessor, who art ever living
     To plead for dying souls that they may live,
     Teach us to know our sin which needs forgiving,
     Teach us to know the love which can forgive.

ADA R. GREENAWAY

Alternative Tune, St. Winifred, 103

Good Friday

THE SECOND WORD FROM THE CROSS

'Verily I say unto thee, To-day shalt thou be with me in Paradise'

'Lord, when thy Kingdom comes, remember me!'
Thus spake the dying lips to dying ears:
O faith, which in that darkest hour could see
The promised glory of the far-off years!

2
No kingly sign declares that glory now,
No ray of hope lights up that awful hour;
A thorny crown surrounds the bleeding brow,
The hands are stretched in weakness, not in power.

3
Hark! through the gloom the dying Saviour saith,
'Thou too shalt rest in Paradise to-day:'
O words of love to answer words of faith!
O words of hope for those who live to pray!

4
Lord, when with dying lips my prayer is said,
Grant that in faith thy Kingdom I may see;
And, thinking on thy Cross and bleeding head,
May breathe my parting words, 'Remember me.'

5*
Remember me, but not my shame or sin:
Thy cleansing Blood hath washed them all away;
Thy precious Death for me did pardon win;
Thy Blood redeemed me in that awful day.

6
Remember me; and, ere I pass away,
Speak thou the assuring word that sets us free,
And make thy promise to my heart, 'To-day
Thou too shalt rest in Paradise with me.'

ARCHBISHOP W. D. MACLAGAN

Alternative Tune, Ellers, 31

141

Good Friday

mf O thou, from whom all goodness flows,
  I lift my heart to thee;
  In all my sorrows, conflicts, woes,
p Good Lord, remember me.

2
mf When on my aching burdened heart
  My sins lie heavily,
  Thy pardon grant, thy peace impart:
p Good Lord, remember me.

3
mf When trials sore obstruct my way,
  And ills I cannot flee,
  Then let my strength be as my day:
p Good Lord, remember me.

4
mf If worn with pain, disease, and grief
  This feeble spirit be,
  Grant patience, rest, and kind relief:
p Good Lord, remember me.

5
mf And O, when in the hour of death
  I bow to thy decree,
  Jesu, receive my parting breath:
p Good Lord, remember me.

T. HAWEIS‡

Alternative Tune, Abridge, 300

Good Friday

THE THIRD WORD FROM THE CROSS

'Woman, behold thy son . . . Behold thy mother'

Stabat Mater dolorosa

mf At the Cross her station keeping
Stood the mournful Mother weeping,
　Where he hung, the dying Lord;
'For her soul, of joy bereavèd,
Bowed with anguish, deeply grievèd,
　Felt the sharp and piercing sword.

2

p O how sad and sore distressèd
Now was she, that Mother blessèd
　Of the Sole-begotten One!
Deep the woe of her affliction,
When she saw the Crucifixion
　Of her ever-glorious Son.

3

mf Who, on Christ's dear Mother gazing
Pierced by anguish so amazing,
　Born of woman, would not weep?
Who, on Christ's dear Mother thinking
Such a cup of sorrow drinking,
　Would not share her sorrows deep?

4

p For his people's sins chastisèd,
She beheld her Son despisèd,
　Scourged, and crowned with thorns entwined;
Saw him then from judgement taken,
And in death by all forsaken,
　Till his spirit he resigned.

5

mf O good Jesu, let me borrow‿
Something of thy Mother's sorrow,
　Fount of love, Redeemer kind,
That my heart fresh ardour gaining,
And a purer love attaining,
　May with thee acceptance find.

Ascribed to JACOPONE DA TODI
Tr. E. Caswall and Compilers

143

Good Friday

HYMN **119**   Cassel — 7 7. 7 7. 7 7   *Christen-schatz* (Basle, 1745)

THE FOURTH WORD FROM THE CROSS

'My God, my God, why hast thou forsaken me?'

Throned upon the awful Tree,
King of grief, I watch with thee;
Darkness veils thine anguished face,
None its lines of woe can trace,
None can tell what pangs unknown
Hold thee silent and alone:

2
Silent through those three dread hours,
Wrestling with the evil powers,
Left alone with human sin,
Gloom around thee and within,
Till the appointed time is nigh,
Till the Lamb of God may die.

3
Hark that cry that peals aloud
Upward through the whelming cloud!
Thou, the Father's only Son,
Thou, his own Anointed One,
Thou dost ask him (can it be?)
'Why hast thou forsaken me?'

4
Lord, should fear and anguish roll⌣
Darkly o'er my sinful soul,
Thou, who once wast thus bereft
That thine own might ne'er be left,
Teach me by that bitter cry
In the gloom to know thee nigh.

J. ELLERTON

144

Good Friday

HYMN **120** Saffron Walden — 8 8 8 6   A. H. Brown, 1830–1926

By permission of the Oxford University Press

THE FIFTH WORD FROM THE CROSS

'I thirst'

His are the thousand sparkling rills
That from a thousand fountains burst,
And fill with music all the hills;
    And yet he saith, 'I thirst.'

2
All fiery pangs on battle-fields,
On fever beds where sick men toss,
Are in that human cry he yields
    To anguish on the Cross.

3
But more than pains that racked him then
Was the deep longing thirst divine
That thirsted for the souls of men :
    Dear Lord! and one was mine.

4
O Love most patient, give me grace;
Make all my soul athirst for thee :
That parched dry lip, that fading face,
    That thirst, were all for me.

MRS. C. F. ALEXANDER

Alternative Tune, Misericordia, 349

145

Good Friday

mf O perfect God, thy love
As perfect Man did share
Here upon earth each form of ill
Thy fellow-men must bear.

2
Now from the Tree of scorn
We hear thy voice again;
Thou who didst take our mortal flesh
Hast felt our mortal pain.

3
p Thy body suffers thirst,
Parched are thy lips and dry:
How poor the offering man can bring
Thy thirst to satisfy!

4
mf O Saviour, by thy thirst
Borne on the Cross of shame,
Grant us in all our sufferings here
To glorify thy name;

5
That through each pain and grief
Our souls may onward move
To gain more likeness to thy life,
More knowledge of thy love.

ADA R. GREENAWAY

Alternative Tune, St. Bride, 322

Good Friday

THE SIXTH WORD FROM THE CROSS

'It is finished'

O perfect life of love!
All, all is finished now;
All that he left his throne above
To do for us below.

2
No work is left undone
Of all the Father willed;
His toils, his sorrows, one by one,
The scripture have fulfilled.

3
No pain that we can share
But he has felt its smart;
All forms of human grief and care
Have pierced that tender heart.

4
And on his thorn-crowned head,
And on his sinless soul,
Our sins in all their guilt were laid,
That he might make us whole.

5
In perfect love he dies;
For me he dies, for me:
O all-atoning Sacrifice,
I cling by faith to thee.

6
In every time of need,
Before the judgement-throne,
Thy works, O Lamb of God, I'll plead,
Thy merits, not my own.

7
Yet work, O Lord, in me
As thou for me hast wrought;
And let my love the answer be
To grace thy love has brought.

SIR H. W. BAKER

Alternative Tune, St. Paul's, 200

Good Friday

HYMN **123** Strength and Stay — 11 10 11 10   J. B. Dykes, 1823–76

(Original harmonies slightly altered)

Good Friday

'Father, into thy hands I commend my spirit'

And now, belovèd Lord, thy soul resigning
  Into thy Father's arms with conscious will,
Calmly, with reverend grace, thy head inclining,
  The throbbing brow and labouring breast grow still.

2
Freely thy life thou yieldest, meekly bending
  E'en to the last beneath our sorrows' load,
Yet, strong in death, in perfect peace commending⌣
  Thy spirit to thy Father and thy God.

3
Sweet Saviour, in mine hour of mortal anguish,
  When earth grows dim, and round me falls the night,
O breathe thy peace, as flesh and spirit languish;
  At that dread eventide let there be light.

4
To thy dear Cross turn thou mine eyes in dying;
  Lay but my fainting head upon thy breast;
Those outstretched arms receive my latest sighing—
  And then, O then, thine everlasting rest.

Mrs. E. S. Alderson

Or

30   The sun is sinking fast.
37   Fast sinks the sun to rest.

GOOD FRIDAY EVENING AND EASTER EVEN

HYMN 124

FIRST TUNE

Batty — 8 7 8 7

Christen-schatz (Basle, 1745)

SECOND TUNE

Portsea — 8 7 8 7

W. Boyce, 1710–79

Good Friday Evening and Easter Even

p   It is finished! blessèd Jesus,
       Thou hast breathed thy latest sigh,
    Teaching us the sons of Adam
       How the Son of God can die.

2
Lifeless lies the piercèd body,
       Resting in its rocky bed;
Thou hast left the Cross of anguish
       For the mansions of the dead.

3
mf In the hidden realms of darkness
       Shines a light unseen before,
When the Lord of dead and living
       Enters at the lowly door.

4
Lo, in spirit, rich in mercy
       Comes he from the world above,
Preaching to the souls in prison
       Tidings of his dying love.

5
Lo, the heavenly light around him,
       As he draws his people near;
All amazed they come rejoicing
       At the gracious words they hear.

6
Patriarch and priest and prophet
       Gather round him as he stands,
In adoring faith and gladness
       Hearing of the piercèd hands.

7
There in lowliest joy and wonder
       Stands the robber at his side,
Reaping now the blessèd promise
       Spoken by the Crucified.

8
p   Jesus, Lord of dead and living,
       Let thy mercy rest on me;
Grant me too, when life is finished,
       Rest in Paradise with thee.

ARCHBISHOP W. D. MACLAGAN
(Revised version by the author, 1902)

Good Friday Evening and Easter Even

By Jesus' grave on either hand,
While night is brooding o'er the land,
The sad and silent mourners stand.

2
At last the weary life is o'er,
The agony and conflict sore‿
Of him who all our sufferings bore.

3
Deep in the rock's sepulchral shade
The Lord by whom the worlds were
The Saviour of mankind, is laid. [made,

4
O hearts bereaved and sore distressed,
Here is for you a place of rest;
Here leave your griefs on Jesus' breast.

I. GREGORY SMITH

Good Friday Evening and Easter Even

O sorrow deep!
Who would not weep
With heartfelt pain and sighing?
God the Father's only Son
In the tomb is lying.

2

O Jesus blest,
My help and rest,
With tears I pray thee, hear me:
Now, and even unto death,
Dearest Lord, be near me.

JOHANN RIST *Tr.* W. Douglas

HYMN **127**   Petra — 7 7. 7 7. 7 7   R. Redhead, 1820–1901

Resting from his work to-day
In the tomb the Saviour lay;
Still he slept, from head to feet
Shrouded in the winding-sheet,
Lying in the rock alone,
Hidden by the sealèd stone.

2

Late at even there was seen
Watching long the Magdalene;
Early, ere the break of day,
Sorrowful she took her way
To the holy garden glade,
Where her buried Lord was laid.

3

So with thee, till life shall end,
I would solemn vigil spend;
Let me hew thee, Lord, a shrine
In this rocky heart of mine,
Where in pure embalmèd cell
None but thou may ever dwell.

4

Myrrh and spices will I bring,
True affection's offering;
Close the door from sight and sound
Of the busy world around;
And in patient watch remain
Till my Lord appear again.

T. WHYTEHEAD‡

153

EASTER

Chorus novae Jerusalem

f Ye choirs of new Jerusalem,
    Your sweetest notes employ,
    The Paschal victory to hymn
    In strains of holy joy.

2

For Judah's Lion bursts his chains,
    Crushing the serpent's head;
And cries aloud through death's domains
    To wake the imprisoned dead.

154

3

Devouring depths of hell their prey‿
At his command restore;
His ransomed hosts pursue their way
Where Jesus goes before.

[UNISON] **4**

Triumphant in his glory now
To him all power is given;
To him in one communion bow
All saints in earth and heaven.

5

mf While we his soldiers praise our King,
His mercy we implore,
Within his palace bright to bring
And keep us evermore.

[UNISON] **6**

f All glory to the Father be,
All glory to the Son,
All glory, Holy Ghost, to thee,
While endless ages run.

Alleluia! Amen.

Al - le - lu - ia! A - men.

St. Fulbert of Chartres
Tr. R. Campbell and Compilers

Note. *In verse 2, lines 1–2, Christ, 'the Lion that is of the tribe of Judah' (Rev. 5. 5), is portrayed as fulfilling the promise of redemption in Gen. 3. 15.*

155

Easter

FIRST TUNE

Ad cenam Agni — L.M.

Mode viii

Ad cenam Agni providi

1 The Lamb's high ban - quet called to share, Ar - rayed in
2 Up - on the al - tar of the Cross His bo - dy
3 Now Christ our Pass - o - ver is slain, The Lamb of
4 Christ ris - es con - queror from the grave, From death re -
5 All praise be thine, O ris - en Lord. From death to

1 gar - ments white and fair, The Red Sea past, we
2 hath re - deemed our loss; And, tast - ing of his
3 God with - out a stain; His flesh, the true un -
4 turn - ing, strong to save; With his right hand the
5 end - less life re - stored; All praise to God the

1 fain would sing To Je - sus our tri - um - phant King.
2 pre - cious Blood, In him we live a - new to God.
3 leav - ened bread, For us is free - ly off - er - èd.
4 ty - rant chains, And Par - a - dise for man re - gains.
5 Fa - ther be And Ho - ly Ghost e - ter - nal - ly.

156

Easter

HYMN **129**   SECOND TUNE

Grenoble — L.M.   Melody from J. B. Croft's *Collection*

May be sung in Unison

Ad cenam Agni providi

The Lamb's high banquet called to share,
Arrayed in garments white and fair,
The Red Sea past, we fain would sing
To Jesus our triumphant King.

2
Upon the altar of the Cross
His body hath redeemed our loss;
And, tasting of his precious Blood,
In him we live anew to God.

3
Now Christ our Passover is slain,
The Lamb of God without a stain;
His flesh, the true unleavened bread,
For us is freely offerèd.

4
Christ rises conqueror from the grave,
From death returning, strong to save;
With his right hand the tyrant chains,
And Paradise for man regains.

[UNISON]   5
All praise be thine, O risen Lord,
From death to endless life restored;
All praise to God the Father be
And Holy Ghost eternally.

Tr. J. M. NEALE and Compilers

Another Office Hymn for Eastertide is
602 Light's glittering morn bedecks the sky.

HYMN 130   O filii et filiae — 8 8 8 with Alleluias   French Melody
(17th cent.)

Easter

O filii et filiae

f   Alleluia! Alleluia! Alleluia!
O sons and daughters, let us sing!
The King of Heaven, the glorious King,
O'er death to-day rose triumphing.
Alleluia!

2
mf   That Easter morn, at break of day,
The faithful women went their way
To seek the tomb where Jesus lay.
Alleluia!

3
An angel clad in white they see,
Who sat, and spake unto the three,
'Your Lord doth go to Galilee.'
Alleluia!

4
p   That night the apostles met in fear;
Amidst them came their Lord most dear,
And said, 'My peace be on all here.'
Alleluia!

5
mf   When Thomas first the tidings heard,
How they had seen the risen Lord,
He doubted the disciples' word.
Alleluia!

6
p   'My piercèd side, O Thomas, see;
My hands, my feet I show to thee;
Not faithless, but believing be.'
Alleluia!

7
mf   No longer Thomas then denied;
He saw the feet, the hands, the side;
f   'Thou art my Lord and God,' he cried.
Alleluia!

8
mf   How blest are they who have not seen,
And yet whose faith hath constant been!
For they eternal life shall win.
Alleluia!

9
f   On this most holy day of days,
To God your hearts and voices raise
In laud and jubilee and praise.
Alleluia!

J. TISSERAND
Tr. J. M. Neale and Compilers

HYMN **131**   FIRST TUNE

Sampford — 7 7 7 7. D   John Ireland

With Movement

SECOND TUNE

St. George — 7 7 7 7. D   Sir G. J. Elvey, 1816–93

Christ the Lord is risen to-day!
Christians, haste your vows to pay;
Offer ye your praises meet
At the Paschal Victim's feet.
For the sheep the Lamb hath bled,
Sinless in the sinner's stead:
'Christ is risen!' to-day we cry;
Now he lives no more to die.

2

Christ, the Victim undefiled,
Man to God hath reconciled;
Whilst in strange and awful strife
Met together death and life.
Christians, on this happy day
Haste with joy your vows to pay:
'Christ is risen!' to-day we cry;
Now he lives no more to die.

3

Christ, who once for sinners bled,
Now the First-born from the dead,
Throned in endless might and power,
Lives and reigns for evermore.
Hail, eternal hope on high!
Hail, thou King of victory!
Hail, thou Prince of Life adored!
Help and save us, gracious Lord.

JANE E. LEESON

Easter

ἀναστάσεως ἡμέρα

f The day of Resurrection!
   Earth, tell it out abroad;
The Passover of gladness,
   The Passover of God!
From death to life eternal,
   From earth unto the sky,
Our God hath brought us over
   With hymns of victory.

2
mf Our hearts be pure from evil,
   That we may see aright‿
The Lord in rays eternal
   Of Resurrection-light;

And, listening to his accents,
   May hear so calm and plain‿
His own 'All hail,' and, hearing,
   May raise the victor strain.

3
f Now let the heavens be joyful,
   And earth her song begin,
The round world keep high triumph,
   And all that is therein;
Let all things seen and unseen
   Their notes of gladness blend,
For Christ the Lord is risen,
   Our joy that hath no end.

ST. JOHN OF DAMASCUS
Tr. J. M. Neale‡

HYMN **133**   St. John Damascene — 7 6 7 6. D   A. H. Brown, 1830–1926

αἴσωμεν πάντες λαοί

Come, ye faithful, raise the strain⌣
  Of triumphant gladness!
God hath brought his Israel
  Into joy from sadness;
Loosed from Pharaoh's bitter yoke
  Jacob's sons and daughters;
Led them with unmoistened foot
  Through the Red Sea waters.

2
'Tis the spring of souls to-day;
  Christ hath burst his prison,
And from three days' sleep in death
  As a sun hath risen:
All the winter of our sins,
  Long and dark, is flying
From his light, to whom we give⌣
  Laud and praise undying.

3
Now the queen of seasons, bright⌣
  With the day of splendour,
With the royal feast of feasts,
  Comes its joy to render;
Comes to glad Jerusalem,
  Who with true affection
Welcomes in unwearied strains
  Jesu's Resurrection.

4
Alleluia now we cry
  To our King immortal,
Who triumphant burst the bars⌣
  Of the tomb's dark portal;
Alleluia, with the Son
  God the Father praising;
Alleluia yet again
  To the Spirit raising.

ST. JOHN OF DAMASCUS
Tr. J. M. Neale and Compilers

Alternative Tune, Ave virgo, 294

HYMN 134 Easter Hymn — 7 7 7 7 with Alleluias *Lyra Davidica,* 1708
(later version)

Al - le - lu - ia!

Al - le - lu - ia!

The Descant may be sung by Trebles in verse 3, the other voices singing the main melody in Unison

Jesus Christ is risen to-day,
    Alleluia!
Our triumphant holy day,
    Alleluia!
Who did once, upon the Cross,
    Alleluia!
Suffer to redeem our loss.
    Alleluia!

2
Hymns of praise then let us sing,
    Alleluia!
Unto Christ, our heavenly King,
    Alleluia!
Who endured the Cross and grave,
    Alleluia!
Sinners to redeem and save.
    Alleluia!

3
But the pains that he endured,
    Alleluia!
Our salvation have procured;
    Alleluia!
Now above the sky he's King,
    Alleluia!
Where the angels ever sing.
    Alleluia!

Lyra Davidica (1708) and the *Supplement* (1816)

Easter

FIRST TUNE

Gelobt sei Gott — 8 8 8 with Alleluias M. Vulpius, *Gesangbuch*, 1609

Harmonized by F. Layriz (1844)

Al - le - lu - ia! . . . . Al - le - lu - ia! . . . Al - le - lu - ia!

Al - le - lu - ia! . . . . Al - le - lu - ia! . . . . Al - le - lu - ia!

SECOND TUNE

Victory — 8 8 8 with Alleluias Adapted from P. da Palestrina, 1525–94

Al - le - lu - ia! Al - le - lu - ia! Al - le - lu - ia!

Org.

Finita jam sunt praelia

f   Alleluia! Alleluia! Alleluia!
The strife is o'er, the battle done;
Now is the Victor's triumph won;
O let the song of praise be sung:
                          Alleluia!

2
Death's mightiest powers have done their worst,
And Jesus hath his foes dispersed;
Let shouts of praise and joy outburst:
                          Alleluia!

3
On the third morn he rose again
Glorious in majesty to reign;
O let us swell the joyful strain:
                          Alleluia!

4
p   Lord, by the stripes which wounded thee
From death's dread sting thy servants free,
f   That we may live, and sing to thee
                          Alleluia!

? 17th cent. *Tr.* F. Pott‡

HYMN **136** Würtemburg — 7 7 7 7 4 *Hundert Arien* (Dresden, 1694)

Al - le - lu - ia!

Christus ist erstanden

f Christ the Lord is risen again!
Christ hath broken every chain!
Hark! angelic voices cry,
Singing evermore on high,
Alleluia!

2
mf He who gave for us his life,
Who for us endured the strife,
Is our Paschal Lamb to-day;
f We too sing for joy, and say
Alleluia!

3
mf He who bore all pain and loss
Comfortless upon the Cross,
,f Lives in glory now on high,
Pleads for us, and hears our cry:
Alleluia!

4*
He whose path no records tell,
Who descended into hell, [bound,
Who the strong man armed hath
Now in highest heaven is crowned.
Alleluia!

5
mf He who slumbered in the grave
f Is exalted now to save;
Now through Christendom it rings
That the Lamb is King of Kings.
Alleluia!

6
mf Now he bids us tell abroad
How the lost may be restored,
How the penitent forgiven,
How we too may enter heaven.
Alleluia!

7
Thou, our Paschal Lamb indeed,
Christ, thy ransomed people feed;
Take our sins and guilt away:
f Let us sing by night and day
Alleluia!

M. WEISSE *Tr.* Catherine Winkworth†

HYMN **137**   Lux Eoi — 8 7 8 7. D   Sir A. Sullivan, 1842–1900

f Alleluia! Alleluia!
  Hearts to heaven and voices raise;
Sing to God a hymn of gladness,
  Sing to God a hymn of praise:
He who on the Cross a Victim
  For the world's salvation bled,
Jesus Christ, the King of Glory,
  Now is risen from the dead.

2
Christ is risen, Christ the first-fruits⌣
  Of the holy harvest field,
Which will all its full abundance
  At his second coming yield;
Then the golden ears of harvest
  Will their heads before him wave,
Ripened by his glorious sunshine,
  From the furrows of the grave.

3
mf Christ is risen, we are risen;
  Shed upon us heavenly grace,
Rain, and dew, and gleams of glory⌣
  From the brightness of thy face;
That we, with our hearts in heaven,
  Here on earth may fruitful be,
And by angel-hands be gathered,
  And be ever, Lord, with thee.

4
f Alleluia! Alleluia!
  Glory be to God on high;
Alleluia to the Saviour,
  Who has gained the victory;
Alleluia to the Spirit,
  Fount of love and sanctity;
Alleluia! Alleluia!
  To the Triune Majesty.

BISHOP CHR. WORDSWORTH

Alternative Tune, Everton, 267

169

HYMN **138** Victimae Paschali — Irregular   Mode i

Victimae Paschali

1 Chris-tians, to the Pas-chal Vic-tim   Of-fer your thank-ful prais-es!

MEN
2 A Lamb the sheep re-deem-eth: Christ, who on-ly is sin-less,
TREBLES
3 Death and life have con-tend-ed   In that com-bat stu-pen-dous:

Re-con-cil-eth sin-ners to   the Fa-ther. 4 Speak, Ma-ry, de-clar-ing
The Prince of Life, who died, reigns im-mor-tal. 6 Bright an-gels at-test-ing,

MEN

TREBLES

TREBLES
What thou saw-est way-far-ing: 5 'The tomb of Christ, who is liv-ing,

TREBLES
The shroud and nap-kin rest-ing. 7 Yea, Christ my hope is a-ris-en:

The glo-ry of Je-sus' Re-sur-rec-tion; 8*Hap-py they who hear the wit-ness,

FULL
To Ga-li-lee he goes be-fore you.' 9 Christ in-deed from death is ris-en,

Ma-ry's word be-liev-ing A - bove the tales of Jew - ry de-ceiv-ing.
Our new life ob-tain-ing: Have mer-cy, Vic-tor King, ev - er reign-ing!

11th cent. *Tr.* cento

171

HYMN **139**   Salzburg — 7 7 7 7. D

J. Hintze, 1622–1702
Harmony by J. S. Bach, 1685–1750

Easter

At the Lamb's high feast we sing
Praise to our victorious King,
Who hath washed us in the tide
Flowing from his piercèd side;
Praise we him, whose love divine⌣
Gives his sacred Blood for wine,
Gives his Body for the feast,
Christ the Victim, Christ the Priest.

2
Where the Paschal blood is poured,
Death's dark angel sheathes his sword;
Israel's hosts triumphant go
Through the wave that drowns the foe.
Praise we Christ, whose Blood was shed,
Paschal Victim, Paschal Bread;
With sincerity and love
Eat we manna from above.

3
Mighty Victim from the sky,
Hell's fierce powers beneath thee lie;
Thou hast conquered in the fight,
Thou hast brought us life and light.
Now no more can death appal,
Now no more the grave enthral:
Thou hast opened Paradise,
And in thee thy saints shall rise.

4
Easter triumph, Easter joy,
Sin alone can this destroy;
From sin's power do thou set free
Souls new-born, O Lord, in thee.
Hymns of glory and of praise,
Risen Lord, to thee we raise;
Holy Father, praise to thee,
With the Spirit, ever be.

R. CAMPBELL
Based on *Ad regias Agni dapes*

HYMN 140 St. Albinus — 7 8 7 8 4 H. J. Gauntlett, 1805–76

Al - le - lu - ia!

Jesus lebt

Jesus lives! thy terrors now꜀
    Can no more, O death, appal us;
Jesus lives! by this we know
    Thou, O grave, canst not enthral us.
                    Alleluia!

2
Jesus lives! henceforth is death꜀
    But the gate of life immortal:
This shall calm our trembling breath,
    When we pass its gloomy portal.
                    Alleluia!

3
Jesus lives! for us he died;
    Then, alone to Jesus living,
Pure in heart may we abide,
    Glory to our Saviour giving.
                    Alleluia!

4
Jesus lives! our hearts know well꜀
    Naught from us his love shall sever;
Life nor death nor powers of hell
    Tear us from his keeping ever.
                    Alleluia!

5
Jesus lives! to him the throne꜀
    Over all the world is given:
May we go where he is gone,
    Rest and reign with him in heaven.
                    Alleluia!

C. F. GELLERT
Tr. Frances E. Cox and others

174

Hymn **141**   Savannah — 7 7 7 7   J. Wesley's *Foundery Collection*, 1742

Love's redeeming work is done;
Fought the fight, the battle won:
Lo, our Sun's eclipse is o'er!
Lo, he sets in blood no more!

2
Vain the stone, the watch, the seal!
Christ has burst the gates of hell;
Death in vain forbids his rise;
Christ has opened Paradise.

3
Lives again our glorious King;
Where, O death, is now thy sting?
Dying once, he all doth save;
Where thy victory, O grave?

4
Soar we now where Christ has led,
Following our exalted Head;
Made like him, like him we rise;
Ours the cross, the grave, the skies.

5
Hail the Lord of earth and heaven!
Praise to thee by both be given:
Thee we greet triumphant now;
Hail, the Resurrection thou!

C. WESLEY

Easter

HYMN **142** St. Michael — S.M.   *Anglo-Genevan Psalms,* 1561

A lower setting of this tune will be found at Hymn 539

The Lord is risen indeed!
Now is his work performed;
Now is the mighty captive freed,
And death's strong castle stormed.

2
The Lord is risen indeed!
Then hell has lost his prey;
With him is risen the ransomed seed
To reign in endless day.

3
The Lord is risen indeed!
He lives, to die no more;
He lives, the sinner's cause to plead,
Whose curse and shame he bore.

4
The Lord is risen indeed!
Attending angels, hear!
Up to the courts of heaven with speed
The joyful tidings bear.

5
Then take your golden lyres,
And strike each cheerful chord;
Join, all ye bright celestial choirs,
To sing our risen Lord.

T. KELLY‡

Alternative Tune, Narenza, 229

HYMN 143 Aethelwold — 8 7. 8 7. 7 7   Sir S. H. Nicholson, 1875–1947

By permission of the Royal School of Church Music

He is risen, he is risen!
  Tell it with a joyful voice;
He has burst his three days' prison;
  Let the whole wide earth rejoice.
Death is conquered, man is free,
Christ has won the victory.

2

Come, ye sad and fearful-hearted,
  With glad smile and radiant brow;
Lent's long shadows have departed,
  All his woes are over now,
And the Passion that he bore:
Sin and pain can vex no more.

3

Come, with high and holy hymning
  Chant our Lord's triumphant lay;
Not one darksome cloud is dimming
  Yonder glorious morning ray,
Breaking o'er the purple east:
Brighter far our Easter-feast.

MRS. C. F. ALEXANDER

Alternative Tune, All Saints, 570

The following hymns are also suitable for this season:

222 Come, ye faithful, raise the anthem.
279 Light's abode, celestial Salem.
602 Light's glittering morn bedecks the sky.

ROGATIONTIDE

HYMN **144**   Lincoln — C.M.   T. Ravenscroft, *Psalms*, 1621

ALTERNATIVE VERSION
(Melody in the Tenor part)

T. Ravenscroft, *Psalms*, 1621

The Alternative Version may be used for verses 2 and 4

Lord, in thy name thy servants plead,
  And thou hast sworn to hear :
Thine is the harvest, thine the seed,
  The fresh and fading year.

2
Our hope, when autumn winds blew wild,
  We trusted, Lord, with thee ;
And still, now spring has on us smiled,
  We wait on thy decree.

3
The former and the latter rain,
  The summer sun and air,

The green ear, and the golden grain,
  All thine, are ours by prayer.

4
Thine too by right, and ours by grace,
  The wondrous growth unseen,
The hopes that soothe, the fears that brace
  The love that shines serene.

5
So grant the precious things brought forth
  By sun and moon below,
That thee in thy new heaven and earth
  We never may forgo.

                                J. KEBLE

See also :   606   To thee our God we fly.

178

ASCENSIONTIDE

Paule, doctor egregie — L.M.

Mode vii

Aeterne Rex altissime

1 O thou e - ter - nal King most high, Whose Blood has brought sal -
2 As - cend - ing to the Fa - ther's throne Thou tak'st the king - dom
3 Be thou our joy, O migh - ty Lord, As thou wilt be our

1 va - tion nigh, The bonds of death are burst by thee,
2 as thine own; While awe - struck an - gels con - tem - plate
3 great re - ward; Let all our glo - ry be in thee

1 And love has won the vic - to - ry.
2 The won - drous change of man's es - tate.
3 Both now and through e - ter - ni - ty.

179

HYMN **145**

A Morning Hymn — L.M.   Melody by J. Clarke, *c.* 1659–1707

Aeterne Rex altissime

O thou eternal King most high,
Whose Blood has brought salvation nigh,
The bonds of death are burst by thee,
And love has won the victory.

2
Ascending to the Father's throne
Thou tak'st the kingdom as thine own;
While awestruck angels contemplate
The wondrous change of man's estate.

3
Be thou our joy, O mighty Lord,
As thou wilt be our great reward;
Let all our glory be in thee
Both now and through eternity.

Tr. COMPILERS† (1904)

Jesu, nostra redemptio

Jesu, our hope, our heart's desire,
  Thy work of grace we sing;
Redeemer of the world art thou,
  Its Maker and its King.

2
How vast the mercy and the love
  Which laid our sins on thee,
And led thee to a cruel death,
  To set thy people free!

3
But now the bonds of death are burst,
  The ransom has been paid;
And thou art on thy Father's throne,
  In glorious robes arrayed.

4
O may thy mighty love prevail
  Our sinful souls to spare!
O may we stand around thy throne,
  And see thy glory there!

5
Jesu, our only joy be thou,
  As thou our prize wilt be;
In thee be all our glory now
  And through eternity.

[UNISON]   6
All praise to thee who art gone up
  Triumphantly to heaven;
All praise to God the Father's name
  And Holy Ghost be given.

Tr. J. CHANDLER *and Compilers*

181

Hymn 147   FIRST TUNE

Ascension — 7 7 7 7 with Alleluias   W. H. Monk, 1823–89

Ascensiontide

Al - le - lu - ia!

Al - le - lu - ia!

The Descant may be sung by Trebles for verses 3 and 6, the main melody being sung in Unison

f Hail the day that sees him rise,   Alleluia!
To his throne above the skies;   Alleluia!
Christ, the Lamb for sinners given, Alleluia!
Enters now the highest heaven.   Alleluia!

2
There for him high triumph waits; Alleluia!
Lift your heads, eternal gates!   Alleluia!
He hath conquered death and sin;   Alleluia!
Take the King of Glory in!   Alleluia!

3
Lo, the heaven its Lord receives, Alleluia!
Yet he loves the earth he leaves; Alleluia!
Though returning to his throne,   Alleluia!
Still he calls mankind his own.   Alleluia!

4
mf See! he lifts his hands above;   Alleluia!
See! he shews the prints of love; Alleluia!
Hark! his gracious lips bestow,   Alleluia!
Blessings on his Church below.   Alleluia!

5
Still for us he intercedes,   Alleluia!
His prevailing Death he pleads;   Alleluia!
Near himself prepares our place,   Alleluia!
He the first-fruits of our race.   Alleluia!

6
Lord, though parted from our sight, Alleluia!
Far above the starry height,   Alleluia!
f Grant our hearts may thither rise, Alleluia!
Seeking thee above the skies.   Alleluia!

C. WESLEY, T. COTTERILL and Compilers

NOTE. *A longer form of this hymn will be found in the 'Processional' section* (**610**)

Ascensiontide

HYMN **147**   SECOND TUNE

Llanfair — 7 7 7 7 with Alleluias   Welsh Hymn Melody

f Hail the day that sees him rise, Alleluia!
To his throne above the skies; Alleluia!
Christ, the Lamb for sinners given, Alleluia!
Enters now the highest heaven. Alleluia!

2
There for him high triumph waits; Alleluia!
Lift your heads, eternal gates! Alleluia!
He hath conquered death and sin; Alleluia!
Take the King of Glory in! Alleluia!

3
Lo, the heaven its Lord receives, Alleluia!
Yet he loves the earth he leaves; Alleluia!
Though returning to his throne, Alleluia!
Still he calls mankind his own. Alleluia!

4
mf See! he lifts his hands above; Alleluia!
See! he shews the prints of love; Alleluia!
Hark! his gracious lips bestow, Alleluia!
Blessings on his Church below. Alleluia!

5
Still for us he intercedes, Alleluia!
His prevailing Death he pleads; Alleluia!
Near himself prepares our place, Alleluia!
He the first-fruits of our race. Alleluia!

[UNISON] 6
Lord, though parted from our sight, Alleluia!
Far above the starry height, Alleluia!
f Grant our hearts may thither rise, Alleluia!
Seeking thee above the skies. Alleluia!

C. WESLEY, T. COTTERILL and Compilers

NOTE. *A longer form of this hymn will be found in the 'Processional' section* (**610**)

Alternative Tune, Chislehurst, 610

HYMN **148** Rex gloriae — 8 7 8 7. D   H. Smart, 1813-79

f See the Conqueror mounts in triumph,
        See the King in royal state
     Riding on the clouds his chariot
        To his heavenly palace gate;
     Hark! the choirs of angel voices
        Joyful Alleluias sing,
     And the portals high are lifted
        To receive their heavenly King.

Ascensiontide

2

mf Who is this that comes in glory,
With the trump of jubilee?
Lord of battles, God of armies,
He has gained the victory;
He who on the Cross did suffer,
f   He who from the grave arose,
He has vanquished sin and Satan,
He by death has spoiled his foes.

3

He has raised our human nature
On the clouds to God's right hand;
There we sit in heavenly places,
There with him in glory stand:
Jesus reigns, adored by angels;
Man with God is on the throne;
Mighty Lord, in thine Ascension
We by faith behold our own.

4*

mf See him who is gone before us
Heavenly mansions to prepare,
See him who is ever pleading‿
For us with prevailing prayer,
See him who with sound of trumpet
And with his angelic train,
Summoning the world to judgement,
On the clouds will come again.

5

f Glory be to God the Father;
Glory be to God the Son,
Dying, risen, ascending for us,
Who the heavenly realm has won;
Glory to the Holy Spirit:
To One God in Persons Three
Glory both in earth and heaven,
Glory, endless glory be.

Bishop Chr. Wordsworth

Ascensiontide

f Thou art gone up on high,
   To mansions in the skies;
And round thy throne unceasingly
   The songs of praise arise :
p But we are lingering here,
   With sin and care oppressed;
Lord, send thy promised Comforter,
   And lead us to thy rest.

2

mf Thou art gone up on high;
   But thou didst first come down,
Through earth's most bitter misery
   To pass unto thy crown;

And girt with griefs and fears
   Our onward course must be;
But only let this path of tears
   'Lead us at last to thee.

3

f Thou art gone up on high;
   But thou shalt come again,
With all the bright ones of the sky
   Attendant in thy train.
Lord, by thy saving power
   So make us live and die,   [hou
That we may stand in that dreac
   At thy right hand on high.

MRS. E. TOKE

188

HYMN **150**   Nun freut euch — 8 7 8 7. 8 8 7   *Etlich Christliche Lyeder,* 1524

Let all the multitudes of light,
   Their songs in concert raising,
With earth's triumphal hymns unite,
   The risen Saviour praising.
Ye heavens, his festival proclaim!
Our King returneth whence he came,
   With victory amazing.

2

For us he bore the bitter Tree,
   To death's dark realm descending;
Our foe he slew, and set us free,
   Man's ancient bondage ending.
No more the tyrant's chains oppress;
O conquering Love, thy name we bless,
   With thee to heaven ascending.

3

Jesus, to thee be endless praise,
   For this thy great salvation;
O holy Father, thine always
   Be thanks and adoration;
Spirit of life and light, to thee⌣
Eternal praise and glory be:
   One God of all creation!

F. B. MACNUTT

Alternative Tune, Laus Deo (Bach), 422

The following hymns are suitable for this season:

Felix dies — L.M.   Mode ii

Beata nobis gaudia

1 O joy, be - cause the circ - ling year
2 Like un - to quiver - ing tongues of flame
3 Thus un - to all was spread a - broad
4 Of old in eve - ry hal - lowed breast

1 Hath brought our day of bless - ing here! The day when first the
2 Up - on each one the Spi - rit came: Tongues, that the earth might
3 The won - der of the works of God; They knew the pro - phet's
4 Thou ca - mest in thy grace to rest: O grant us now from

1 light di - vine Up - on the Church be - gan to shine.
2 hear their call, And fire, that love might burn in all.
3 word ful - filled, And owned the work which God had willed.
4 sin re - lease, And in our time, good Lord, give peace.

Erfurt — L.M. *Geistliche Lieder* (Leipzig, 1539)

Beata nobis gaudia

O joy, because the circling year
Hath brought our day of blessing here!
The day when first the light divine
Upon the Church began to shine.

2
Like unto quivering tongues of flame
Upon each one the Spirit came:
Tongues, that the earth might hear their call,
And fire, that love might burn in all.

3
Thus unto all was spread abroad
The wonder of the works of God;
They knew the prophet's word fulfilled,
And owned the work which God had willed.

4
Of old in every hallowed breast
Thou camest in thy grace to rest:
O grant us now from sin release,
And in our time, good Lord, give peace.

Tr. J. ELLERTON and Compilers† (1904)

HYMN **152**   Veni creator No. 2 — L.M.   J. B. Dykes, 1823–76

Veni, creator Spiritus

Come, O Creator Spirit, come,
And make within our hearts thy home;
To us thy grace celestial give,
Who of thy breathing move and live.

2
O Paraclete, that name is thine,
Of God most high the gift divine;
The well of life, the fire of love,
Our soul's anointing from above.

3
Thou dost appear in sevenfold dower
The sign of God's almighty power;
The Father's promise, making rich⌣
With saving truth our earthly speech.

4
Our senses with thy light inflame,
Our hearts to heavenly love reclaim;
Our bodies' poor infirmity
With strength perpetual fortify.

5
Our mortal foe afar repel,
Grant us henceforth in peace to dwell;
And so to us, with thee for guide,
No ill shall come, no harm betide.

6
May we by thee the Father learn,
And know the Son, and thee discern,
Who art of Both; and thus adore
In perfect faith for evermore.

? ARCHBISHOP RABANUS MAURUS
Tr. Yattendon Hymnal

NOTE. *'Paraclete' in verse 2, line 1, is the English form of 'Parakletos,' a title of the Holy Spirit used by St. John and translated 'Comforter' (or 'Advocate')*

Whitsuntide

Spirit of mercy, truth, and love,
O shed thine influence from above,
And still from age to age convey⌣
The wonders of this sacred day.

2

In every clime, by every tongue,
Be God's surpassing glory sung;
Let all the listening earth be taught
The acts our great Redeemer wrought.

3

Unfailing comfort, heavenly guide,
Still o'er thy holy Church preside;
Still let mankind thy blessings prove,
Spirit of mercy, truth, and love.

Foundling Hospital Collection† (1774)

Alternative Tune, Melcombe, 4

Whitsuntide

FIRST TUNE

Sudeley — C.M.

Sir J. Stainer, 1840–1901

SECOND TUNE

Winchester Old — C.M.

Este, *Psalms*, 1592

A lower setting of this tune with an Alternative Version will be found at Hymn 62. The Alternative Version may be used for verses 3 and 5

f   When God of old came down from heaven,
      In power and wrath he came;
   Before his feet the clouds were riven,
      Half darkness and half flame:

2

p   But, when he came the second time,
      He came in power and love;
   Softer than gale at morning prime
      Hovered his holy Dove.

3

f   The fires, that rushed on Sinai down
      In sudden torrents dread,
   Now gently light, a glorious crown,
      On every sainted head.

4

And as on Israel's awestruck ear
   The voice exceeding loud,
The trump that angels quake to hear,
   Thrilled from the deep, dark cloud;

5

So, when the Spirit of our God
   Came down his flock to find,
A voice from heaven was heard abroad,
   A rushing, mighty wind.

6

mf It fills the Church of God; it fills⌣
     The sinful world around:
   Only in stubborn hearts and wills
     No place for it is found.

7

p   Come, Lord, come Wisdom, Love, and Power,
      Open our ears to hear;
   Let us not miss the accepted hour:
      Save, Lord, by love or fear.

J. KEBLE

HYMN **155**   Naphill — 7 7 7 7. D   H. E. Darke

3
The centuries go gliding,
But still we have abiding
With us that Spirit Holy
To make us brave and lowly—
    Lowly, for we feel our need :
    God alone is strong indeed ;
    Brave, for with the Spirit's aid
    We can venture unafraid.

Our Lord, his Passion ended,
Hath gloriously ascended,
Yet though from him divided,
He leaves us not unguided ;
    All his benefits to crown
    He hath sent his Spirit down,
    Burning like a flame of fire
    His disciples to inspire.

2
God's Spirit is directing ;
No more they sit expecting ;
But forth to all the nation
They go with exultation ;   [wrought
    That which God in them hath
    Fills their life and soul and thought ;
    So their witness now can do
    Work as great in others too.

4
O Lord of every nation,
Fill us with inspiration !
We know our own unfitness,
Yet for thee would bear witness.
    By thy Spirit now we raise
    To the heavenly Father praise :
    Holy Spirit, Father, Son,
    Make us know thee, ever One.

F. C. BURKITT

HYMN **156**   Veni, Sancte Spiritus — 7 7 7. 7 7 7   S. Webbe, 1740–1816

Veni, Sancte Spiritus

Come, thou Holy Spirit, come,
And from thy celestial home
  Shed a ray of light divine;
Come, thou Father of the poor,
Come, thou source of all our store,
  Come, within our bosoms shine:

2
Thou of comforters the best,
Thou the soul's most welcome guest,
  Sweet refreshment here below;
In our labour rest most sweet,
Grateful coolness in the heat,
  Solace in the midst of woe.

3
O most blessèd Light divine,
Shine within these hearts of thine,
  And our inmost being fill;
Where thou art not, man hath naught,
Nothing good in deed or thought,
  Nothing free from taint of ill.

4
Heal our wounds; our strength renew;
On our dryness pour thy dew;
  Wash the stains of guilt away;
Bend the stubborn heart and will;
Melt the frozen, warm the chill;
  Guide the steps that go astray.

5
On the faithful, who adore◡
And confess thee, evermore◡
  In thy sevenfold gifts descend:
Give them virtue's sure reward,
Give them thy salvation, Lord,
  Give them joys that never end.

ARCHBISHOP STEPHEN LANGTON
Tr. E. Caswall and Compilers

HYMN **157**   Veni, creator Spiritus — L.M.   Mode viii

1 Come, Ho - ly Ghost, our souls in - spire, And light - en
2 Thy bless - èd unc - tion from a - bove Is com - fort,
3 A - noint and cheer our soil - èd face With the a -
4 Teach us to know the Fa - ther, Son, And thee, of

1 with ce - les - tial fire; Thou the a - noint - ing
2 life, and fire of love; En - a - ble with per -
3 bun - dance of thy grace: Keep far our foes, give
4 Both, to be but One; That through the a - ges

1 Spi - rit art, Who dost thy seven - fold gifts im - part.
2 pet - ual light The dul - ness of our blind - ed sight.
3 peace at home; Where thou art guide no ill can come.
4 all a - long This .... may be our end - less song,

CONCLUSION

'Praise to thy e - ter - nal mer - it,

Fa - ther, Son, and Ho - ly Spi - rit.'

BISHOP J. COSIN
Based on *Veni, creator Spiritus*

The following hymns are suitable for this season:

TRINITY SUNDAY

O Pater sancte — 11 11 11 5   Mode iv

O Pater sancte

1 Fa - ther most ho - ly, mer - ci - ful and lo - ving,
2 Three in a won - drous U - ni - ty un - bro - ken,
3 All thy cre - a - tion ser - veth its Cre - a - tor,
4 Lord God Al - migh - ty, un - to thee be glo - ry,

1 Je - su, Re - deem - er, ev - er to be wor - shipped, Life - giv -
2 One per - fect God - head, love that ne - ver fail - eth, Light of
3 Thee eve - ry crea - ture prais - eth with - out ceas - ing; We too
4 One in three Per - sons, ov - er all ex - alt - ed. Thine, as

1 ing Spi - rit, Com - for - ter most gra - cious, God ev - er - last - ing;
2 the an - gels, suc - cour of the need - y, Hope of all liv - ing;
3 would sing thee psalms of true de - vo - tion: Hear, we be - seech thee.
4 is meet, be hon - our, praise and bless - ing Now and for ev - er.

200

Trinity Sunday

SECOND TUNE

Angers — 11 11 11 5   Melody from J. B. Croft's *Collection*

May be sung in Unison

O Pater sancte

Father most holy, merciful and loving,
Jesu, Redeemer, ever to be worshipped,
Life-giving Spirit, Comforter most gracious,
    God everlasting;

2
Three in a wondrous Unity unbroken,
One perfect Godhead, love that never faileth,
Light of the angels, succour of the needy,
    Hope of all living;

3
All thy creation serveth its Creator,
Thee every creature praiseth without ceasing;
We too would sing thee psalms of true devotion:
    Hear, we beseech thee.

4
Lord God Almighty, unto thee be glory,
One in three Persons, over all exalted.
Thine, as is meet, be honour, praise and blessing
    Now and for ever.

Before 10th cent.
Tr. A. E. ALSTON

Trinity Sunday

HYMN **159**   St. Flavian — C.M.   Psalm cxxxii, adapted from *Psalms*, 1562

ALTERNATIVE VERSION

(Melody in the Tenor part)

Harmonized by T. Ravenscroft (1621)

The Alternative Version may be used for verses 2 and 4

Trinity Sunday

Most ancient of all mysteries,
  Before thy throne we lie;
Have mercy now, most merciful,
  Most holy Trinity.

2
When heaven and earth were yet unmade,
  When time was yet unknown,
Thou in thy bliss and majesty
  Didst live and love alone.

3
Thou wast not born; there was no fount⌣
  From which thy being flowed;
There is no end which thou canst reach:
  But thou art simply God.

4
How wonderful creation is,
  The work which thou didst bless!
And O what then must thou be like,
  Eternal loveliness!

5
Most ancient of all mysteries,
  Low at thy throne we lie;
Have mercy now, most merciful,
  Most holy Trinity.

F. W. FABER

The following hymns are suitable:

160 Holy, Holy, Holy! Lord God Almighty.
161 Bright the vision that delighted.
162 I bind unto myself to-day.
163 Three in One, and One in Three.
164 Father of heaven, whose love profound.

GENERAL HYMNS

Hymn **160**   Nicaea — 11 12 12 10   J. B. Dykes, 1823–76

mf Holy, Holy, Holy! Lord God Almighty!
     Early in the morning our song shall rise to thee;
    Holy, Holy, Holy! merciful and mighty!
     God in three Persons, blessèd Trinity!

2
Holy, Holy, Holy! all the saints adore thee,
     Casting down their golden crowns around the glassy sea;
    Cherubim and seraphim falling down before thee,
     Which wert and art and evermore shalt be.

3
p Holy, Holy, Holy! though the darkness hide thee,
     Though the eye of sinful man thy glory may not see,
mf Only thou art holy, there is none beside thee
     Perfect in power, in love, and purity.

4
Holy, Holy, Holy! Lord God Almighty!
f   All thy works shall praise thy name in earth and sky and sea;
    Holy, Holy, Holy! merciful and mighty!
     God in three Persons, blessèd Trinity!

Bishop R. Heber

HYMN **161**   Laus Deo — 8 7 8 7   R. Redhead, 1820–1901

DESCANT

The Descant may be sung by Trebles for verses 3 and 6, the main melody being sung in Unison

if Bright the vision that delighted⌣
  Once the sight of Judah's seer;
Sweet the countless tongues united
  To entrance the prophet's ear.

2
Round the Lord in glory seated
  Cherubim and seraphim⌣
Filled his temple, and repeated⌣
  Each to each the alternate hymn:

[UNISON]   3
'Lord, thy glory fills the heaven;
  Earth is with its fulness stored;
Unto thee be glory given,
  Holy, Holy, Holy, Lord.'

4
Heaven is still with glory ringing,
  Earth takes up the angels' cry,
'Holy, Holy, Holy,' singing,   [high.⸱
  'Lord of Hosts, the Lord most

5
mf With his seraph train before him,
  With his holy Church below,
Thus unite we to adore him,
  Bid we thus our anthem flow:

[UNISON]   6
f 'Lord, thy glory fills the heaven;
  Earth is with its fulness stored;
Unto thee be glory given,
  Holy, Holy, Holy, Lord.'

BISHOP R. MANT†

NOTE. *This hymn is based on the account of Isaiah's vision in Is. 6*

HYMN **162** St. Patrick's Breastplate — Irregular   Old Irish Melodies

Arranged by Sir C. V. Stanford, 1852–1924

Ατοmμιuμ ιnoιu

VOICES. *Full Unison. Rather quickly and with strong rhythm*

1 *f* I bind un - to my - self to - day The strong name

of the Trin - i - ty, By in - vo - ca - tion

of the same, The Three in One, and One in Three.

MEN
2 *mf* I bind this day to me for ev - er, By power of
TREBLE
4* *mf* I bind un - to my - self to - day The vir - tues
FULL
7* A - gainst all Sa - tan's spells and wiles, A - gainst false

2 faith, Christ's In - car - na-tion, His Bap - tism in the Jor - dan
4* of the star - lit hea-ven, The glo - rious sun's life - giv - ing
7* words of her - e - sy, A - gainst the know-ledge that de-

2 riv-er, His death on Cross for my sal - va-tion: (FULL)*f* His
4* ray, The white - ness of the moon at ev - en, (FULL)*f* The
7* files, A - gainst the heart's i - dol - a - try, A-

207

2 burst - ing from the spic - èd tomb, His rid - ing
4* flash - ing of the light - ning free, The whirl - ing
7* gainst the wiz - ard's e - vil craft, A - gainst the

2 up the heaven - ly way, His com - ing at the
4* winds' tem - pest - uous shocks, The sta - ble earth, the
7* death-wound and the burn-ing, The chok - ing wave, the

2 day of doom, I bind un - to my - self to - day.
4* deep salt sea A - round the old e - ter - nal rocks.
7* poi-soned shaft, Pro - tect me, Christ, till thy re - turning.

General

VOICES *in Harmony with Organ*

3* *mf* I bind un - to my - self the power Of the great love of

5 *mf* I bind un - to my - self to - day The power of God to

6* *mf* A - gainst the de - mon snares of sin, The vice that gives temp-

3* cher - u - bim; The sweet 'Well done!' in judge - ment

5 hold and lead, His eye to watch, His might to

6* ta - tion force, The na - tu - ral lusts that war with-

3* hour; The ser - vice of the ser - a - phim, *mf* Con-

5 stay, His ear to heark - en to my need; *mp* The

6* in, The hos - tile men that mar my course — *p* Or

(Org.)

3* fess - ors' faith, a - pos - tles' word, The pa - triarchs'

5 wis - dom of my God to teach, His hand to

6* few or ma - ny, far or nigh, In ev - ery

209

General

3* prayers, the   pro - phets' scrolls, *p* All   good   deeds   done   un -
5   guide, his   shield   to   ward, The   word   of   God   to
6* place, and   in   all   hours, A - gainst their   fierce   hos -

3* to the   Lord, And   pu - ri - ty   of   vir - gin   souls.
5   give me   speech, His   heaven - ly   host   to   be   my   guard.
6* til - i - ty   I   bind   to   me   these   ho - ly   powers.

PART II

In moderate time

8 Christ   be   with me,   Christ with - in   me,   Christ   be - hind   me,

Christ   be - fore   me,   Christ   be - side me,   Christ   to   win   me,

8 Christ to com-fort and re - store me, Christ be-neath me, Christ a-bove me, Christ in qui - et, Christ in dan - ger,

rall. - - - -

Christ in hearts of all that love me, Christ in mouth of friend and stran - ger.

DOXOLOGY

FULL *A little slower*

9† I bind un - to my - self the name, The strong name

† *The accompaniment for verse 2 may be used*

211

HYMN **162** (*continued*)

of the Trin - i - ty, By in - vo - ca - tion of the

ff

same, The Three in One, and One in Three,

Of whom all na - ture hath cre - a - tion, E - ter - nal

General

Fa - ther, Spi - rit, Word. Praise to the Lord of
my sal - va - tion: Sal - va - tion is of Christ the
Lord. A - - men.

Ascribed to St. Patrick
Tr. Mrs. C. F. Alexander

HYMN **163**   Capetown — 7 7 7 5   F. Filitz, 1804–76

·   Three in One, and One in Three,
Ruler of the earth and sea,
Hear us, while we lift to thee⌣
    Holy chant and psalm.

2
Light of lights! with morning shine;
Lift on us thy light divine;
And let charity benign
    Breathe on us her balm.

3
Light of lights! when falls the even,
Let it close on sin forgiven;
Fold us in the peace of heaven;
    Shed a holy calm.

4
Three in One and One in Three,
Dimly here we worship thee;
With the saints hereafter we⌣
    Hope to bear the palm.

G. RORISON†

214

HYMN 164   FIRST TUNE

Song 5 — L.M.   Orlando Gibbons, 1583–1625

Father of heaven, whose love profound
A ransom for our souls hath found,
Before thy throne we sinners bend,
To us thy pardoning love extend.

2
Almighty Son, incarnate Word,
Our Prophet, Priest, Redeemer, Lord,
Before thy throne we sinners bend,
To us thy saving grace extend.

3
Eternal Spirit, by whose breath
The soul is raised from sin and death,
Before thy throne we sinners bend,
To us thy quickening power extend.

4
Thrice Holy! Father, Spirit, Son;
Mysterious Godhead, Three in One,
Before thy throne we sinners bend,
Grace, pardon, life to us extend.

E. COOPER†

General

SECOND TUNE

Rivaulx — L.M.

J. B. Dykes, 1823–76

Father of heaven, whose love profound
A ransom for our souls hath found,
Before thy throne we sinners bend,
To us thy pardoning love extend.

2
Almighty Son, incarnate Word,
Our Prophet, Priest, Redeemer, Lord,
Before thy throne we sinners bend,
To us thy saving grace extend.

3
Eternal Spirit, by whose breath
The soul is raised from sin and death,
Before thy throne we sinners bend,
To us thy quickening power extend.

4
Thrice Holy! Father, Spirit, Son;
Mysterious Godhead, Three in One,
Before thy throne we sinners bend,
Grace, pardon, life to us extend.

E. Cooper†

HYMN **165** St. Anne — C.M.   *Supplement to the New Version,* 1708

DESCANT

The Descant may be sung by Trebles for verse 6, the main melody being sung in Unison

Psalm 90

f O God, our help in ages past,
　Our hope for years to come,
　Our shelter from the stormy blast,
　And our eternal home;

mf Beneath the shadow of thy throne
　Thy saints have dwelt secure;
　Sufficient is thine arm alone,
　And our defence is sure.

3
Before the hills in order stood,
　Or earth received her frame,
From everlasting thou art God,
　To endless years the same.

4
p A thousand ages in thy sight
　Are like an evening gone; [night
Short as the watch that ends the
　Before the rising sun.

5*
Time, like an ever-rolling stream,
　Bears all its sons away;
They fly forgotten, as a dream⌣
　Dies at the opening day.

[UNISON]　6
f O God, our help in ages past,
　Our hope for years to come, [last,
Be thou our guard while troubles
　And our eternal home.

I. WATTS†

General

ALTERNATIVE VERSION

(Melody in the Tenor part)

Harmonized by J. Dowland, 1563–1626

The Alternative Version may be used for verses 2 and 4

Psalm 100

f   All people that on earth do dwell,
    Sing to the Lord with cheerful voice:
  Him serve with fear, his praise forth tell,
    Come ye before him, and rejoice.

2

mf   The Lord, ye know, is God indeed;
    Without our aid he did us make;
  We are his folk, he doth us feed,
    And for his sheep he doth us take.

3

f   O enter then his gates with praise,
    Approach with joy his courts unto;
  Praise, laud, and bless his name always,
    For it is seemly so to do.

4

mf   For why? the Lord our God is good;
    His mercy is for ever sure;
  His truth at all times firmly stood,
    And shall from age to age endure.

[UNISON]   5

  To Father, Son, and Holy Ghost,
    The God whom heaven and earth adore,
  From men and from the angel-host
    Be praise and glory evermore.

W. KETHE, *Day's Psalter* (1561)

General

Old 104th — 10 10 11 11

T. Ravenscroft, *Psalms*, 1621

Descant by Alan Gray, 1855–1935

Descant by permission of the Cambridge University Press

The Descant may be sung by Trebles for verse 6, the main melody being sung in Unison

General

Psalm 104

f   O worship the King all glorious above;
O gratefully sing his power and his love;
Our Shield and Defender, the Ancient of Days,
Pavilioned in splendour and girded with praise.

2
O tell of his might, O sing of his grace,
Whose robe is the light, whose canopy space;
His chariots of wrath the deep thunder clouds form,
And dark is his path on the wings of the storm.

3*
mf   The earth with its store of wonders untold,
Almighty, thy power hath founded of old;
Hath stablished it fast by a changeless decree,
And round it hath cast, like a mantle, the sea.

4
Thy bountiful care what tongue can recite?
It breathes in the air, it shines in the light;
It streams from the hills, it descends to the plain,
And sweetly distils in the dew and the rain.

5
p   Frail children of dust and feeble as frail,
In thee do we trust, nor find thee to fail;
Thy mercies how tender, how firm to the end!
Our Maker, Defender, Redeemer, and Friend.

[UNISON] 6
f   O measureless Might, ineffable Love,
While angels delight to hymn thee above,
Thy ransomed creation, though feeble their lays,
With true adoration shall sing to thy praise.

SIR R. GRANT†
Based on W. Kethe (1561)

General

SECOND TUNE

Hanover — 10 10 11 11

Supplement to the New Version, 1708
Descant by Alan Gray, 1855–1935

DESCANT

Descant by permission of the Cambridge University Press

The Descant may be sung by Trebles for verse 6, the main melody being sung in Unison

A lower setting of this tune will be found at Hymn 506

222

Psalm 104

f O worship the King all glorious above;
O gratefully sing his power and his love;
Our Shield and Defender, the Ancient of Days,
Pavilioned in splendour and girded with praise.

2
O tell of his might, O sing of his grace,
Whose robe is the light, whose canopy space;
His chariots of wrath the deep thunder clouds form,
And dark is his path on the wings of the storm.

3*
mf The earth with its store of wonders untold,
Almighty, thy power hath founded of old;
Hath stablished it fast by a changeless decree,
And round it hath cast, like a mantle, the sea.

4
Thy bountiful care what tongue can recite?
It breathes in the air, it shines in the light;
It streams from the hills, it descends to the plain,
And sweetly distils in the dew and the rain.

5
p Frail children of dust and feeble as frail,
In thee do we trust, nor find thee to fail;
Thy mercies how tender, how firm to the end!
Our Maker, Defender, Redeemer, and Friend.

[UNISON] 6
f O measureless Might, ineffable Love,
While angels delight to hymn thee above,
Thy ransomed creation, though feeble their lays,
With true adoration shall sing to thy praise.

SIR R. GRANT†
Based on W. Kethe (1561)

HYMN **168**   Tranmere — D.C.M.   W. Hayes, 1706–77

Alternative Tune, St. Matthew, 478

General

mf   There is a book, who runs may read,
     Which heavenly truth imparts,
  And all the lore its scholars need,
     Pure eyes and Christian hearts.
  The works of God above, below,
     Within us and around,
  Are pages in that book, to show
     How God himself is found.

2

  The glorious sky, embracing all,
     Is like the Maker's love,
  Wherewith encompassed, great and small
     In peace and order move.
  The moon above, the Church below,
     A wondrous race they run;
  But all their radiance, all their glow,
     Each borrows of its sun.

3*

  The Saviour lends the light and heat
     That crown his holy hill;
  The saints, like stars, around his seat
     Perform their courses still.
  The dew of heaven is like thy grace,
     It steals in silence down;
  But where it lights, the favoured place
     By richest fruits is known.

4

f   One name, above all glorious names,
     With its ten thousand tongues
  The everlasting sea proclaims,
     Echoing angelic songs.
  The raging fire, the roaring wind,
     Thy boundless power display;
  But in the gentler breeze we find
     Thy Spirit's viewless way.

5

mf   Two worlds are ours : 'tis only sin
     Forbids us to descry
  The mystic heaven and earth within,
     Plain as the sea and sky.
  Thou who hast given me eyes to see
     And love this sight so fair,
  Give me a heart to find out thee,
     And read thee everywhere.

J. KEBLE

HYMN **169** Westminster — C.M.   J. Turle, 1802–82

mf My God, how wonderful thou art,
   Thy majesty how bright,
   How beautiful thy mercy-seat,
   In depths of burning light!

2

p How dread are thine eternal years,
   O everlasting Lord,
   By prostrate spirits day and night
   Incessantly adored!

3

mf How wonderful, how beautiful,
   The sight of thee must be,
   Thine endless wisdom, boundless
     power,
   And aweful purity!

4

p O how I fear thee, living God,
   With deepest, tenderest fears,
   And worship thee with trembling
     hope,
   And penitential tears!

5

mf Yet I may love thee too, O Lord,
   Almighty as thou art,
   For thou hast stooped to ask of me
   The love of my poor heart.

6

No earthly father loves like thee,
   No mother, e'er so mild,
   Bears and forbears as thou hast done
   With me thy sinful child

7

Father of Jesus, love's reward,
   What rapture will it be,
   Prostrate before thy throne to lie,
   And gaze and gaze on thee!

F. W. FABER

HYMN **170** Addison's — D.L.M.   J. Sheeles, 1688–1761

The spacious firmament on high,
With all the blue ethereal sky,
And spangled heavens, a shining frame,
Their great Original proclaim.
The unwearied sun from day to day
Does his Creator's power display,
And publishes to every land
The works of an almighty hand.

2

Soon as the evening shades prevail
The moon takes up the wondrous tale,
And nightly to the listening earth
Repeats the story of her birth;
Whilst all the stars that round her burn,
And all the planets in their turn,
Confirm the tidings, as they roll,
And spread the truth from pole to pole.

3

What though in solemn silence all
Move round the dark terrestrial ball;
What though nor reàl voice nor sound
Amid their radiant orbs be found;
In reason's ear they all rejoice,
And utter forth a glorious voice,
For ever singing as they shine,
'The hand that made us is divine.'

J. ADDISON

The last line of each verse is repeated

227

HYMN **171**   Dix — 7 7. 7 7. 7 7   C. Kocher, 1786–1872

DESCANT

If preferred, the harmonies for lines 1 and 2 may be repeated for lines 3 and 4.   The Descant may be sung by Trebles for verse 5, the main melody being sung in Unison.   In this case th above harmonies should be played on the organ.

General

mf For the beauty of the earth,
  For the beauty of the skies,
  For the love which from our birth
  Over and around us lies,
f Lord of all, to thee we raise⌣
  This our grateful hymn of praise.

2

mf For the beauty of each hour⌣
  Of the day and of the night,
  Hill and vale, and tree and flower,
  Sun and moon and stars of light,
f Lord of all, to thee we raise⌣
  This our grateful hymn of praise.

3

mf For the joy of human love,
  Brother, sister, parent, child,
  Friends on earth, and friends above,
  Pleasures pure and undefiled,
f Lord of all, to thee we raise⌣
  This our grateful hymn of praise.

4

mf For each perfect gift of thine,
  To our race so freely given,
  Graces human and divine,
  Flowers of earth and buds of heaven,
f Lord of all, to thee we raise⌣
  This our grateful hymn of praise.

[UNISON] **5**
For thy Church which evermore⌣
  Lifteth holy hands above,
Offering up on every shore
  Her pure sacrifice of love,
Lord of all, to thee we raise⌣
This our grateful hymn of praise.

F. S. PIERPOINT†

HYMN 172 Easter Song — 8 8 8. 8 8 6. 12   *Catholische Kirchengesänge*
(Cologne, 1623)

Al - le - lu - ia, al - le - lu - ia!

O   praise him, O   praise him, Al - le -

lu - ia, al - le - lu - ia, al - le - lu - ia!

A setting of this tune with an Alternative Version will be found at Hymn 602

General

f   All creatures of our God and King,
    Lift up your voice and with us sing
      Alleluia, alleluia!
    Thou burning sun with golden beam,
    Thou silver moon with softer gleam,
      O praise him, O praise him,
      Alleluia, alleluia, alleluia!

2

Thou rushing wind that art so strong,
Ye clouds that sail in heaven along,
    O praise him, alleluia!
Thou rising morn, in praise rejoice,
Ye lights of evening, find a voice;
    O praise him, etc.

3

mf   Thou flowing water, pure and clear,
    Make music for thy Lord to hear,
      Alleluia, alleluia!
    Thou fire so masterful and bright,
    That givest man both warmth and light,
      O praise him, etc.

4*

Dear mother earth, who day by day
Unfoldest blessings on our way,
    O praise him, alleluia!
The flowers and fruits that in thee grow,
Let them his glory also show;
    O praise him, etc.

5

And all ye men of tender heart,
Forgiving others, take your part,
    O sing ye alleluia!
Ye who long pain and sorrow bear,
Praise God and on him cast your care;
    O praise him, etc.

6*

p   And thou, most kind and gentle death,
    Waiting to hush our latest breath,
      O praise him, alleluia!
    Thou leadest home the child of God,
    And Christ our Lord the way hath trod;
      O praise him, etc.

7

f   Let all things their Creator bless,
    And worship him in humbleness;
      O praise him, alleluia!
    Praise, praise the Father, praise the Son,
    And praise the Spirit, Three in One;
      O praise him, etc.

W. H. DRAPER Based on St. Francis
of Assisi's *Canticle of the Sun*

HYMN **173** Nature — 8 8. 8 8. 8 8   Sir C. H. H. Parry, 1848–1918

I praised the earth, in beauty seen,
With garlands gay of various green;
I praised the sea, whose ample field⌣
Shone glorious as a silver shield—
And earth and ocean seemed to say,
'Our beauties are but for a day.'

2
I praised the sun, whose chariot rolled
On wheels of amber and of gold;
I praised the moon, whose softer eye⌣
Gleamed sweetly through the summer sky—
And moon and sun in answer said,
'Our days of light are numberèd.'

3
O God, O good beyond compare,
If thus thy meaner works are fair,
If thus thy beauties gild the span⌣
Of ruined earth and sinful man,
How glorious must the mansion be
Where thy redeemed shall dwell with thee!

BISHOP R. HEBER

Alternative Tune, Surrey, 179

HYMN **174**   St. Audrey — 8 7. 8 7. 8 7   B. Harwood, 1859–1949

3
Lord of beauty, thine the splendour
 Shewn in earth and sky and sea,
Burning sun and moonlight tender,
 Hill and river, flower and tree :
Lest we fail our praise to render
 Touch our eyes that they may see.

Lord of life, alone sustaining
 All below and all above,
Lord of love, by whose ordaining
 Sun and stars sublimely move :
In our earthly spirits reigning,
 Lift our hearts that we may love.

2
Lord of wisdom, whom obeying
 Mighty waters ebb and flow,
While unhasting, undelaying,
 Planets on their courses go :
In thy laws thyself displaying,
 Teach our minds thyself to know.

4
Lord of beauty, bid us own thee,
 Lord of truth, our footsteps guide,
Till as Love our hearts enthrone thee,
 And, with vision purified,
Lord of all, when all have known thee,
 Thou in all art glorified.

C. A. ALINGTON

Alternative Tune, Regent Square, 279

233

HYMN **175** Ivyhatch — L.M.   B. Luard Selby, 1853-1919

The Lord is King! lift up thy voice,
O earth, and all ye heavens, rejoice;
From world to world the joy shall ring,
'The Lord omnipotent is King!'

2
The Lord is King! who then shall dare
Resist his will, distrust his care,
Or murmur at his wise decrees,
Or doubt his royal promises?

3
He reigns! ye saints, exalt your strains;
Your God is King, your Father reigns;
And he is at the Father's side,
The Man of love, the Crucified.

4*
Alike pervaded by his eye
All parts of his dominion lie:
This world of ours and worlds unseen,
And thin the boundary between.

5
One Lord one empire all secures;
He reigns, and life and death are yours;
Through earth and heaven one song shall ring,
'The Lord omnipotent is King!'

J. CONDER

234

HYMN **176**   Offertorium — 7 6 7 6. D   M. Haydn, 1737-1806

3
Sometimes a light surprises⌣   It can bring with it nothing
  The Christian while he sings :   But he will bear us through;
It is the Lord who rises   Who gives the lilies clothing
  With healing in his wings;   Will clothe his people too :
When comforts are declining,   Beneath the spreading heavens
  He grants the soul again   No creature but is fed;
A season of clear shining   And he who feeds the ravens
  To cheer it after rain.   Will give his children bread.

2
In holy contemplation   Though vine nor fig-tree neither⌣
  We sweetly then pursue   Their wonted fruit should bear,
The theme of God's salvation,   Though all the fields should wither,
  And find it ever new :   Nor flocks nor herds be there;
Set free from present sorrow,   Yet, God the same abiding,
  We cheerfully can say,   His praise shall tune my voice;
E'en let the unknown morrow   For, while in him confiding,
  Bring with it what it may,   I cannot but rejoice.

W. COWPER

235

HYMN **177**   Contemplation — C.M.   Sir F. A. G. Ouseley, 1825–89

mf When all thy mercies, O my God,
My rising soul surveys,
Transported with the view, I'm lost⌣
In wonder, love, and praise.

2

Unnumbered comforts to my soul
Thy tender care bestowed,
Before my infant heart conceived
From whom those comforts flowed.

3

p When in the slippery paths of youth
With heedless steps I ran,
mf Thine arm unseen conveyed me safe,
And led me up to man.

4*

Ten thousand thousand precious gifts
My daily thanks employ,
And not the least a cheerful heart
Which tastes those gifts with joy.

5

f Through every period of my life
Thy goodness I'll pursue,
And after death in distant worlds
The glorious theme renew.

6

Through all eternity to thee⌣
A joyful song I'll raise ;
For O, eternity's too short
To utter all thy praise.

J. ADDISON

236

Hymn **178** University — C.M.   C. Collignon, 1725–85

Psalm 23

mf The God of love my Shepherd is,
      And he that doth me feed;
      While he is mine and I am his,
      What can I want or need?

2
He leads me to the tender grass,
Where I both feed and rest;
Then to the streams that gently pass :
In both I have the best.

3
Or if I stray, he doth convert,
And bring my mind in frame,
And all this not for my desert,
But for his holy name.

4
p Yea, in death's shady black abode
     Well may I walk, not fear;
     For thou art with me, and thy rod
     To guide, thy staff to bear.

5
mf Surely thy sweet and wondrous love
      Shall measure all my days;
f   And, as it never shall remove,
      So neither shall my praise.

GEORGE HERBERT

General

Psalm 23

mf The Lord my pasture shall prepare,
And feed me with a shepherd's care;
His presence shall my wants supply,
And guard me with a watchful eye;
My noonday walks he shall attend,
And all my midnight hours defend.

2

p When in the sultry glebe I faint,
Or on the thirsty mountain pant,
To fertile vales and dewy meads
My weary wandering steps he leads,
Where peaceful rivers, soft and slow,
Amid the verdant landscape flow.

3

mf Though in a bare and rugged way
Through devious lonely wilds I stray,
Thy bounty shall my pains beguile;
The barren wilderness shall smile
With sudden greens and herbage crowned,
And streams shall murmur all around.

4

p Though in the paths of death I tread,
With gloomy horrors overspread,
mf My steadfast heart shall fear no ill,
For thou, O Lord, art with me still:
Thy friendly crook shall give me aid,
And guide me through the dreadful shade.

J. ADDISON

238

HYMN **180**   Collingwood — C.M.   H. A. Bate

Father, whate'er of earthly bliss
   Thy sovereign will denies,
Accepted at thy throne of grace
   Let this petition rise:

2

Give me a calm and thankful heart,
   From every murmur free;
The blessings of thy grace impart,
   And let me live to thee.

3

Let the sweet hope that thou art mine
   My path of life attend;
Thy presence through my journey shine,
   And crown my journey's end.

ANNE STEELE†

HYMN **181**   London New — C.M.   *Psalms* (Edinburgh, 1635)

God moves in a mysterious way
   His wonders to perform;
He plants his footsteps in the sea,
   And rides upon the storm.

2
Deep in unfathomable mines‿
   Of never-failing skill
He treasures up his bright designs,
   And works his sovereign will.

3
Ye fearful saints, fresh courage take;
   The clouds ye so much dread
Are big with mercy, and shall break‿
   In blessings on your head.

4
Judge not the Lord by feeble sense,
   But trust him for his grace;
Behind a frowning providence
   He hides a smiling face.

5
His purposes will ripen fast,
   Unfolding every hour;
The bud may have a bitter taste,
   But sweet will be the flower.

6
Blind unbelief is sure to err,
   And scan his work in vain;
God is his own interpreter,
   And he will make it plain.

W. COWPER

240

HYMN **182**   Marching — 8 7 8 7   Martin Shaw

Father, hear the prayer we offer:
   Not for ease that prayer shall be,
But for strength that we may ever⌣
   Live our lives courageously.

2
Not for ever in green pastures
   Do we ask our way to be;
But the steep and rugged pathway
   May we tread rejoicingly.

3
Not for ever by still waters
   Would we idly rest and stay;
But would smite the living fountains⌣
   From the rocks along our way.

4
Be our strength in hours of weakness,
   In our wanderings be our guide;
Through endeavour, failure, danger,
   Father, be thou at our side.

                    MRS. L. M. WILLIS (1864)

HYMN **183** A stronghold sure — 8 7 8 7. 6 6 6 6 7   M. Luther,
1483–1546

General

Ein' feste Burg

A safe stronghold our God is still,
A trusty shield and weapon;
He'll keep us clear from all the ill
That hath us now o'ertaken.
The ancient prince of hell
Hath risen with purpose fell;
Strong mail of craft and power
He weareth in this hour;
On earth is not his fellow.

2

With force of arms we nothing can,
Full soon were we down-ridden;
But for us fights the proper Man,
Whom God himself hath bidden.
Ask ye, Who is this same?
Christ Jesus is his name,
The Lord Sabaoth's Son;
He, and no other one,
Shall conquer in the battle.

3

And were this world all devils o'er,
And watching to devour us,
We lay it not to heart so sore;
Not they can overpower us.
And let the prince of ill
Look grim as e'er he will,
He harms us not a whit;
For why?—his doom is writ;
A word shall quickly slay him

4

God's word, for all their craft and force,
One moment will not linger,
But, spite of hell, shall have its course;
'Tis written by his finger.
And though they take our life,
Goods, honour, children, wife,
Yet is their profit small;
These things shall vanish all:
The City of God remaineth!

M. Luther
Tr. T. Carlyle

243

General

FIRST TUNE

Repton — 8 6. 8 8 6

Sir C. H. H. Parry, 1848–1918 (from *Judith*)

When the above tune is used the last line of the words must be repeated

SECOND TUNE

Engedi — 8 6. 8 8 6

S. S. Wesley, 1810–7(

Dear Lord and Father of mankind,
　Forgive our foolish ways!
Re-clothe us in our rightful mind,
In purer lives thy service find,
　In deeper reverence praise.

2
In simple trust like theirs who heard,
　Beside the Syrian sea,
The gracious calling of the Lord,
Let us, like them, without a word
　Rise up and follow thee.

3*
O Sabbath rest by Galilee!
　O calm of hills above,
Where Jesus knelt to share with thee
The silence of eternity,
　Interpreted by love!

4
Drop thy still dews of quietness,
　Till all our strivings cease;
Take from our souls the strain and stress,
And let our ordered lives confess
　The beauty of thy peace.

5
Breathe through the heats of our desire
　Thy coolness and thy balm;
Let sense be dumb, let flesh retire;
Speak through the earthquake, wind, and fire,
　O still small voice of calm!

J. G. WHITTIER

HYMN **185**   FIRST TUNE

Gerontius — C.M.   J. B. Dykes, 1823-76

SECOND TUNE

Somervell — C.M.   Sir A. Somervell, 1863-1937

f   Praise to the Holiest in the height,
      And in the depth be praise :
    In all his words most wonderful,
      Most sure in all his ways.

2

mf O loving wisdom of our God!
      When all was sin and shame,
    A second Adam to the fight
      And to the rescue came.

3

O wisest love! that flesh and blood,
    Which did in Adam fail,
Should strive afresh against the foe,
    Should strive and should prevail;

4

And that a higher gift than grace
    Should flesh and blood refine,
God's presence and his very self,
    And essence all-divine.

5

O generous love! that he, who smote
    In Man for man the foe,
The double agony in Man
    For man should undergo;

6

p   And in the garden secretly,
      And on the Cross on high,
    Should teach his brethren, and inspire
      To suffer and to die.

7

f   Praise to the Holiest in the height,
      And in the depth be praise :
    In all his words most wonderful,
      Most sure in all his ways.

CARDINAL J. H. NEWMAN

Alternative Tune, Richmond, 258

Hymn **186**   Halton Holgate — 8 7 8 7   W. Boyce, 1710–79

Firmly I believe and truly
  God is Three and God is One;
And I next acknowledge duly
  Manhood taken by the Son.

2
And I trust and hope most fully
  In that Manhood crucified;
And each thought and deed unruly
  Do to death, as he has died.

3
Simply to his grace and wholly
  Light and life and strength belong,
And I love supremely, solely,
  Him the Holy, him the Strong.

4
And I hold in veneration,
  For the love of him alone,
Holy Church as his creation,
  And her teachings as his own.

5
Adoration ay be given,
  With and through the angelic host,
To the God of earth and heaven,
  Father, Son, and Holy Ghost.

CARDINAL J. H. NEWMAN

Alternative Tune, Stuttgart, 76

HYMN **187** Eisenach — L.M. J. H. Schein, 1586–1630

O amor quam ecstaticus

mf O love, how deep, how broad, how high!
It fills the heart with ecstasy,
That God, the Son of God, should take
Our mortal form for mortals' sake.

2
He sent no angel to our race
Of higher or of lower place,
But wore the robe of human frame⌣
Himself, and to this lost world came.

3
For us he was baptized, and bore⌣
His holy fast, and hungered sore;
For us temptations sharp he knew;
For us the tempter overthrew.

4
p For us to wicked men betrayed,
Scourged, mocked, in purple robe arrayed,
He bore the shameful Cross and death;
For us at length gave up his breath.

5
f For us he rose from death again,
For us he went on high to reign,
For us he sent his Spirit here
To guide, to strengthen, and to cheer.

6
To him whose boundless love has won
Salvation for us through his Son,
To God the Father, glory be
Both now and through eternity.

Ascribed to THOMAS À KEMPIS
Tr. B. Webb‡

HYMN 188 FIRST TUNE

Jesu dulcis memoria — L.M. Mode i

Jesu dulcis memoria

1. Je - su! the ve - ry thought is sweet; In that dear
2. No word is sung more sweet than this, No sound is
3. Je - su, the hope of souls for - lorn, How good to
4. No tongue of mor - tal can ex - press, No pen can
5*. O Je - su, King of won - drous might! O Vic - tor,
6. A - bide with us, O Lord, to - day, Ful - fil us

1. name all heart - joys meet; But O, than hon - ey
2. heard more full of bliss, No thought brings sweet - er
3. them for sin that mourn! To them that seek thee,
4. write, the bless - ed - ness: He on - ly who hath
5*. glo - rious from the fight! Sweet - ness that may not
6. with thy grace, we pray; And with thine own true

1. sweet - er far The glimp - ses of his pre - sence are.
2. com - fort nigh, Than Je - sus, Son of God most high.
3. O how kind! But what art thou to them that find?
4. proved it knows What bliss from love of Je - sus flows.
5*. be ex - prest, And al - to - geth - er love - li - est!
6. sweet - ness feed Our souls from sin and dark - ness freed.

St. Bernard — L.M.   W. H. Monk, 1823–89

Jesu dulcis memoria

Jesu! the very thought is sweet;
In that dear name all heart-joys meet;
But O, than honey sweeter far
The glimpses of his presence are.

2
No word is sung more sweet than this,
No sound is heard more full of bliss,
No thought brings sweeter comfort nigh,
Than Jesus, Son of God most high.

3
Jesu, the hope of souls forlorn,
How good to them for sin that mourn!
To them that seek thee, O how kind!
But what art thou to them that find?

4
No tongue of mortal can express,
No pen can write, the blessedness:
He only who hath proved it knows
What bliss from love of Jesus flows.

5*
O Jesu, King of wondrous might!
O Victor, glorious from the fight!
Sweetness that may not be exprest,
And altogether loveliest!

6
Abide with us, O Lord, to-day,
Fulfil us with thy grace, we pray;
And with thine own true sweetness feed
Our souls from sin and darkness freed.

c. 12th century
Tr. J. M. NEALE and Compilers

General

FIRST TUNE

Metzler's Redhead — C.M.

R. Redhead, 1820–1901

SECOND TUNE

Belmont — C.M.

Adapted from W. Gardiner's *Sacred Melodies*, 1812

Jesu dulcis memoria

PART I

Jesu, the very thought of thee
   With sweetness fills the breast;
But sweeter far thy face to see,
   And in thy presence rest.

2

No voice can sing, no heart can frame,
　Nor can the memory find,
A sweeter sound than Jesu's name,
　The Saviour of mankind.

3

O hope of every contrite heart,
　O joy of all the meek,
To those who ask how kind thou art,
　How good to those who seek!

4

But what to those who find? Ah, this⌣
　Nor tongue nor pen can show;
The love of Jesus, what it is
　None but his loved ones know.

5

Jesu, our only joy be thou,
　As thou our prize wilt be;
In thee be all our glory now,
　And through eternity.

PART **2**

6

O Jesu, King most wonderful,
　Thou Conqueror renowned,
Thou sweetness most ineffable,
　In whom all joys are found!

7

When once thou visitest the heart,
　Then truth begins to shine,
Then earthly vanities depart,
　Then kindles love divine.

8

Thee, Jesu, may our voices bless,
　Thee may we love alone,
And ever in our lives express
　The image of thine own.

9

Abide with us, and let thy light⌣
　Shine, Lord, on every heart;
Dispel the darkness of our night,
　And joy to all impart.

10

Jesu, our love and joy, to thee,
　The Virgin's holy Son,
All might and praise and glory be
　While endless ages run.

c. 12th century
Tr. E. CASWALL‡

General

FIRST TUNE

Oriel — 8 7. 8 7. 8 7

C. Ett, *Cantica Sacra*, 1840
Descant by Alan Gray, 1855–1935

Descant by permission of the Cambridge University Press

The Descant may be sung by Trebles for verses 3 and 6, the main melody being sung in Unison

A higher setting of this tune will be found at Hymn 474

General

Gloriosi Salvatoris

To the name of our salvation
    Laud and honour let us pay,
Which for many a generation
    Hid in God's foreknowledge lay,
But with holy exultation
    We may sing aloud to-day.

2
Jesus is the name we treasure,
    Name beyond what words can tell;
Name of gladness, name of pleasure,
    Ear and heart delighting well;
Name of sweetness passing measure,
    Saving us from sin and hell.

3*
'Tis the name for adoration,
    Name for songs of victory,
Name for holy meditation
    In this vale of misery,
Name for joyful veneration
    By the citizens on high.

4
'Tis the name that whoso preacheth
    Speaks like music to the ear;
Who in prayer this name beseecheth
    Sweetest comfort findeth near;
Who its perfect wisdom reacheth
    Heavenly joy possesseth here.

5
Jesus is the name exalted
    Over every other name;
In this name, whene'er assaulted,
    We can put our foes to shame:
Strength to them who else had halted,
    Eyes to blind, and feet to lame.

6
Therefore we in love adoring
    This most blessèd name revere,
Holy Jesu, thee imploring
    So to write it in us here,
That hereafter heavenward soaring
    We may sing with angels there.

c. 15th century
Tr. J. M. NEALE and Compilers

General

St. Nicholas — 8 7. 8 7. 8 7 W. Ellis, 1868-1947

Slow

By permission of the Royal School of Church Music

General

Gloriosi Salvatoris

To the name of our salvation
Laud and honour let us pay,
Which for many a generation
Hid in God's foreknowledge lay,
But with holy exultation
We may sing aloud to-day.

2
Jesus is the name we treasure,
Name beyond what words can tell:
Name of gladness, name of pleasure,
Ear and heart delighting well; ·
Name of sweetness passing measure,
Saving us from sin and hell.

3*
'Tis the name for adoration,
Name for songs of victory,
Name for holy meditation
In this vale of misery,
Name for joyful veneration
By the citizens on high.

4
'Tis the name that whoso preacheth
Speaks like music to the ear;
Who in prayer this name beseecheth
Sweetest comfort findeth near;
Who its perfect wisdom reacheth
Heavenly joy possesseth here.

5
Jesus is the name exalted
Over every other name;
In this name, whene'er assaulted,
We can put our foes to shame:
Strength to them who else had halted,
Eyes to blind, and feet to lame.

6
Therefore we in love adoring
This most blessèd name revere,
Holy Jesu, thee imploring
So to write it in us here,
That hereafter heavenward soaring
We may sing with angels there.

c. 15th century
Tr. J. M. NEALE and Compilers

General

FIRST TUNE

Hartford — 7 7 7 7

B. Milgrove, 1731-1810

SECOND TUNE

Innocents — 7 7 7 7

The Parish Choir, 1850

General

Victis sibi cognomina

Conquering kings their titles take
From the foes they captive make :
Jesus, by a nobler deed,
From the thousands he hath freed.

2
Yes, none other name is given
Unto mortals under heaven,
Which can make the dead arise,
And exalt them to the skies.

3
That which Christ so hardly wrought,
That which he so dearly bought,
That salvation, brethren, say,
Shall we madly cast away?

4
Rather gladly for that name
Bear the cross, endure the shame :
Joyfully for him to die
Is not death but victory.

5
Jesu, who dost condescend
To be called the sinner's friend,
Hear us, as to thee we pray,
Glorying in thy name to-day.

[UNISON] 6
Glory to the Father be,
Glory, holy Son, to thee,
Glory to the Holy Ghost,
From the saints and angel-host.

18th century
Tr. J. CHANDLER and Compilers

HYMN **192** St. Peter — C.M.　　　　A. R. Reinagle, 1799–1877

A lower setting of this tune will be found at Hymn 13

How sweet the name of Jesus sounds
　In a believer's ear!
It soothes his sorrows, heals his wounds,
　And drives away his fear.

2
It makes the wounded spirit whole,
　And calms the troubled breast;
'Tis manna to the hungry soul,
　And to the weary rest.

3
Dear name! the rock on which I build,
　My shield and hiding-place,
My never-failing treasury filled⏝
　With boundless stores of grace.

4
Jesus! my Shepherd, Brother, Friend,
　My Prophet, Priest, and King,
My Lord, my Life, my Way, my End,
　Accept the praise I bring.

5
Weak is the effort of my heart,
　And cold my warmest thought;
But when I see thee as thou art,
　I'll praise thee as I ought.

6
Till then I would thy love proclaim
　With every fleeting breath;
And may the music of thy name
　Refresh my soul in death.

J. NEWTON†

HYMN **193** Hollingside — 7 7 7 7. D   J. B. Dykes, 1823–76

f Jesu, lover of my soul,
 Let me to thy bosom fly,
While the gathering waters roll,
 While the tempest still is high :
Hide me, O my Saviour, hide,
 Till the storm of life is past ;
Safe into the haven guide,
 O receive my soul at last.

2

Other refuge have I none ;
 Hangs my helpless soul on thee ;
Leave, ah, leave me not alone,
 Still support and comfort me.

All my trust on thee is stayed,
 All my help from thee I bring ;
Cover my defenceless head
 With the shadow of thy wing.

3

f Plenteous grace with thee is found,
 Grace to cleanse from every sin ;
Let the healing streams abound ;
 Make and keep me pure within :
[UNISON]
Thou of life the fountain art ;
 Freely let me take of thee ;
Spring thou up within my heart,
 Rise to all eternity.

C. WESLEY†

Alternative Tune, Aberystwyth, 86

HYMN **194**   St. Constantine — 6 5 6 5   W. H. Monk, 1823–89

<table>
<tr><td></td><td></td></tr>
</table>

p Jesu, meek and gentle,
   Son of God most high,
Pitying, loving Saviour,
   Hear thy children's cry.

2
Pardon our offences,
   Loose our captive chains,
Break down every idol
   Which our soul detains.

3
mf Give us holy freedom,
   Fill our hearts with love,
Draw us, holy Jesus,
   To the realms above.

4
Lead us on our journey,
   Be thyself the Way
Through terrestrial darkness
   To celestial day.

5
p   Jesu, meek and gentle,
   Son of God most high,
Pitying, loving Saviour,
   Hear thy children's cry.

Hear   thy   chil - dren's   cry.

G. R. PRYNNE

HYMN **195**   Cornwall — 8 8 6. 8 8 6   S. S. Wesley, 1810–76

O love divine, how sweet thou art!
When shall I find my longing heart
  All taken up by thee?
I thirst, I faint and die to prove
The greatness of redeeming love,
  The love of Christ to me.

2
Stronger his love than death or hell;
Its riches are unsearchable:
  The first-born sons of light
Desire in vain its depth to see;
They cannot reach the mystery,
  The length and breadth and height.

3*
God only knows the love of God;
O that it now were shed abroad
  In this poor stony heart!
For love I sigh, for love I pine;
This only portion, Lord, be mine,
  Be mine this better part.

4
For ever would I take my seat
With Mary at the Master's feet:
  Be this my happy choice;
My only care, delight, and bliss,
My joy, my heaven on earth, be this,
  To hear the Bridegroom's voice.

C. WESLEY†

General

FIRST TUNE

Oxford New — C.M.

Isaac Smith's *Collection, c.* 1770

SECOND TUNE

Selby — C.M.

A. J. Eyre, 1853-1919

General

3 He speaks; and, listen - ing
5 My gra - cious Mas - ter

O for a thousand tongues to sing
  My dear Redeemer's praise,
The glories of my God and King,
  The triumphs of his grace!

2
Jesus! the name that charms our fears,
  That bids our sorrows cease;
'Tis music in the sinner's ears,
  'Tis life and health and peace.

3
He speaks; and, listening to his voice,
  New life the dead receive,
The mournful broken hearts rejoice,
  The humble poor believe.

4
Hear him, ye deaf; his praise, ye dumb,
  Your loosened tongues employ;
Ye blind, behold your Saviour come;
  And leap, ye lame, for joy!

5
My gracious Master and my God,
  Assist me to proclaim
And spread through all the earth abroad
  The honours of thy name.

C. WESLEY

265

General

Dominus regit me — 8 7 8 7   J. B. Dykes, 1823–76

The Descant may be sung by Trebles for verse 6, the main melody being sung in Unison

Psalm 23

mf The King of love my Shepherd is,
    Whose goodness faileth never;
  I nothing lack if I am his
    And he is mine for ever.

2

Where streams of living water flow
    My ransomed soul he leadeth,
And where the verdant pastures grow
    With food celestial feedeth.

3

Perverse and foolish oft I strayed,
    But yet in love he sought me,
And on his shoulder gently laid,
    And home rejoicing brought me.

4

p In death's dark vale I fear no ill
    With thee, dear Lord, beside me;
Thy rod and staff my comfort still,
    Thy Cross before to guide me.

5

mf Thou spread'st a table in my sight;
    Thy unction grace bestoweth;
And O what transport of delight
    From thy pure chalice floweth!

[UNISON]   **6**

f And so through all the length of days
    Thy goodness faileth never:
Good Shepherd, may I sing thy prais
    Within thy house for ever.

SIR H. W. BAK

HYMN **198**   St. George — S.M.   H. J. Gauntlett, 1805-76

Summi Parentis Filio

mf   To Christ, the Prince of Peace,
        And Son of God most high,
    The Father of the world to come,
        We lift our joyful cry.

2
p   Deep in his heart for us
        The wound of love he bore,
    That love which he enkindles still
        In hearts that him adore.

3
mf   O Jesu, Victim blest,
        What else but love divine
    Could thee constrain to open thus⌣
        That sacred heart of thine?

4
    O wondrous fount of love,
        O well of waters free,
    O heavenly flame, refining fire,
        O burning charity!

5
p   Hide us in thy dear heart,
        Jesu, our Saviour blest,
mf So shall we find thy plenteous grace,
        And heaven's eternal rest.

18th century
Tr. E. CASWALL and Compilers

HYMN **199**   St. James — C.M.   R. Courteville (1697)

A lower setting of this tune will be found at Hymn 557

mf Thou art the Way : by thee alone‿
     From sin and death we flee ;
     And he who would the Father seek
     Must seek him, Lord, by thee.

2
Thou art the Truth : thy word alone‿
True wisdom can impart ;
Thou only canst inform the mind
And purify the heart.

3
f Thou art the Life : the rending tomb‿
    Proclaims thy conquering arm ;
    And those who put their trust in thee
    Nor death nor hell shall harm.

4
mf Thou art the Way, the Truth, the Life :
     Grant us that Way to know,
     That Truth to keep, that Life to win,
     Whose joys eternal flow.

BISHOP G. W. DOANE

HYMN **200** St. Paul's — S.M.   Sir J. Stainer, 1840–1901

μνώεο Χριστέ

Lord Jesus, think on me,
And purge away my sin;
From earthborn passions set me free,
And make me pure within.

2
Lord Jesus, think on me
With many a care opprest;
Let me thy loving servant be,
And taste thy promised rest.

3
Lord Jesus, think on me,
Nor let me go astray;
Through darkness and perplexity
Point thou the heavenly way.

4
Lord Jesus, think on me,
That, when the flood is past,
I may the eternal brightness see,
And share thy joy at last.

BISHOP SYNESIUS OF CYRENE
Tr. A. W. Chatfield†

HYMN **201**   Eatington — C.M.   W. Croft, 1678–1727

Amor, Jesu dulcissime

Jesu, thy mercies are untold
    Through each returning day;
Thy love exceeds a thousandfold
    Whatever we can say·

2

That love which in thy Passion drained
    For us thy precious Blood;
That love whereby the saints have gained
    The vision of their God.

3

'Tis thou hast loved us from the womb,
    Pure source of all our bliss,
Our only hope of life to come,
    Our happiness in this

4

Lord, grant us, while on earth we stay,
    Thy love to feel and know;
And, when from hence we pass away,
    To us thy glory show.

Cento from *Jesu, dulcis memoria*
Tr. E. CASWALL

Alternative Tune, St. Fulbert, 128

HYMN **202**   St. Chrysostom — 8 8. 8 8. 8 8   Sir J. BARNBY, 1838–96

mf Jesu, my Lord, my God, my all,
  Hear me, blest Saviour, when I call;
  Hear me, and from thy dwelling-place
  Pour down the riches of thy grace.
    Jesu, my Lord, I thee adore,
    O make me love thee more and
    more.

2

p Jesu, too late I thee have sought:
mf How can I love thee as I ought?
  And how extol thy matchless fame,
  The glorious beauty of thy name?
    Jesu, my Lord, I thee adore,
    O make me love thee more and
    more.

3

p   Jesu, what didst thou find in me,
    That thou hast dealt so lovingly?
f   How great the joy that thou hast brought,
    So far exceeding hope or thought!
mf   Jesu, my Lord, etc.

4

f   Jesu, of thee shall be my song,
    To thee my heart and soul belong;
    All that I have or am is thine,
    And thou, blest Saviour, thou art mine.
mf   Jesu, my Lord, etc.

H. COLLINS†

Alternative Tune, St. Matthias, 203

271

General

FIRST TUNE

St. Matthias — 8 8. 8 8. 8 8   W. H. Monk, 1823–89

A lower setting of this tune will be found at Hymn 28

SECOND TUNE

Stella — 8 8. 8 8. 8 8   *Easy Hymns for Catholic Schools,* 1851

272

Liebe, die du mich zum Bilde

mf   O Love, who formedst me to wear⌣
      The image of thy Godhead here;
  Who soughtest me with tender care
      Through all my wanderings wild and drear:
  O Love, I give myself to thee,
  Thine ever, only thine to be.

2

  O Love, who ere life's earliest dawn
      On me thy choice hast gently laid;
  O Love, who here as Man wast born,
      And wholly like to us wast made:
  O Love, I give myself to thee,
  Thine ever, only thine to be.

3

p   O Love, who once in time wast slain,
      Pierced through and through with bitter woe;
  O Love, who wrestling thus didst gain
      That we eternal joy might know:
mf   O Love, I give myself to thee,
  Thine ever, only thine to be.

4

f   O Love, who once shalt bid me rise
      From out this dying life of ours;
  O Love, who once o'er yonder skies
      Shalt set me in the fadeless bowers:
  O Love, I give myself to thee,
  Thine ever, only thine to be.

J. Scheffler
Tr. Catherine Winkworth†

HYMN **204**   Almsgiving — L.M.   S. S. Wesley, 1810–76

mf   Where high the heavenly temple stands,
The house of God not made with hands,
A great High Priest our nature wears,
The guardian of mankind appears.

2
He who for men their surety stood,
And poured on earth his precious Blood,
Pursues in heaven his mighty plan,
The Saviour and the Friend of man.

3
Though now ascended up on high,
He bends on earth a brother's eye;
Partaker of the human name,
He knows the frailty of our frame.

4
p   In every pang that rends the heart
The Man of Sorrows had a part;
He sympathizes with our grief,
And to the sufferer sends relief.

5
mf   With boldness therefore at the throne
Let us make all our sorrows known;
And ask the aid of heavenly power
To help us in the evil hour.

M. BRUCE

HYMN **205**   FIRST TUNE

Airedale — 8 7 8 7. D   Sir C. V. Stanford, 1852-1924

f Love divine, all loves excelling,
　Joy of heaven, to earth come down,
Fix in us thy humble dwelling,
　All thy faithful mercies crown.
Jesu, thou art all compassion,
　Pure unbounded love thou art;
Visit us with thy salvation,
　Enter every trembling heart.

2
Come, almighty to deliver,
　Let us all thy grace receive;
Suddenly return, and never,
　Never more thy temples leave.

Thee we would be always blessing,
　Serve thee as thy hosts above;
Pray, and praise thee, without
　Glory in thy perfect love. [ceasing,

3
f Finish then thy new creation:
　Pure and spotless let us be;
Let us see thy great salvation,
　Perfectly restored in thee;
Changed from glory into glory,
　Till in heaven we take our place,
Till we cast our crowns before thee,
　Lost in wonder, love, and praise.

C. WESLEY†

Love Divine — 8 7 8 7   Sir J. Stainer, 1840-1901

mf Love divine, all loves excelling,
Joy of heaven, to earth come down,
Fix in us thy humble dwelling,
All thy faithful mercies crown.

2
Jesu, thou art all compassion,
Pure unbounded love thou art;
Visit us with thy salvation,
Enter every trembling heart.

3
Come, almighty to deliver,
Let us all thy grace receive;
Suddenly return, and never,
Never more thy temples leave.

4
Thee we would be always blessing,
Serve thee as thy hosts above;
Pray, and praise thee, without ceasing,
Glory in thy perfect love.

5
f Finish then thy new creation:
Pure and spotless let us be;
Let us see thy great salvation,
Perfectly restored in thee;

6
Changed from glory into glory,
Till in heaven we take our place,
Till we cast our crowns before thee,
Lost in wonder, love, and praise.

C. WESLEY†

HYMN **206** Bow Church — 5 5. 8 8. 5 5   G. Bullivant, 1883-1937

Jesu, geh' voran

mf   Jesus, still lead on,
Till our rest be won,
And, although the way be cheerless,
We will follow calm and fearless;
Guide us by thy hand
To our fatherland.

2

p   If the way be drear,
If the foe be near,
Let not faithless fears o'ertake us,
Let not faith and hope forsake us;
For, through many a foe,
To our home we go.

3

mf   Jesus, still lead on,
Till our rest be won;
Heavenly leader, still direct us,
Still support, console, protect us,
Till we safely stand
In our fatherland.

COUNT N. L. ZINZENDORF
Tr. Jane L. Borthwick

HYMN 207   Everton — 8 7 8 7. D   H. Smart, 1813–79

General

Son of God, eternal Saviour,
  Source of life and truth and grace,
Son of Man, whose birth incarnate
  Hallows all our human race,
Thou, our Head, who, throned in glory,
  For thine own dost ever plead,
Fill us with thy love and pity;
  Heal our wrongs, and help our need.

2

As thou, Lord, hast lived for others,
  So may we for others live;
Freely have thy gifts been granted,
  Freely may thy servants give:
Thine the gold and thine the silver,
  Thine the wealth of land and sea,
We but stewards of thy bounty,
  Held in solemn trust for thee.

3

Come, O Christ, and reign among us,
  King of love, and Prince of Peace;
Hush the storm of strife and passion,
  Bid its cruel discords cease;
By thy patient years of toiling,
  By thy silent hours of pain,
Quench our fevered thirst of pleasure,
  Shame our selfish greed of gain.

4

Son of God, eternal Saviour,
  Source of life and truth and grace,
Son of Man, whose birth incarnate
  Hallows all our human race,
Thou who prayedst, thou who willest,
  That thy people should be one,
Grant, O grant our hope's fruition:
  Here on earth thy will be done.

S. C. LOWRY

Alternative Tune, Rex gloriae, 148

HYMN **208**   Bishopthorpe — C.M.   J. Clarke, *c.* 1659–1707

3

Immortal love for ever full,
 For ever flowing free,
For ever shared, for ever whole,
 A never-ebbing sea!

We may not climb the heavenly steeps
 To bring the Lord Christ down;
In vain we search the lowest deeps,
 For him no depths can drown:

2

Our outward lips confess the name
 All other names above;
Love only knoweth whence it came
 And comprehendeth love.

4

But warm, sweet, tender, even yet‿
 A present help is he;
And faith has still its Olivet,
 And love its Galilee.

5

The healing of his seamless dress
 Is by our beds of pain;
We touch him in life's throng and press,
 And we are whole again.

6*

Through him the first fond prayers are said
 Our lips of childhood frame;
The last low whispers of our dead
 Are burdened with his name.

7

Alone, O Love ineffable,
 Thy saving name is given;
To turn aside from thee is hell,
 To walk with thee is heaven.

J. G. WHITTIER

HYMN **209** Dunfermline — C.M.   *Scottish Psalter,* 1615

> *mf* Light of the lonely pilgrim's heart,
> Star of the coming day,
> Arise, and with thy morning beams
> Chase all our griefs away.

> **2**
> *f* Come, blessèd Lord, bid every shore‿
> And answering island sing
> The praises of thy royal name,
> And own thee as their King.

> **3**
> Bid the whole world, responsive now‿
> To the bright world above,
> Break forth in rapturous strains of joy
> In answer to thy love.

> **4**
> *mf* Jesus, thy fair creation groans—
> The air, the earth, the sea—
> In unison with all our hearts,
> And calls aloud for thee.

> **5**
> Thine was the Cross, with all its fruits‿
> Of grace and peace divine :
> *f* Be thine the crown of glory now,
> The palm of victory thine.

SIR E. DENNY†

HYMN **210**   Petra — 7 7. 7 7. 7 7   R. Redhead, 1820–1901

mf Rock of ages, cleft for me,
   Let me hide myself in thee ;
   Let the water and the blood,
   From thy riven side which flowed,
   Be of sin the double cure :
   Cleanse me from its guilt and power.

2
   Not the labours of my hands
   Can fulfil thy law's demands ;
   Could my zeal no respite know,
   Could my tears for ever flow,
   All for sin could not atone :
   Thou must save, and thou alone

3
p   Nothing in my hand I bring,
   Simply to thy Cross I cling ;
   Naked, come to thee for dress ;
   Helpless, look to thee for grace ;
   Foul, I to the fountain fly ;
   Wash me, Saviour, or I die.

4
   While I draw this fleeting breath,
   When my eyelids close in death,
   When I soar through tracts unknown,
   See thee on thy judgement throne ;
mf   Rock of ages, cleft for me,
   Let me hide myself in thee.

A. M. TOPLADY†

HYMN **211**   Song 13 — 7 7 7 7   Orlando Gibbons, 1583–1625

Dignare me, O Jesu, rogo te

Jesu, grant me this, I pray,
Ever in thy heart to stay;
Let me evermore abide
Hidden in thy wounded side.

2
If the world or Satan lay⌣
Tempting snares about my way,
I am safe when I abide
In thy heart and wounded side.

3
If the flesh, more dangerous still,
Tempt my soul to deeds of ill,
Naught I fear when I abide
In thy heart and wounded side.

4
Death will come one day to me;
Jesu, cast me not from thee:
Dying let me still abide
In thy heart and wounded side.

17th century
Tr. SIR H. W. BAKER†

HYMN **212**   Wigan — 6 6 6 4. 8 8 4   S. S. Wesley, 1810–76
(Harmonies slightly altered)

2

mf   Behold the Lamb of God!   Behold the Lamb of God!
p   O thou for sinners slain,   All hail, incarnate Word,
    Let it not be in vain   Thou everlasting Lord,
      That thou hast died: Saviour most blest!
mf Thee for my Saviour let me take,   Fill us with love that never faints,
    My only refuge let me make   Grant us with all thy blessèd saints
      Thy piercèd side.   Eternal rest.

3
Behold the Lamb of God!
f   Worthy is he alone
    To sit upon the throne⌣
      Of God above;
    One with the Ancient of all Days,
    One with the Comforter in praise,
      All Light and Love.

M. BRIDGES and Compilers

284

HYMN **213**　　　　　FIRST TUNE

Ave radix — 6 6 6 6　　　　　　*Sens Processional,* 1728

mf　Jesu, meek and lowly,
　　Saviour, pure and holy,
　　On thy love relying
　　Hear me humbly crying.

2

　　Prince of life and power,
　　My salvation's tower,
p　On the Cross I view thee
　　Calling sinners to thee.

3

mf　There behold me gazing ꓹ
　　At the sight amazing;
　　Bending low before thee,
　　Helpless I adore thee.

4

p　By thy red wounds streaming
　　With thy life-blood gleaming,
　　Blood for sinners flowing,
　　Pardon free bestowing;

5

mf　By that fount of blessing,
　　Thy dear love expressing,
　　All my aching sadness
　　Turn thou into gladness.

6

　　Lord, in mercy guide me,
　　Be thou e'er beside me;
　　In thy ways direct me,
　　'Neath thy wings protect me.

H. COLLINS

HYMN 213 SECOND TUNE

St. Martin — 6 6 6 6 C. Ett, *Cantica Sacra*, 184●

mf Jesu, meek and lowly,
Saviour, pure and holy,
On thy love relying
Hear me humbly crying.

2
Prince of life and power,
My salvation's tower,
p On the Cross I view thee
Calling sinners to thee.

3
mf There behold me gazing⌣
At the sight amazing;
Bending low before thee,
Helpless I adore thee.

4
p By thy red wounds streaming
With thy life-blood gleaming,
Blood for sinners flowing,
Pardon free bestowing;

5
mf By that fount of blessing,
Thy dear love expressing,
All my aching sadness
Turn thou into gladness.

6
Lord, in mercy guide me,
Be thou e'er beside me;
In thy ways direct me,
'Neath thy wings protect me.

H. COLLINS

286

mf There is a green hill far away,
    Without a city wall,
p Where the dear Lord was crucified,
    Who died to save us all.

2

mf We may not know, we cannot tell,
    What pains he had to bear,
But we believe it was for us
    He hung and suffered there.

3

He died that we might be forgiven,
    He died to make us good,
That we might go at last to heaven,
    Saved by his precious Blood.

4

There was no other good enough
    To pay the price of sin;
He only could unlock the gate
    Of heaven, and let us in.

5

O dearly, dearly has he loved,
    And we must love him too,
And trust in his redeeming Blood,
    And try his works to do.

MRS. C. F. ALEXANDER

287

HYMN **215**   Bow Brickhill — L.M.   Sir S. H. Nicholson, 1875–1947

[UNISON]
We sing the praise of him who died,
　Of him who died upon the Cross;
The sinner's hope let men deride,
　For this we count the world but loss.

2
Inscribed upon the Cross we see
　In shining letters, 'God is love;'
He bears our sins upon the Tree;
　He brings us mercy from above.

3
The Cross! it takes our guilt away;
　It holds the fainting spirit up;
It cheers with hope the gloomy day,
　And sweetens every bitter cup.

4
It makes the coward spirit brave,
　And nerves the feeble arm for fight;
It takes its terror from the grave,
　And gilds the bed of death with light

[UNISON]　**5**
The balm of life, the cure of woe,
　The measure and the pledge of love,
The sinner's refuge here below,
　The angels' theme in heaven above.

T. KELLY

Alternative Tune, Breslau, 333

HYMN **216** Gopsal — 6 6 6 6. 8 8 G. F. Handel, 1685-1759

Rejoice! the Lord is King!
Your Lord and King adore;
Mortals, give thanks and sing,
And triumph evermore:
Lift up your heart, lift up your voice;
Rejoice, again I say, rejoice.

2

mf Jesus, the Saviour, reigns,
The God of truth and love;
When he had purged our stains,
He took his seat above:
f Lift up your heart, lift up your voice;
Rejoice, again I say, rejoice.

3

mf His kingdom cannot fail;
He rules o'er earth and heaven;
The keys of death and hell
Are to our Jesus given:
f Lift up your heart, lift up your voice;
Rejoice, again I say, rejoice.

4

mf He sits at God's right hand
Till all his foes submit,
And bow to his command,
And fall beneath his feet:
f Lift up your heart, lift up your voice;
Rejoice, again I say, rejoice.

C. WESLEY

HYMN **217**   Miles Lane — C.M.   W. Shrubsole, 1760–1806

f   All hail the power of Jesus' name!
   Let angels prostrate fall;
   Bring forth the royal diadem
   And crown him Lord of all.

2

mf Crown him, ye morning stars of light,
   Who fixed this floating ball;
   Now hail the Strength of Israel's
      might,
f   And crown him Lord of all.

3

mf Crown him, ye martyrs of your God,
   Who from his altar call;
   Extol the Stem-of-Jesse's Rod,
f   And crown him Lord of all.

4

mf Ye seed of Israel's chosen race,
   Ye ransomed of the fall,
   Hail him who saves you by his grace
f   And crown him Lord of all.

5

p Sinners, whose love can ne'er forget
   The wormwood and the gall,
mf Go spread your trophies at his feet,
f   And crown him Lord of all.

6

Let every tribe and every tongue
Before him prostrate fall,
And shout in universal song
The crownèd Lord of all.

E. PERRONET‡

Alternative Tune, Ladywell, **297**

HYMN 218 St. Magnus — C.M. J. Clarke, *c.* 1659–1707

A lower setting of this tune will be found at Hymn 461

The head that once was crowned with
    thorns
Is crowned with glory now:
A royal diadem adorns⌣
    The mighty Victor's brow.

2
The highest place that heaven affords
    Is his, is his by right,
The King of Kings, and Lord of
    Lords,
    And heaven's eternal Light;

3
mf The joy of all who dwell above,
    The joy of all below,
    To whom he manifests his love,
    And grants his name to know.

4
p To them the Cross, with all its shame,
    With all its grace, is given:
f Their name an everlasting name,
    Their joy the joy of heaven.

5
p They suffer with their Lord below,
f   They reign with him above;
    Their profit and their joy to know⌣
    The mystery of his love.

6
mf The Cross he bore is life and health,
    Though shame and death to him;
f His people's hope, his people's wealth,
    Their everlasting theme.

T. KELLY

HYMN **219**   Crüger — 7 6 7 6. D   J. Crüger, 1598–1662

f   Hail to the Lord's Anointed,
      Great David's greater Son!
      Hail, in the time appointed,
      His reign on earth begun!
      He comes to break oppression,
      To set the captive free,
      To take away transgression,
      And rule in equity.

2*

      He comes with succour speedy
      To those who suffer wrong;
      To help the poor and needy,
      And bid the weak be strong;
      To give them songs for sighing,
      Their darkness turn to light,
      Whose souls, condemned and dying,
      Were precious in his sight.

3

mf He shall come down like showers
    Upon the fruitful earth,
And love, joy, hope, like flowers,
    Spring in his path to birth:
Before him on the mountains
    Shall peace, the herald, go;
And righteousness in fountains
    From hill to valley flow.

4*

Arabia's desert-ranger
    To him shall bow the knee;
The Ethiopian stranger
    His glory come to see;
With offerings of devotion
    Ships from the isles shall meet,
To pour the wealth of ocean⌣
    In tribute at his feet.

5

Kings shall bow down before him,
    And gold and incense bring;
All nations shall adore him,
    His praise all people sing:
To him shall prayer unceasing
    And daily vows ascend;
His kingdom still increasing,
    A kingdom without end.

6

f O'er every foe victorious,
    He on his throne shall rest;
From age to age more glorious,
    All-blessing and all-blest:
The tide of time shall never⌣
    His covenant remove;
His name shall stand for ever,
    His changeless name of Love.

J. MONTGOMERY

General

FIRST TUNE

Truro — L.M.

Psalmodia Evangelica, 1789

SECOND TUNE

Galilee — L.M.

P. Armes, 1836–1908

Jesus shall reign where'er the sun
Does his successive journeys run;
His kingdom stretch from shore to shore,
Till moons shall wax and wane no more.

2

People and realms of every tongue
Dwell on his love with sweetest song,

And infant voices shall proclaim
Their early blessings on his name.

3

Blessings abound where'er he reigns :
The prisoner leaps to lose his chains ;
The weary find eternal rest,
And all the sons of want are blest.

4*
To him shall endless prayer be made,
And praises throng to crown his head ;
His name like incense shall arise
With every morning sacrifice.

5
Let every creature rise and bring
Peculiar honours to our King ;
Angels descend with songs again,
And earth repeat the loud Amen.

I. WATTS†

HYMN **221**   Nativity — C.M.   H. Lahee, 1826–1912

Come, let us join our cheerful songs
  With angels round the throne ;
Ten thousand thousand are their
  tongues,
But all their joys are one.

2
'Worthy the Lamb that died,' they
  cry,
'To be exalted thus ;'
'Worthy the Lamb,' our lips reply,
  'For he was slain for us.'

3
mf Jesus is worthy to receive
    Honour and power divine ;
    And blessings, more than we can give,
    Be, Lord, for ever thine.

4
f Let all creation join in one
    To bless the sacred name
    Of him that sits upon the throne,
    And to adore the Lamb.

I. WATTS†

295

HYMN **222**   Unser Herrscher — 8 7. 8 7. 8 7   J. Neander, 1640–80

The Descant may be sung by Trebles for verse 6, the main melody being sung in Unison

f   Come, ye faithful, raise the anthem,
     Cleave the skies with shouts of praise;
   Sing to him who found the ransom,
     Ancient of eternal Days,
   God of God, the Word incarnate,
     Whom the heaven of heaven obeys.

2

mf Ere he raised the lofty mountains,
  Formed the seas, or built the sky,
Love eternal, free, and boundless,
  Moved the Lord of Life to die,
Fore-ordained the Prince of Princes
  For the throne of Calvary.

3*

p There, for us and our redemption,
  See him all his life-blood pour!
mf There he wins our full salvation,
  Dies that we may die no more;
f Then, arising, lives for ever,
  Reigning where he was before.

4

High on yon celestial mountains
  Stands his sapphire throne, all bright,
Midst unending Alleluias
  Bursting from the sons of light;
Sion's people tell his praises,
  Victor after hard-won fight.

5

mf Bring your harps, and bring your incense,
  Sweep the string and pour the lay;
f Let the earth proclaim his wonders,
  King of that celestial day;
He the Lamb once slain is worthy,
  Who was dead, and lives for ay.

[UNISON] **6**
Laud and honour to the Father,
  Laud and honour to the Son,
Laud and honour to the Spirit,
  Ever Three and ever One,
Consubstantial, co-eternal,
  While unending ages run.

J. HUPTON and J. M. NEALE†

HYMN **223**   FIRST TUNE

Barnet — 6 6 6. 6 6 6   R. H. Jesson

By permission of the Royal School of Church Music

SECOND TUNE

Laudes Domini — 6 6 6. 6 6 6   Sir J. Barnby, 1838–9

General

Beim frühen Morgenlicht

When morning gilds the skies,
My heart awaking cries,
　　May Jesus Christ be praised:
Alike at work and prayer
To Jesus I repair;
　　May Jesus Christ be praised.

2
Whene'er the sweet church bell
Peals over hill and dell,
　　May Jesus Christ be praised:
O hark to what it sings,
As joyously it rings,
　　May Jesus Christ be praised.

3
My tongue shall never tire
Of chanting with the choir,
　　May Jesus Christ be praised:
This song of sacred joy,
It never seems to cloy,
　　May Jesus Christ be praised.

4
Does sadness fill my mind?
A solace here I find,
　　May Jesus Christ be praised:
Or fades my earthly bliss?
My comfort still is this,
　　May Jesus Christ be praised.

5*
The night becomes as day,
When from the heart we say,
　　May Jesus Christ be praised:
The powers of darkness fear,
When this sweet chant they hear,
　　May Jesus Christ be praised.

6
Be this, while life is mine,
My canticle divine,
　　May Jesus Christ be praised:
Be this the eternal song
Through ages all along,
　　May Jesus Christ be praised.

19th century
Tr. E. CASWALL

299

General

FIRST TUNE

Corona — D.S.M.   C. Hylton Stewart, 1884–1932

By permission of the Oxford University Press

SECOND TUNE

Diademata — D.S.M.   Sir G. J. Elvey, 1816–93

Crown him with many crowns,
The Lamb upon his throne;
Hark! how the heavenly anthem
All music but its own: [drowns⌣
Awake, my soul, and sing
Of him who died for thee,
And hail him as thy matchless King
Through all eternity.

2
mf Crown him the Virgin's Son,
The God incarnate born,
Whose arm those crimson trophies
won
Which now his brow adorn:
Fruit of the mystic Rose,
As of that Rose the Stem;
The Root whence mercy ever flows,
The Babe of Bethlehem.

3
mf Crown him the Lord of love;
p Behold his hands and side,
Those wounds yet visible above
In beauty glorified:
No angel in the sky
Can fully bear that sight,
But downward bends his burning eye
At mysteries so bright.

4
mf Crown him the Lord of peace,
f Whose power a sceptre sways
From pole to pole, that wars may
cease,
And all be prayer and praise:
His reign shall know no end,
mf And round his piercèd feet
Fair flowers of Paradise extend⌣
Their fragrance ever sweet.

[UNISON] 5
f Crown him the Lord of years,
The Potentate of time,
Creator of the rolling spheres,
Ineffably sublime:
All hail, Redeemer, hail!
For thou hast died for me;
Thy praise shall never, never fail
Throughout eternity.

M. BRIDGES‡

NOTE. *The expression 'mystic Rose' in verse 2, line* 5, *is a medieval title for the Blessed Virgin,*
and is combined here with a reference to Isaiah 11. 1

HYMN **225** Evelyns — 6 5 6 5. D W. H. Monk, 1823–89

* *In verse 5 sing this chord to the first words of line 2, dividing the ♩ of the melody into two ♩ ♩*

mf At the name of Jesus
　　Every knee shall bow,
　Every tongue confess him
　　King of glory now :
　'Tis the Father's pleasure ⌣
　　We should call him Lord,
　Who from the beginning
　　Was the mighty Word.

　　　　2*
f At his voice creation ⌣
　　Sprang at once to sight,
　All the angel faces,
　　All the hosts of light,

Thrones and Dominations,
　Stars upon their way,
All the heavenly orders,
　In their great array.

　　　　3
p Humbled for a season,
　　To receive a name
From the lips of sinners
　Unto whom he came,
mf Faithfully he bore it
　　Spotless to the last,
Brought it back victorious,
　When from death he passed :

302

4

f Bore it up triumphant
    With its human light,
Through all ranks of creatures,
    To the central height,
To the throne of Godhead,
    To the Father's breast;
Filled it with the glory⌣
    Of that perfect rest.

5

Name him, brothers, name him,
    With love as strong as death,
p But with awe and wonder
    And with bated breath :
mf He is God the Saviour,
    He is Christ the Lord,
Ever to be worshipped,
    Trusted, and adored.

6*

In your hearts enthrone him ;
    There let him subdue⌣
All that is not holy,
    All that is not true :
Crown him as your Captain ·
    In temptation's hour ;
Let his will enfold you
    In its light and power.

7

f Brothers, this Lord Jesus
    Shall return again,
With his Father's glory,
    With his angel train ;
For all wreaths of empire
    Meet upon his brow,
And our hearts confess him
    King of glory now.

CAROLINE M. NOEL

HYMN **226**   Paderborn — 10 10 11 11   *Paderborn Gesangbuch,* 1765

Ye servants of God, your Master proclaim,
And publish abroad his wonderful name;
The name all-victorious of Jesus extol:
His Kingdom is glorious, and rules over all.

2
God ruleth on high, almighty to save;
And still he is nigh: his presence we have.
The great congregation his triumph shall sing,
Ascribing salvation to Jesus our King.

3
Salvation to God who sits on the throne!
Let all cry aloud, and honour the Son.
The praises of Jesus the angels proclaim,
Fall down on their faces, and worship the Lamb.

[UNISON]   4
Then let us adore, and give him his right:
All glory and power, all wisdom and might,
And honour and blessing, with angels above,
And thanks never-ceasing, and infinite love.

C. WESLEY

O quickly come, dread Judge of all;
  For, aweful though thine advent be,
All shadows from the truth will fall,
  And falsehood die, in sight of thee:
O quickly come! for doubt and fear⌣
Like clouds dissolve when thou art near.

2

O quickly come, great King of all;
  Reign all around us, and within;
Let sin no more our souls enthral,
  Let pain and sorrow die with sin:
O quickly come! for thou alone⌣
Canst make thy scattered people one.

3

O quickly come, true Life of all;
  For death is mighty all around;
On every home his shadows fall,
  On every heart his mark is found:
O quickly come! for grief and pain⌣
Can never cloud thy glorious reign.

4

O quickly come, sure Light of all,
  For gloomy night broods o'er our
And weakly souls begin to fall   [way;
  With weary watching for the day:
O quickly come! for round thy throne⌣
No eye is blind, no night is known.

L. TUTTIETT

HYMN **228**   Babylon's Streams — L.M.   T. Campion, *c.* 1575–1619

mf   That day of wrath, that dreadful day,
     When heaven and earth shall pass away,
     What power shall be the sinner's stay?
     How shall he meet that dreadful day?

2

f   When, shrivelling like a parchèd scroll,
     The flaming heavens together roll;
     When louder yet, and yet more dread,
     Swells the high trump that wakes the dead:

3

p   O on that day, that wrathful day,
     When man to judgement wakes from clay,
     Be thou, O Christ, the sinner's stay,
     Though heaven and earth shall pass away.

SIR WALTER SCOTT
Based on *Dies irae*

306

HYMN **229** Narenza — S.M. J. Leisentrit, *Catholicum Hymnologium*, 1587

Ye servants of the Lord,
Each in his office wait,
Observant of his heavenly word,
And watchful at his gate.

2
Let all your lamps be bright,
And trim the golden flame;
Gird up your loins as in his sight,
For aweful is his name.

3
Watch! 'tis your Lord's command,
And while we speak, he's near;
Mark the first signal of his hand,
And ready all appear.

4
O happy servant he
In such a posture found!
He shall his Lord with rapture see,
And be with honour crowned.

5
Christ shall the banquet spread
With his own royal hand,
And raise that faithful servant's head
Amid the angelic band.

P. DODDRIDGE†

General

FIRST TUNE

St. Cuthbert — 8 6 8 4

J. B. Dykes, 1823–7(

SECOND TUNE

Shrewsbury — 8 6 8 4

J. E. Hun

p   Our blest Redeemer, ere he breathed
His tender last farewell,
A guide, a Comforter, bequeathed
With us to dwell.

2

mf He came sweet influence to impart,
A gracious willing guest,
While he can find one humble heart
Wherein to rest.

308

General

3

p And his that gentle voice we hear,
Soft as the breath of even,
That checks each fault, that calms
And speaks of heaven. [each fear,

4

mf And every virtue we possess,
And every conquest won,

And every thought of holiness,
Are his alone.

5

Spirit of purity and grace,
Our weakness, pitying, see:
O make our hearts thy dwelling-place,
And worthier thee.

HARRIET AUBER

HYMN **231**   Tallis — C.M.   T. Tallis, c. 1505–85

A higher setting of this tune will be found at Hymn 78

O fons amoris, Spiritus

mf   O Holy Spirit, Lord of grace,
Eternal fount of love,
Inflame, we pray, our inmost hearts
With fire from heaven above.

2

As thou in bond of love dost join
The Father and the Son,
So fill us all with mutual love,
And knit our hearts in one.

[UNISON]   **3**

f   All glory to the Father be,
All glory to the Son,
All glory, Holy Ghost, to thee,
While endless ages run.

C. COFFIN *Tr.* J. Chandler‡

309

General

HYMN **232**   Hawkhurst — L.M.   H. J. Gauntlett, 1805–76

A lower setting of this tune will be found at Hymn 427

Come, gracious Spirit, heavenly Dove,
With light and comfort from above;
Be thou our guardian, thou our guide,
O'er every thought and step preside.

2
The light of truth to us display,
And make us know and choose thy way;
Plant holy fear in every heart,
That we from God may ne'er depart.

3
Lead us to Christ, the living Way,
Nor let us from his pastures stray;
Lead us to holiness, the road
That we must take to dwell with God.

4
Lead us to heaven, that we may share
Fulness of joy for ever there;
Lead us to God, our final rest,
To be with him for ever blest.

S. BROWNE and others

310

General

VOICES IN UNISON

mf Gracious Spirit, Holy Ghost,
Taught by thee, we covet most
Of thy gifts at Pentecost,
  Holy, heavenly love.

2
Love is kind, and suffers long,
Love is meek, and thinks no wrong,
Love than death itself more strong;
  Therefore give us love.

3
Prophecy will fade away,
Melting in the light of day;
Love will ever with us stay;
  Therefore give us love.

4
Faith will vanish into sight;
Hope be emptied in delight;
Love in heaven will shine more bright;
  Therefore give us love.

5
Faith and hope and love we see
Joining hand in hand agree;
But the greatest of the three,
  And the best, is love.

6
p From the overshadowing
Of thy gold and silver wing
Shed on us, who to thee sing,
  Holy, heavenly love.

BISHOP CHR. WORDSWORTH

Alternative Tune, Capetown, 163

311

HYMN **234**   St. Timothy — C.M.   Sir H. W. Baker, 1821-77

A lower setting of this tune will be found at Hymn 5

mf O Holy Ghost, thy people bless
    Who long to feel thy might,
    And fain would grow in holiness
    As children of the light.

2
To thee we bring, who art the Lord,
    Our selves to be thy throne;
Let every thought and deed and word
    Thy pure dominion own.

3
Life-giving Spirit, o'er us move,
    As on the formless deep;
Give life and order, light and love,
    Where now is death or sleep.

4
f Great gift of our ascended King,
    His saving truth reveal;
Our tongues inspire his praise to sing,
    Our hearts his love to feel.

5
mf True wind of heaven, from south or north,
    For joy or chastening, blow;
The garden-spices shall spring forth
    If thou wilt bid them flow.

6
f O Holy Ghost, of sevenfold might,
    All graces come from thee;
Grant us to know and serve aright
    One God in Persons Three.

SIR H. W. BAKER

General

Discendi, Amor santo

mf Come down, O Love divine,
  Seek thou this soul of mine,
And visit it with thine own ardour
    glowing;
O Comforter, draw near,
Within my heart appear,
And kindle it, thy holy flame bestow-
    ing.

2
O let it freely burn,
Till earthly passions turn⌣
To dust and ashes in its heat consum-
    ing;
And let thy glorious light
Shine ever on my sight,
And clothe me round, the while my
  path illuming.

3
mf Let holy charity
  Mine outward vesture be,
And lowliness become mine inner
    clothing:
True lowliness of heart,
Which takes the humbler part,
And o'er its own shortcomings weeps
  with loathing.

4
f And so the yearning strong,
  With which the soul will long,
Shall far outpass the power of human
    telling;
For none can guess its grace,
Till he become the place
Wherein the Holy Spirit makes his
    dwelling.

BIANCO DA SIENA
Tr. R. F. Littledale

313

General

HYMN **236**   Aylesbury — S.M.   J. Chetham, *Psalms*, 1718

mf   Breathe on me, Breath of God,
Fill me with life anew,
That I may love what thou dost love,
And do what thou wouldst do.

2
Breathe on me, Breath of God,
Until my heart is pure;
Until with thee I will one will,
To do and to endure.

3
Breathe on me, Breath of God,
Till I am wholly thine;
Until this earthly part of me
Glows with thy fire divine.

4
Breathe on me, Breath of God:
f   So shall I never die,
But live with thee the perfect life
Of thine eternity.

E. HATCH

Alternative Tune, Carlisle, 362

314

HYMN **237** Amen Court — 6 6 8 4   J. Dykes Bower

βασιλεῦ οὐράνιε, Παράκλητε

O King enthroned on high,
Thou Comforter divine,
Blest Spirit of all truth, be nigh‿
And make us thine.

2
Thou art the source of life,
Thou art our treasure-store;
Give us thy peace, and end our strife‿
For evermore.

3
Descend, O heavenly Dove,
Abide with us alway;
And in the fulness of thy love
Cleanse us, we pray.

Pentecostarion, c. 8th cent.
Tr. J. BROWNLIE

Alternative Tune, Totteridge, 302

315

HYMN **238**   Song 22 — 10 10 10 10   Orlando Gibbons, 1583–1625

Love of the Father, Love of God the Son,
From whom all came, in whom was all begun;
Who formest heavenly beauty out of strife,
Creation's whole desire and breath of life:

2

Thou the all-holy, thou supreme in might,
Thou dost give peace, thy presence maketh right;
Thou with thy favour all things dost enfold,
With thine all-kindness free from harm wilt hold.

3*

Hope of all comfort, splendour of all aid,
That dost not fail nor leave the heart afraid;
To all that cry thou dost all help accord,
The angels' armour, and the saints' reward.

4

Purest and highest, wisest and most just,
There is no truth save only in thy trust;
Thou dost the mind from earthly dreams recall,
And bring, through Christ, to him for whom are all.

General

5

Eternal glory, all men thee adore,
Who art and shalt be worshipped evermore:
Us whom thou madest, comfort with thy might,
And lead us to enjoy thy heavenly light.

Yattendon Hymnal
Based on *Amor Patris et Filii*, 12th cent.

HYMN **239**   Störl — C.M.   J. G. C. Störl, 1675-1719

Spirit divine, attend our prayers,
  And make this house thy home;
Descend with all thy gracious powers;
  O come, great Spirit, come!

2

Come as the light : to us reveal
  Our emptiness and woe;
And lead us in those paths of life
  Where all the righteous go.

3

Come as the fire : and purge our hearts
  Like sacrificial flame;
Let our whole soul an offering be
  To our Redeemer's name.

4

Come as the dew : and sweetly bless
  This consecrated hour;
May barrenness rejoice to own
  Thy fertilizing power.

5

Come as the dove: and spread thy wings,
  The wings of peaceful love;
And let thy Church on earth become
  Blest as the Church above.

6

Come as the wind, with rushing sound
  And Pentecostal grace,
That all of woman born may see
  The glory of thy face.

7

Spirit divine, attend our prayers;
  Make a lost world thy home;
Descend with all thy gracious powers;
  O come, great Spirit, come!

A. REED

Hymn 240 FIRST TUNE

Salzburg — 7 7 7 7. D J. Hintze, 1622–1702

SECOND TUNE

Maidstone — 7 7 7 7. D W. B. Gilbert, 1829–191(

General

Psalm 84

mf Pleasant are thy courts above
In the land of light and love;
Pleasant are thy courts below
In this land of sin and woe:
O, my spirit longs and faints
For the converse of thy saints,
For the brightness of thy face,
For thy fulness, God of grace.

3

Happy souls, their praises flow
Even in this vale of woe;
Waters in the desert rise,
Manna feeds them from the skies;
f On they go from strength to strength,
Till they reach thy throne at length,
At thy feet adoring fall,
Who hast led them safe through all.

2

Happy birds that sing and fly
Round thy altars, O Most High;
Happier souls that find a rest
In a heavenly Father's breast!
Like the wandering dove that found
No repose on earth around,
They can to their ark repair,
And enjoy it ever there.

4

p Lord, be mine this prize to win,
Guide me through a world of sin,
Keep me by thy saving grace,
Give me at thy side a place.
mf Sun and Shield alike thou art;
Guide and guard my erring heart:
f Grace and glory flow from thee;
Shower, O shower them, Lord, on me.

H. F. LYTE

319

General

FIRST TUNE

Praises — 8 8 8 8 7

B. Luard Selby, 1853–1919

SECOND TUNE

Hosanna — 8 8 8 8 7

J. W. Elliott, 1833–1915

UNISON

HARMONY

rit.

Hosanna to the living Lord!
Hosanna to the incarnate Word!
To Christ, Creator, Saviour, King,
Let earth, let heaven Hosanna sing,
        Hosanna in the highest!

2
O Saviour, with protecting care
Abide in this thy house of prayer,
Where we thy parting promise claim,
Assembled in thy sacred name :
        Hosanna in the highest!

3
But, chiefest, in our cleansèd breast,
Eternal, bid thy Spirit rest;
And make our secret soul to be
A temple pure and worthy thee :
        Hosanna in the highest!

4
To God the Father, God the Son,
And God the Spirit, Three in One,
Be honour, praise, and glory given
By all on earth and all in heaven :
        Hosanna in the highest!

BISHOP R. HEBER†

General

mf We love the place, O God,
　　Wherein thine honour dwells;
　　The joy of thine abode
　　All earthly joy excels.

2
It is the house of prayer,
　　Wherein thy servants meet;
　　And thou, O Lord, art there
　　Thy chosen flock to greet.

3
We love the sacred font;
　　For there the holy Dove
　　To pour is ever wont⌣
　　His blessing from above.

4
We love thine altar, Lord;
　　O what on earth so dear?
　　For there, in faith adored,
　　We find thy presence near.

5
We love the word of life,
　　The word that tells of peace,
　　Of comfort in the strife,
　　And joys that never cease.

6
f　We love to sing below
　　For mercies freely given;
　　But O, we long to know⌣
　　The triumph-song of heaven.

7
mf　Lord Jesus, give us grace
　　On earth to love thee more,
f　In heaven to see thy face,
　　And with thy saints adore.

W. BULLOCK and
SIR H. W. BAKER

HYMN **243** Harewood — 6 6 6 6. 4 4 4 4 S. S. Wesley, 1810–76

Angularis fundamentum

f Christ is our Corner-stone,
  On him alone we build;
With his true saints alone
  The courts of heaven are filled:
    On his great love
    Our hopes we place
    Of present grace
    And joys above.

2

O then with hymns of praise
  These hallowed courts shall ring;
Our voices we will raise
  The Three in One to sing;
    And thus proclaim
    In joyful song,
    Both loud and long,
    That glorious name.

3

mf Here, gracious God, do thou
  For evermore draw nigh;
Accept each faithful vow,
  And mark each suppliant sigh;
    In copious shower
    On all who pray
    Each holy day
    Thy blessings pour.

4

p Here may we gain from heaven
  The grace which we implore;
And may that grace, once given,
  Be with us evermore,
    Until that day
    When all the blest
    To endless rest
    Are called away.

Tr. J. CHANDLER†

HYMN **244** Canon viii — L.M.   G. C. E. Ryley, 1866–1947

By permission of the Royal School of Church Music

O quam juvat fratres, Deus

O Lord, how joyful 'tis to see
The brethren join in love to thee!
On thee alone their heart relies,
Their only strength thy grace supplies.

2
How sweet within thy holy place
With one accord to sing thy grace,
Besieging thine attentive ear
With all the force of fervent prayer!

3
O may we love the house of God,
Of peace and joy the blest abode;

O may no angry strife destroy
That sacred peace, that holy joy.

4
The world without may rage, but we
Will only cling more close to thee,
With hearts to thee more wholly given,
More weaned from earth, more fixed o heaven.

5
Lord, shower upon us from above
The sacred gift of mutual love;
Each other's wants may we supply,
And reign together in the sky.

C. COFFIN *Tr.* J. Chand

Alternative Tune, Melcombe, 4

HYMN **245** Wareham — L.M.   W. Knapp, 1698–17

General

The Descant may be sung by Trebles for verses 3 and 5, the main melody being sung in Unison

Lower settings of this tune will be found at Hymns 502 and 582

mf Jesus, where'er thy people meet,
There they behold thy mercy-seat;
Where'er they seek thee thou art found,
And every place is hallowed ground.

2
For thou, within no walls confined,
Inhabitest the humble mind;
Such ever bring thee when they come,
And, going, take thee to their home.

[UNISON] 3
f Dear Shepherd of thy chosen few,
Thy former mercies here renew;
Here to our waiting hearts proclaim
The sweetness of thy saving name.

4
mf Here may we prove the power of prayer
To strengthen faith and sweeten care,
To teach our faint desires to rise,
And bring all heaven before our eyes.

[UNISON] 5
Lord, we are few, but thou art near;
Nor short thine arm, nor deaf thine ear:
f O rend the heavens, come quickly down,
And make a thousand hearts thine own.

W. COWPER

325

HYMN **246** Angel voices — 8 5 8 5. 8 4 3 E. G. Monk, 1819–1900

mf Angel-voices ever singing
 Round thy throne of light,
 Angel-harps for ever ringing,
 Rest not day nor night;
f Thousands only live to bless thee
  And confess thee
   Lord of might.

2
mf Thou who art beyond the farthest‿
 Mortal eye can scan,
 Can it be that thou regardest‿
 Songs of sinful man?
 Can we know that thou art near us,
  And wilt hear us?
f   Yea, we can.

3
mf Yea, we know that thou rejoicest‿
 O'er each work of thine;
 Thou didst ears and hands and voices
 For thy praise design;
 Craftsman's art and music's measure
  For thy pleasure
   All combine.

4
 In thy house, great God, we offer‿
 Of thine own to thee;
 And for thine acceptance proffer
 All unworthily   [voices
 Hearts and minds and hands and
  In our choicest
   Psalmody.

5
f   Honour, glory, might, and merit
    Thine shall ever be,
   Father, Son, and Holy Spirit,
    Blessèd Trinity!
   Of the best that thou hast given
    Earth and heaven
     Render thee.

F. POTT‡

326

HYMN **247**   Oswald's Tree — C.M.   Sir H. Walford Davies, 1869–1941

> *f*   Great Shepherd of thy people, hear,
>   Thy presence now display;
>   As thou hast given a place for prayer,
>   So give us hearts to pray.

> **2**
> *mf* Within these walls let holy peace
>   And love and concord dwell;
>   Here give the troubled conscience ease,
>   The wounded spirit heal.

> **3**
>   May we in faith receive thy word,
>   In faith present our prayers,
>   And in the presence of our Lord
>   Unbosom all our cares.

> **4**
>   The hearing ear, the seeing eye,
>   The contrite heart, bestow;
> *f*   And shine upon us from on high,
>   That we in grace may grow

J. NEWTON†

HYMN 248 Croft's 148th — 6 6 6 6. 4 4 4 4   W. Croft, 1678–1727

A lower setting of this tune will be found at Hymn 552

Psalm 84

Lord of the worlds above,
  How pleasant and how fair
The dwellings of thy love,
  Thy earthly temples, are!
    To thine abode
    My heart aspires,
    With warm desires
  To see my God.

2

O happy souls that pray
  Where God appoints to hear!
O happy men that pay
  Their constant service there!
    They praise thee still;
    And happy they
    That love the way
  To Zion's hill.

3

They go from strength to strength
  Through this dark vale of tears,
Till each arrives at length,
  Till each in heaven appears :
    O glorious seat!
    When God our King
    Shall thither bring
  Our willing feet.

I. WATTS

Alternative Tune, Darwall's 148th, 371

328

HYMN **249**   Althorp — 8 8. 8 8. 8 8   James Green's *Psalmody*, 1744

Gott ist gegenwärtig!

mf Lo, God is here! let us adore,
　　And own how dreadful is this place!
　　Let all within us feel his power,
　　And silent bow before his face;
　　Who know his power, his grace who prove,
p 　Serve him with awe, with reverence love.

2

mf Lo, God is here! him day and night
　　Rejoicing choirs of angels sing;
　　To him, enthroned above all height,
　　The hosts of heaven their praises bring:
p 　Disdain not, Lord, our meaner song,
　　Who praise thee with a faltering tongue.

3

f 　Being of beings! may our praise
　　Thy courts with grateful fragrance fill;
　　Still may we stand before thy face,
　　Still hear and do thy sovereign will;
　　To thee may all our thoughts arise
　　A true and ceaseless sacrifice.

G. TERSTEEGEN *Tr.* J. Wesley†

Alternative Tune, Colchester, 90

HYMN **250** Ravenshaw — 6 6 6 6   German Medieval Melody

Lord, thy word abideth,
And our footsteps guideth;
Who its truth believeth
Light and joy receiveth.

2
When our foes are near us,
Then thy word doth cheer us,
Word of consolation,
Message of salvation.

3
When the storms are o'er us,
And dark clouds before us,
Then its light directeth,
And our way protecteth.

4
Who can tell the pleasure,
Who recount the treasure,
By thy word imparted
To the simple-hearted?

5
Word of mercy, giving
Succour to the living;
Word of life, supplying
Comfort to the dying!

6
O that we discerning
Its most holy learning,
Lord, may love and fear thee,
Evermore be near thee.

SIR H. W. BAKER

HYMN **251**   Angmering — C.M.   Sir C. H. H. Parry, 1848-1918

Father of mercies, in thy word
What endless glory shines!
For ever be thy name adored
For these celestial lines.

2
Here may the blind and hungry come,
And light and food receive;
Here shall the lowliest guest have room,
And taste and see and live.

3
Here springs of consolation rise
To cheer the fainting mind,
And thirsting souls receive supplies,
And sweet refreshment find.

4
Here the Redeemer's welcome voice
Spreads heavenly peace around,
And life and everlasting joys
Attend the blissful sound.

5
O may these heavenly pages be
My ever dear delight,
And still new beauties may I see,
And still increasing light.

6
Divine instructor, gracious Lord,
Be thou for ever near;
Teach me to love thy sacred word,
And view my Saviour here.

ANNE STEELE

Alternative Tune, Southwell (Irons), 282

HYMN **252**   Alfreton — L.M.   *Supplement to the New Version,* 1708

A lower setting of this tune will be found at Hymn 95

Psalm 19

The heavens declare thy glory, Lord;
  In every star thy wisdom shines;
But when our eyes behold thy word,
  We read thy name in fairer lines.

2

Sun, moon, and stars convey thy praise
  Round the whole earth, and never stand;
So, when thy truth began its race,
  It touched and glanced on every land.

3

Nor shall thy spreading Gospel rest
  Till through the world thy truth has run;
Till Christ has all the nations blest
  That see the light or feel the sun.

4

Great Sun of Righteousness, arise;
  Bless the dark world with heavenly light;
Thy Gospel makes the simple wise,
  Thy laws are pure, thy judgements right.

5

Thy noblest wonders here we view,
  In souls renewed and sins forgiven:
Lord, cleanse my sins, my soul renew,
  And make thy word my guide to heaven.

                         I. WATTS

HYMN **253** FIRST TUNE

Iste Confessor — 11 11 11 5 French Melody

May be sung in Unison

mf Lord of our life, and God of our salvation,
Star of our night, and hope of every nation,
Hear and receive thy Church's supplication,
f   Lord God Almighty.

2

mf See round thine ark the hungry billows curling;
See how thy foes their banners are unfurling;
Lord, while their darts envenomed they are hurling,
f   Thou canst preserve us.

3

f Lord, thou canst help when earthly armour faileth,
Lord, thou canst save when deadly sin assaileth;
Lord, o'er thy Church nor death nor hell prevaileth:
p   Grant us thy peace, Lord.

4

mf Grant us thy help till foes are backward driven,
Grant them thy truth, that they may be forgiven,
p Grant peace on earth, and, after we have striven,
Peace in thy heaven.

P. PUSEY† Based on *Christe du
Beistand*, M. von Löwenstern

HYMN 253　　　SECOND TUNE

Cloisters — 11 11 11 5　　　　　　Sir J. Barnby, 1838–96

mf Lord of our life, and God of our salvation,
Star of our night, and hope of every nation,
Hear and receive thy Church's supplication,
　　f　　Lord God Almighty.

2

mf See round thine ark the hungry billows curling;
See how thy foes their banners are unfurling;
Lord, while their darts envenomed they are hurling,
　　f　　Thou canst preserve us.

3

f Lord, thou canst help when earthly armour faileth,
Lord, thou canst save when deadly sin assaileth;
Lord, o'er thy Church nor death nor hell prevaileth:
　　p　　Grant us thy peace, Lord.

4

mf Grant us thy help till foes are backward driven,
Grant them thy truth, that they may be forgiven,
p Grant peace on earth, and, after we have striven,
　　　Peace in thy heaven.

P. PUSEY† Based on *Christe du
Beistand*, M. von Löwenstern

334

Hymn **254**   University — C.M.   C. Collignon, 1725–85

f The Church of God a kingdom is,
    Where Christ in power doth reign ;
mf Where spirits yearn till, seen in bliss,
    Their Lord shall come again.

2
f Glad companies of saints possess‿
    This Church below, above ;
  And God's perpetual calm doth
    Their paradise of love.   [bless‿

3
An altar stands within the shrine
    Whereon, once sacrificed,
Is set, immaculate, divine,
    The Lamb of God, the Christ.

4
There rich and poor, from countless
    Praise Christ on mystic Rood ; [lands,
There nations reach forth holy hands
    To take God's holy food.

5
mf There pure life-giving streams o'erflow‿
    The sower's garden-ground ;
  And faith and hope fair blossoms show,
    And fruits of love abound.

6
O King, O Christ, this endless grace
    To us and all men bring,
f To see the vision of thy face
    In joy, O Christ, our King.

L. B. C. L. Muirhead

HYMN **255**   Aurelia — 7 6 7 6. D   S. S. Wesley, 1810–76

mf   The Church's one foundation
   Is Jesus Christ her Lord;
She is his new creation
   By water and the word:
From heaven he came and sought her
   To be his holy Bride;
With his own Blood he bought her,
   And for her life he died.

2

Elect from every nation,
  Yet one o'er all the earth,
Her charter of salvation
  One Lord, one faith, one birth;
One holy name she blesses,
  Partakes one holy food,
And to one hope she presses
  With every grace endued.

3*

p Though with a scornful wonder
  Men see her sore opprest,
By schisms rent asunder,
  By heresies distrest,
mf Yet saints their watch are keeping,
  Their cry goes up, 'How long?'
f And soon the night of weeping
  Shall be the morn of song.

4

mf Mid toil and tribulation,
  And tumult of her war,
She waits the consummation‿
  Of peace for evermore;
Till with the vision glorious
  Her longing eyes are blest,
f And the great Church victorious
  Shall be the Church at rest.

5

mf Yet she on earth hath union
  With God the Three in One,
And mystic sweet communion
  With those whose rest is won:
O happy ones and holy!
  Lord, give us grace that we,
Like them the meek and lowly,
  On high may dwell with thee.

S. J. STONE

HYMN **256**   Thornbury — 7 6 7 6. D   B. Harwood, 1859–1949

VERSES 1, 2, 4 AND 6, UNISON

1 Thy hand, O God, has guid - ed_ Thy flock, from age to
2 Thy her - alds brought glad tid - ings To great - est, as to
4 Through many a day of dark - ness, Through many a scene of
6 Thy mer - cy will not fail us, Nor leave thy work un-

1 age; The won - drous tale is writ - ten, Full
2 least; They bade men rise, and hast - en To
4 strife, The faith - ful few fought brave - ly, To
6 done; With thy right hand to help us, The

1 clear, on ev - ery page; Our fa - thers owned thy
2 share the great King's feast; And this was all their
4 guard the na - tion's life. Their Gos - pel of re-
6 vic - tory shall be won; And then, by men and

General

Verses 3 and 5, see next page

VERSES 3 AND 5, HARMONY

3* When sha-dows thick were fall-ing, And all seemed sunk in
5* And we, shall we be faith-less? Shall hearts fail, hands hang

3* night, Thou, Lord, didst send thy ser - vants, Thy
5* down? Shall we e - vade the con - flict, And

3* cho - sen sons of light. On them and on thy
5* cast a - way our crown? Not so: in God's deep

3* peo - ple Thy plen - teous grace was poured,
5* coun - sels Some bet - ter thing is stored;

General

VOICES

One *ff*

| 3* And | this | was | still | their | mes - | sage: | One |
| 5* We | will | main - tain, | un - | flinch - | ing, | One |

ORGAN

ff

ff

Church, one faith, one Lord.

| 3* Church, | one | faith, | one | Lord, | one | faith, | one | Lord. |
| 5* Church, | one | faith, | one | Lord, | one | faith, | one | Lord. |

E. H. PLUMPTRE

General

Abbot's Leigh — 8 7 8 7. D   C. V. Taylor

Reprinted by permission of the Oxford University Press

342

Glorious things of thee are spoken,
  Zion, city of our God;
He whose word cannot be broken
  Formed thee for his own abode.
On the Rock of ages founded,
  What can shake thy sure repose?
With salvation's walls surrounded,
  Thou may'st smile at all thy foes.

2
See, the streams of living waters,
  Springing from eternal love,
Well supply thy sons and daughters,
  And all fear of want remove.
Who can faint while such a river
  Ever flows their thirst to assuage:
Grace which, like the Lord the giver,
  Never fails from age to age?

3*
Round each habitation hovering,
  See the cloud and fire appear
For a glory and a covering,
  Showing that the Lord is near.
Thus they march, the pillar leading,
  Light by night and shade by day;
Daily on the manna feeding
  Which he gives them when they pray.

4
Saviour, since of Zion's city
  I through grace a member am,
Let the world deride or pity,
  I will glory in thy name.
Fading is the worldling's pleasure,
  All his boasted pomp and show;
Solid joys and lasting treasure
  None but Zion's children know.

                    J. Newton‡

General

HYMN **257**   SECOND TUNE

Austria — 8 7 8 7. D   F. J. Haydn, 1732–1809

A higher setting of this tune will be found at Hymn 368

344

General

Glorious things of thee are spoken,
 Zion, city of our God;
He whose word cannot be broken
 Formed thee for his own abode.
On the Rock of ages founded,
 What can shake thy sure repose?
With salvation's walls surrounded,
 Thou may'st smile at all thy foes.

2
See, the streams of living waters,
 Springing from eternal love,
Well supply thy sons and daughters,
 And all fear of want remove.
Who can faint while such a river
 Ever flows their thirst to assuage:
Grace which, like the Lord the giver,
 Never fails from age to age?

3*
Round each habitation hovering,
 See the cloud and fire appear
For a glory and a covering,
 Showing that the Lord is near.
Thus they march, the pillar leading,
 Light by night and shade by day;
Daily on the manna feeding
 Which he gives them when they pray.

4
Saviour, since of Zion's city
 I through grace a member am,
Let the world deride or pity,
 I will glory in thy name.
Fading is the worldling's pleasure,
 All his boasted pomp and show;
Solid joys and lasting treasure
 None but Zion's children know.

J. NEWTON‡

HYMN **258**   Richmond — C.M.   T. Haweis, 1734–1820

City of God, how broad and far
 Outspread thy walls sublime!
The true thy chartered freemen are
 Of every age and clime:

2
One holy Church, one army strong,
 One steadfast, high intent;
One working band, one harvest-song,
 One King omnipotent.

3
How purely hath thy speech come down
 From man's primeval youth!
How grandly hath thine empire grown
 Of freedom, love, and truth!

4
How gleam thy watch-fires through the night
 With never-fainting ray!
How rise thy towers, serene and bright,
 To meet the dawning day!

[UNISON]   5
In vain the surge's angry shock,
 In vain the drifting sands:
Unharmed upon the eternal Rock
 The eternal city stands.

S. JOHNSON

HYMN **259**   Old 120th — 6 6. 6 6. 6 6   *Psalms*, 1570

A lower setting of this tune will be found at Hymn 544

O thou not made with hands,
　Not throned above the skies,
Nor walled with shining walls,
　Nor framed with stones of price,
More bright than gold or gem,
God's own Jerusalem!

2
Where'er the gentle heart
　Finds courage from above;
Where'er the heart forsook
　Warms with the breath of love;
Where faith bids fear depart,
City of God, thou art.

3
Thou art where'er the proud‿
　In humbleness melts down;
Where self itself yields up;
　Where martyrs win their crown;
Where faithful souls possess‿
Themselves in perfect peace;

4
Where in life's common ways
　With cheerful feet we go;
Where in his steps we tread,
　Who trod the way of woe;
Where he is in the heart,
City of God, thou art.

5
Not throned above the skies,
　Nor golden-walled afar,
But where Christ's two or three‿
　In his name gathered are,
Be in the midst of them,
God's own Jerusalem!

F. T. PALGRAVE

HYMN 260   Hyfrydol — 8 7 8 7. D   R. H. Prichard, 1811-87

Ye that know the Lord is gracious,
　Ye for whom a Corner stone⏝
Stands, of God elect and precious,
　Laid that ye may build thereon,
See that on that sure foundation
　Ye a living temple raise,
Towers that may tell forth salvation,
　Walls that may re-echo praise.

2

Living stones, by God appointed
　Each to his allotted place,
Kings and priests, by God anointed,
　Shall ye not declare his grace?
Ye, a royal generation,
　Tell the tidings of your birth,
Tidings of a new creation
　To an old and weary earth.

3

Tell the praise of him who called you
　Out of darkness into light,
Broke the fetters that enthralled you,
　Gave you freedom, peace and sight:
Tell the tale of sins forgiven,
　Strength renewed and hope restored,
Till the earth, in tune with heaven,
　Praise and magnify the Lord!

C. A. ALINGTON

349

HYMN **261** Binchester — C.M. W. Croft, 1678-1727

Happy are they, they that love God,
  Whose hearts have Christ confest,
Who by his Cross have found their life,
  And 'neath his yoke their rest.

2

Glad is the praise, sweet are the songs,
  When they together sing;
And strong the prayers that bow the ear
  Of heaven's eternal King.

3

Christ to their homes giveth his peace,
  And makes their loves his own:
But ah, what tares the evil one
  Hath in his garden sown!

4

Sad were our lot, evil this earth,
  Did not its sorrows prove
The path whereby the sheep may find
  The fold of Jesus' love.

5

Then shall they know, they that love him,
  How all their pain is good;
And death itself cannot unbind
  Their happy brotherhood.

Yattendon Hymnal
Based on *O quam juvat*, C. COFFIN

Hymn 262   St. Cecilia — 6 6 6 6   L. G. Hayne, 1836–83

mf Thy Kingdom come, O God,
    Thy rule, O Christ, begin;
  Break with thine iron rod
    The tyrannies of sin.

2
p Where is thy reign of peace
    And purity and love?
  When shall all hatred cease,
    As in the realms above?

3
When comes the promised time
    That war shall be no more,
And lust, oppression, crime
    Shall flee thy face before?

4
mf We pray thee, Lord, arise,
    And come in thy great might;
  Revive our longing eyes,
    Which languish for thy sight.

5
p Men scorn thy sacred name,
    And wolves devour thy fold;
  By many deeds of shame
    We learn that love grows cold.

6
O'er heathen lands afar
    Thick darkness broodeth yet:
f Arise, O morning star,
    Arise, and never set!

L. Hensley

351

HYMN **263** Irish — C.M.   *Hymns and Sacred Poems* (Dublin, 1749)

Thy Kingdom come! on bended knee
  The passing ages pray;
And faithful souls have yearned to see
  On earth that Kingdom's day:

2
But the slow watches of the night
  Not less to God belong;
And for the everlasting right
  The silent stars are strong.

3
And lo, already on the hills
  The flags of dawn appear;
Gird up your loins, ye prophet souls,
  Proclaim the day is near:

4
The day in whose clear-shining light
  All wrong shall stand revealed,
When justice shall be throned in might
  And every hurt be healed;

5
When knowledge, hand in hand with peace,
  Shall walk the earth abroad:
The day of perfect righteousness,
  The promised day of God.

F. L. HOSMER

HYMN **264**   Heathlands — 7 7. 7 7. 7 7   H. Smart, 1813–79

Psalm 67

mf God of mercy, God of grace,
Show the brightness of thy face;
Shine upon us, Saviour, shine,
Fill thy Church with light divine;
And thy saving health extend⁀
Unto earth's remotest end.

2

f Let the people praise thee, Lord!
Be by all that live adored;
Let the nations shout and sing
Glory to their Saviour King;
mf At thy feet their tribute pay,
And thy holy will obey.

3

f Let the people praise thee, Lord!
Earth shall then her fruits afford;
God to man his blessing give,
Man to God devoted live;
All below, and all above,
One in joy and light and love.

H. F. LYTE

HYMN 265   Aurelia — 7 6 7 6. D   S. S. Wesley, 1810–76

mf From Greenland's icy mountains,
    From India's coral strand,
Where Afric's sunny fountains
    Roll down their golden sand,
From many an ancient river,
    From many a palmy plain,
They call us to deliver
    Their land from error's chain.

2

What though the spicy breezes
    Blow soft o'er Java's isle,
Though every prospect pleases
    And only man is vile :
In vain with lavish kindness
    The gifts of God are strown ;
The heathen in his blindness
    Bows down to wood and stone.

3

Can we, whose souls are lighted
    With wisdom from on high,
Can we to men benighted
    The lamp of life deny?
f Salvation! O salvation!
    The joyful sound proclaim,
Till each remotest nation
    Has learned Messiah's name.

4

Waft, waft, ye winds, his story,
    And you, ye waters, roll,
Till, like a sea of glory,
    It spreads from pole to pole ;
Till o'er our ransomed nature
    The Lamb for sinners slain,
Redeemer, King, Creator,
    In bliss returns to reign.

BISHOP R. HEBER

HYMN **266**   Moscow — 6 6 4. 6 6 6 4   F. Giardini, 1716–96

f   Thou, whose almighty word
Chaos and darkness heard,
    And took their flight;
mf Hear us, we humbly pray,
And where the Gospel-day⌣
Sheds not its glorious ray,
f   Let there be light!

2
mf Thou, who didst come to bring⌣
On thy redeeming wing
    Healing and sight,
Health to the sick in mind,
Sight to the inly blind,
O now to all mankind
f   Let there be light!

3
mf Spirit of truth and love,
Life-giving, holy Dove,
    Speed forth thy flight;
Move on the water's face,
Bearing the lamp of grace,
And in earth's darkest place
f   Let there be light!

4
Holy and blessèd Three,
Glorious Trinity,
    Wisdom, Love, Might;
Boundless as ocean's tide
Rolling in fullest pride,
Through the earth far and wide
    Let there be light!

J. MARRIOTT†

HYMN **267**   Everton — 8 7 8 7. D   H. Smart, 1813–79

mf Lord, her watch thy Church is keep-
    ing;
    When shall earth thy rule obey?
    When shall end the night of weeping?
       When shall break the promised
       day?
    See the whitening harvest languish,
      Waiting still the labourers' toil;
f Was it vain, thy Son's deep anguish?
    Shall the strong retain the spoil?

2
Tidings, sent to every creature,
    Millions yet have never heard;
    Can they hear without a preacher?
f Lord almighty, give the word:

f Give the word; in every nation‿
    Let the Gospel-trumpet sound,
    Witnessing a world's salvation
      To the earth's remotest bound.

3
Then the end: thy Church com-
    pleted,
    All thy chosen gathered in,
With their King in glory seated,
    Satan bound, and banished sin;
Gone for ever parting, weeping,
    Hunger, sorrow, death, and pain:
Lo, her watch thy Church is keep-
    ing;
    Come, Lord Jesus, come to reign!

H. DOWNTON

HYMN **268**   Duke Street — L.M.   Attributed to J. Hatton, *d.* 1793

Fling out the banner! let it float⌣
  Skyward and seaward, high and wide :
Our glory only in the Cross,
  Our only hope the Crucified.

2
Fling out the banner! angels bend⌣
  In anxious silence o'er the sign,
And vainly seek to comprehend
  The wonders of the love divine.

3
Fling out the banner! heathen lands⌣
  Shall see from far the glorious sight,
And nations, crowding to be born,
  Baptize their spirits in its light.

4
Fling out the banner! wide and high,
  Seaward and skyward let it shine ;
Nor skill nor might nor merit ours :
  We conquer only in that sign.

BISHOP G. W. DOANE

HYMN **269**   Little Cornard — 6 6 6 6. 8 8   Martin Shaw

By permission of J. Curwen & Sons, Ltd., from Curwen edition No. 80634

Hills of the north, rejoice;
  River and mountain-spring,
Hark to the advent voice;
  Valley and lowland, sing:
Though absent long, your Lord is nigh;
He judgement brings and victory.

2
Isles of the southern seas,
  Deep in your coral caves
Pent be each warring breeze,
  Lulled be your restless waves:
He comes to reign with boundless sway,
And makes your wastes his great high-
    way.

3
Lands of the east, awake,
  Soon shall your sons be free;
The sleep of ages break,
  And rise to liberty.
On your far hills, long cold and grey,
Has dawned the everlasting day.

4
Shores of the utmost west,
  Ye that have waited long,
Unvisited, unblest,
  Break forth to swelling song;
High raise the note, that Jesus died,
Yet lives and reigns, the Crucified.

[UNISON]   5
Shout, while ye journey home;
  Songs be in every mouth;
Lo, from the north we come,
  From east and west and south.
City of God, the bond are free,
We come to live and reign in thee!

C. E. OAKLEY

HYMN 270 Rangoon — Irregular   C. Wood, 1866–1926

Trumpet of God, sound high,
Till the hearts of the heathen shake,
And the souls that in slumber lie
At the voice of the Lord awake.
Till the fencèd cities fall
At the blast of the Gospel call,
Trumpet of God, sound high!

2
Hosts of the Lord, go forth:
Go, strong in the power of his rest,
Till the south be at one with the north,
And peace upon east and west;
Till the far-off lands shall thrill
With the gladness of God's good will,
Hosts of the Lord, go forth!

3
Come, as of old, like fire;
O force of the Lord, descend,
Till with love of the world's Desire
Earth burn to its utmost end;
Till the ransomed people sing
To the glory of Christ the King,
Come, as of old, like fire!

A. BROOKS

HYMN **271**   Benson — Irregular   Millicent D. Kingham (1894)

mf God is working his | purpose out as | year succeeds to | year,
God is working his | purpose out and the | time is drawing | near;
Nearer and nearer | draws the time, the | time that shall surely | be,
f When the | earth shall be filled with the | glory of God as the | waters cover
the | sea.

2

mf From | utmost east to | utmost west wher- | e'er man's foot hath | trod,
By the | mouth of many | messengers goes | forth the voice of | God,
f 'Give | ear to me, ye | continents, ye | isles, give ear to | me,
That the | earth may be filled with the | glory of God as the | waters cover
the | sea.'

3

p What can we do to | work God's work, to | prosper and in- | crease
The | brotherhood of | all mankind, the | reign of the Prince of | Peace?
What can we do to | hasten the time, the | time that shall surely | be,
f When the | earth shall be filled with the | glory of God as the | waters cover
the | sea?

4

March we forth in the | strength of God with the | banner of Christ un- | furled,
That the | light of the glorious | Gospel of truth may | shine throughout the |
world.
Fight we the fight with | sorrow and sin, to | set their captives | free,
That the | earth may be filled with the | glory of God as the | waters cover
the | sea.

5

p All we can do is | nothing worth un- | less God blesses the | deed;
Vainly we hope for the | harvest-tide till | God gives life to the | seed;
mf Yet | nearer and nearer | draws the time, the | time that shall surely | be,
When the | earth shall be filled with the | glory of God as the | waters cover
the | sea.

A. C. AINGER

HYMN 272   Dundee — C.M.   *Psalms* (Edinburgh, 1615)

Higher settings of this tune will be found at Hymns 80 and 628

ALTERNATIVE VERSION

(Melody in the Tenor part)

Harmonized by T. Ravenscroft (1621)

The Alternative Version may be used for verses 2 and 4

mf Let saints on earth in concert sing
    With those whose work is done;
    For all the servants of our King
    In heaven and earth are one.

2
One family, we dwell in him,
    One Church, above, beneath;
p Though now divided by the stream,
    The narrow stream of death.

3
mf One army of the living God,
    To his command we bow: [flood
    Part of the host have crossed th
p   And part are crossing now.

4
E'en now to their eternal home
    There pass some spirits blest;
While others to the margin come,
    Waiting their call to rest.

5
mf Jesu, be thou our constant guide;
f   Then, when the word is given,
Bid Jordan's narrow stream divide,
And bring us safe to heaven.

C. WESLEY and others

HYMN **273**   Vienna — 7 7 7 7   J. H. Knecht, 1752–1817

They whose course on earth is o'er,
Think they of their brethren more?
They before the throne who bow,
Feel they for their brethren now?

2
We by enemies distrest,
They in Paradise at rest;
We the captives, they the freed—
We and they are one indeed.

3
Those whom many a land divides,
Many mountains, many tides,
Have they with each other part,
Fellowship of heart with heart?

4
Each to each may be unknown,
Wide apart their lots be thrown;

Differing tongues their lips may
    speak,
One be strong, and one be weak:

5
mf Yet in Sacrament and prayer
Each with other hath a share;
Hath a share in tear and sigh,
Watch and fast and litany.

6
Saints departed even thus
Hold communion still with us;
Still with us, beyond the veil
Praising, pleading, without fail.

7
f With them still our hearts we raise,
Share their work and join their praise,
Rendering worship, thanks, and love
To the Trinity above.

J. M. NEALE and Compilers

HYMN **274** Uffingham — L.M. J. Clarke, *c.* 1659–1707

He wants not friends that hath thy love,
  And may converse and walk with thee,
And with thy saints here and above,
  With whom for ever I must be.

2

In the blest fellowship of saints
  Is wisdom, safety, and delight;
And when my heart declines and faints,
  It's raisèd by their heat and light.

3

As for my friends, they are not lost;
  The several vessels of thy fleet,
Though parted now, by tempests tost,
  Shall safely in the haven meet.

4

Still we are centred all in thee,
  Members, though distant, of one Head;
In the same family we be,
  By the same faith and spirit led.

5

Before thy throne we daily meet
  As joint-petitioners to thee;
In spirit we each other greet,
  And shall again each other see.

6

The heavenly hosts, world without end,
  Shall be my company above;
And thou, my best and surest Friend,
  Who shall divide me from thy love?

R. Baxter†

HYMN **275**   FIRST TUNE

Werde munter — 7 6 7 6. D   J. Schop, *d.* 1644

HYMN **275** SECOND TUNE

St. Alphege — 7 6 7 6 H. J. Gauntlett, 1805-76

A lower setting of this tune will be found at Hymn 569

Hic breve vivitur

p Brief life is here our portion,
   Brief sorrow, short-lived care :
mf The life that knows no ending,
   The tearless life, is there.
O happy retribution :
   Short toil, eternal rest;
For mortals and for sinners
   A mansion with the blest!

2

And now we fight the battle,
   But then shall wear the crown
Of full and everlasting,
   And passionless renown.
nf And now we watch and struggle,
   And now we live in hope,
And Sion in her anguish
   With Babylon must cope.

3

f But he whom now we trust in
   Shall then be seen and known,
And they that know and see him
   Shall have him for their own.
The morning shall awaken,
   The shadows shall decay,
And each true-hearted servant
   Shall shine as doth the day.

4

There God, our King and portion,
   In fulness of his grace,
Shall we behold for ever,
   And worship face to face.
Then all the halls of Sion
   For ay shall be complete,
And in the Land of Beauty
   All things of beauty meet.

BERNARD OF CLUNY
Tr. J. M. Neale†

HYMN **276**   Pearsall — 7 6 7 6. D   R. L. Pearsall, 1795–1856

General

Hora novissima

mf The world is very evil,
  The times are waxing late;
Be sober and keep vigil,
  The Judge is at the gate:
The Judge who comes in mercy,
  The Judge who comes with might,
Who comes to end the evil,
  Who comes to crown the right.

2
Arise, arise, good Christian,
  Let right to wrong succeed;
Let penitential sorrow⌣
  To heavenly gladness lead,
To light that has no evening,
  That knows no moon nor sun,
The light so new and golden,
  The light that is but one.

3
O home of fadeless splendour,
  Of flowers that bear no thorn,
Where they shall dwell as children
p   Who here as exiles mourn!
mf 'Midst power that knows no limit,
  Where wisdom has no bound,
The beatific vision⌣
  Shall glad the saints around.

4
O happy, holy portion,
  Refection for the blest,
True vision of true beauty,
  True cure of the distrest!
f Strive, man, to win that glory;
  Toil, man, to gain that light;
Send hope before to grasp it,
  Till hope be lost in sight.

BERNARD OF CLUNY
Tr. J. M. Neale†

HYMN **277** Holy Well — 7 6 7 6. D Traditional Carol

General

O bona patria

mf For thee, O dear, dear country,
    Mine eyes their vigils keep;
For very love, beholding
    Thy happy name, they weep.
The mention of thy glory
    Is unction to the breast,
And medicine in sickness,
    And love and life and rest.

2

O one, O only mansion!
    O Paradise of joy!
Where tears are ever banished,
    And smiles have no alloy;
The Lamb is all thy splendour,
    The Crucified thy praise;
His laud and benediction
    Thy ransomed people raise.

3

With jasper glow thy bulwarks,
    Thy streets with emeralds blaze;
The sardius and the topaz
    Unite in thee their rays;
Thine ageless walls are bonded
    With amethyst unpriced;
The saints build up thy fabric,
    Thy Corner-stone is Christ.

4

Thou hast no shore, fair ocean!
    Thou hast no time, bright day!
Dear fountain of refreshment
    To pilgrims far away!
f Upon the Rock of ages
    They raise thy holy tower;
Thine is the victor's laurel,
    And thine the golden dower.

BERNARD OF CLUNY
Tr. J. M. Neale†

HYMN **278**   Ewing — 7 6 7 6. D   A. Ewing, 1830–95

General

Urbs Sion aurea

mf Jerusalem the golden,
    With milk and honey blest,
    Beneath thy contemplation
    Sink heart and voice opprest.
    I know not, O, I know not
    What joys await us there,
    What radiancy of glory,
    What bliss beyond compare.

2

f They stand, those halls of Sion,
    All jubilant with song,
    And bright with many an angel,
    And all the martyr throng;
    The Prince is ever with them,
    The daylight is serene,
    The pastures of the blessèd
    Are decked in glorious sheen.

3

mf There is the throne of David;
    And there, from care released,
    The shout of them that triumph,
    The song of them that feast;
f And they, who with their Leader
    Have conquered in the fight,
    For ever and for ever
    Are clad in robes of white.

4

mf O sweet and blessèd country,
    The home of God's elect!
    O sweet and blessèd country
    That eager hearts expect!
p Jesu, in mercy bring us‿
    To that dear land of rest;
mf Who art, with God the Father
    And Spirit, ever blest.

BERNARD OF CLUNY
Tr. J. M. Neale and Compilers

375

General

A lower setting of this tune will be found at Hymn 573

Jerusalem luminosa

Light's abode, celestial Salem,
  Vision whence true peace doth spring,
Brighter than the heart can fancy,
  Mansion of the highest King;
O how glorious are the praises
  Which of thee the prophets sing!

2
There for ever and for ever
  Alleluia is outpoured;
For unending, for unbroken
  Is the feast-day of the Lord;
All is pure and all is holy
  That within thy walls is stored.

3
There no cloud or passing vapour
  Dims the brightness of the air;
Endless noon-day, glorious noon-day,
  From the Sun of suns is there;
There no night brings rest from labour,
  For unknown are toil and care.

4*
O how glorious and resplendent,
  Fragile body, shalt thou be,
When endued with so much beauty,
  Full of health and strong and free,
Full of vigour, full of pleasure
  That shall last eternally!

5*
Now with gladness, now with courage,
  Bear the burden on thee laid,
That hereafter these thy labours
  May with endless gifts be paid;
And in everlasting glory
  Thou with brightness be arrayed.

[UNISON] 6
Laud and honour to the Father,
  Laud and honour to the Son,
Laud and honour to the Spirit,
  Ever Three and ever One,
Consubstantial, co-eternal,
  While unending ages run.

Ascribed to THOMAS À KEMPIS
Tr. J. M. Neale†

376

General

mf Jerusalem on high
  My song and city is,
  My home whene'er I die,
  The centre of my bliss :
f   O happy place !
  When shall I be,
  My God, with thee,
  To see thy face?

2
mf There dwells my Lord, my King,
  Judged here unfit to live ;
  There angels to him sing,
  And lowly homage give :
f   O happy, etc.

3
mf The patriarchs of old
  There from their travels cease ;
  The prophets there behold
  Their longed-for Prince of Peace :
f   O happy, etc.

4
mf The Lamb's apostles there
  I might with joy behold,
  The harpers I might hear
  Harping on harps of gold :
f   O happy, etc.

5
mf The bleeding martyrs, they‿
  Within those courts are found,
  Clothèd in pure array,
  Their scars with glory crowned :
f   O happy, etc.

6
p Ah me ! ah me ! that I‿
  In Kedar's tents here stay :
  No place like that on high ;
  Lord, thither guide my way ;
f   O happy, etc.

S. CROSSMAN

Hʏᴍɴ **281** O quanta qualia — 10 10 10 10 La Feillée, *Méthode*, 1808

* *For the first verse the slur is better over the 3rd and 4th notes of this bar*

General

mf O what their joy and their glory must be,
Those endless sabbaths the blessèd ones see!
Crown for the valiant, to weary ones rest;
God shall be all, and in all ever blest.

2*

What are the Monarch, his court, and his throne?
What are the peace and the joy that they own?
O that the blest ones, who in it have share,
All that they feel could as fully declare!

3

Truly Jerusalem name we that shore,
'Vision of peace,' that brings joy evermore!
Wish and fulfilment can severed be ne'er,
Nor the thing prayed for come short of the prayer.

4

There, where no troubles distraction can bring,
We the sweet anthems of Sion shall sing,
While for thy grace, Lord, their voices of praise
Thy blessèd people eternally raise.

5*

There dawns no sabbath, no sabbath is o'er,
Those sabbath-keepers have one evermore;
f One and unending is that triumph-song
Which to the angels and us shall belong.

6

p Now in the meanwhile, with hearts raised on high,
We for that country must yearn and must sigh;
Seeking Jerusalem, dear native land,
Through our long exile on Babylon's strand.

7

mf Low before him with our praises we fall,
Of whom, and in whom, and through whom are all:
f Of whom, the Father; and in whom, the Son;
Through whom, the Spirit, with them ever One.

PETER ABELARD
Tr. J. M. Neale‡

Hymn **282**   Southwell — C.M.   H. S. Irons, 1834–1905

mf Jerusalem, my happy home,
  Name ever dear to me,
When shall my labours have an end?
  Thy joys when shall I see?

2
When shall these eyes thy heaven-
    built walls
And pearly gates behold?
Thy bulwarks with salvation strong,
And streets of shining gold?

3
f Apostles, martyrs, prophets, there‿
  Around my Saviour stand;

And all I love in Christ below
  Will join the glorious band.

4
mf Jerusalem, my happy home,
  When shall I come to thee?
When shall my labours have an end?
  Thy joys when shall I see?

5
O Christ, do thou my soul prepare
  For that bright home of love;
That I may see thee and adore,
  With all thy saints above.

'F.B.P.' (*c.* 1600) and Compilers

Note. *The poem on which this hymn is based will be found (abbreviated) in the* 'Processional' *section* (**623**)

Hymn **283**   St. Sebastian — 10 10 7   Sir P. C. Buck, 1871–1947

UNISON

General

Alleluia piis edite laudibus

[FULL]
Sing Alleluia forth in duteous praise,
Ye citizens of heaven; O sweetly raise⌣
                An endless Alleluia.

[MEN]   2
Ye powers who stand before the eternal Light,
In hymning choirs re-echo to the height
                An endless Alleluia.

[TREBLES]   3
The holy city shall take up your strain,
And with glad songs resounding wake again
                An endless Alleluia.

[MEN]   4
In blissful antiphons ye thus rejoice
To render to the Lord with thankful voice
                An endless Alleluia.

[TREBLES]   5
Ye who have gained at length your palms in bliss,
Victorious ones, your chant shall still be this:
                An endless Alleluia.

[MEN]   6
There, in one grand acclaim, for ever ring
The strains which tell the honour of your King:
                An endless Alleluia.

[TREBLES]   7
This is sweet rest for weary ones brought back,
This is glad food and drink which ne'er shall lack:
                An endless Alleluia.

[MEN]   8
While thee, by whom were all things made, we praise⌣
For ever, and tell out in sweetest lays
                An endless Alleluia.

[FULL]   9
Almighty Christ, to thee our voices sing⌣
Glory for evermore; to thee we bring⌣
                An endless Alleluia.

                    MOZARABIC (5th–8th cent.)
                    Tr. J. Ellerton

HYMN 284   Alford — 7 6 8 6. D   J. B. Dykes, 1823–76

f   Ten thousand times ten thousand,
      In sparkling raiment bright,
      The armies of the ransomed saints
      Throng up the steeps of light:
mf 'Tis finished! all is finished,
      Their fight with death and sin;
f   Fling open wide the golden gates,
      And let the victors in.

2

What rush of Alleluias
      Fills all the earth and sky!
What ringing of a thousand harps
      Bespeaks the triumph nigh!
O day, for which creation
      And all its tribes were made!
O joy, for all its former woes
      A thousand-fold repaid!

3

mf O then what raptured greetings
      On Canaan's happy shore,
What knitting severed friendships up,
      Where partings are no more!
Then eyes with joy shall sparkle
      That brimmed with tears of late:
Orphans no longer fatherless,
      Nor widows desolate.

4

Bring near thy great salvation,
      Thou Lamb for sinners slain,
f   Fill up the roll of thine elect,
      Then take thy power and reign:
mf Appear, Desire of Nations;
      Thine exiles long for home;
f   Show in the heavens thy promised sign;
      Thou Prince and Saviour, come.

H. ALFORD

383

HYMN **285**   Beulah — C.M.   G. M. Garrett, 1834–97

A lower setting of this tune will be found at Hymn 32

f There is a land of pure delight,
    Where saints immortal reign;
    Infinite day excludes the night,
    And pleasures banish pain.

2
There everlasting spring abides,
    And never-withering flowers;
p Death, like a narrow sea, divides
    That heavenly land from ours.

3
mf Sweet fields beyond the swelling flood
    Stand dressed in living green;
    So to the Jews old Canaan stood,
    While Jordan rolled between.

4
p But timorous mortals start and shrink
    To cross the narrow sea,
    And linger shivering on the brink,
    And fear to launch away.

5
mf O could we make our doubts remove,
    Those gloomy doubts that rise,
    And see the Canaan that we love
    With unbeclouded eyes;

6
f Could we but climb where Moses stood,
    And view the landscape o'er;
    Not Jordan's stream, nor death's cold flood,
    Should fright us from the shore.

I. WATTS

General

HYMN **286**   Vulpius — 7 6 7 6   Melody by M. Vulpius, c. 1560–1616
Harmony by J. S. Bach, 1685–1750

1 My soul, there is a coun - try
2 There a - bove noise, and dan - ger, Sweet
3 He is thy gra - cious Friend, And —
4 If thou canst get but thi - ther, There
5 Leave then thy fool - ish ran - ges, For

1 Far be - yond the stars, Where stands a wing - èd
2 peace sits crowned with smiles, And One born in a
3 O my soul, a - wake! — Did in pure love de -
4 grows the flower of peace, The Rose that can - not
5 none can thee se - cure But one who ne - ver

1 sen - try All skil - ful in the wars:
2 man - ger Com - mands the beau - teous files.
3 scend, To die here for thy sake.
4 wi - ther, Thy fort - ress and thy ease.
5 chan - ges, Thy God, thy life, thy cure.

HENRY VAUGHAN

385

HYMN **287** Woolmer's — L.M.   Sir F. A. G. Ouseley, 1825-89

mf They come, God's messengers of love,
They come from realms of peace above,
From homes of never-fading light,
From blissful mansions ever bright.

2
They come to watch around us here,
To soothe our sorrow, calm our fear :
Ye heavenly guides, speed not away ;
God willeth you with us to stay.

3
p But chiefly at its journey's end
'Tis yours the spirit to befriend,
And whisper to the faithful heart,
'O Christian soul, in peace depart.'

4
Blest Jesu, thou whose groans and tears
Have sanctified frail nature's fears,
To earth in bitter sorrow weighed,
Thou didst not scorn thine angel's aid :

5
mf An angel guard to us supply,
When on the bed of death we lie ;
And by thine own almighty power
p O shield us in the last dread hour.

6
f To God the Father, God the Son,
And God the Spirit, Three in One,
From all above and all below
Let joyful praise unceasing flow.

R. CAMPBELL and others

HYMN **288**   Trisagion — 10 10 10 10   H. Smart, 1813–79

Org.

f   Stars of the morning, so gloriously bright,
Filled with celestial virtue and light,
These that, where night never followeth day,
Praise the Thrice-Holy for ever and ay :

2
mf   These are thy ministers, these dost thou own,
Lord God of Sabaoth, nearest thy throne ;
These are thy messengers, these dost thou send,
Help of the helpless ones, man to defend.

3
These keep the guard amidst Salem's dear bowers,
Thrones, Principalities, Virtues, and Powers,
Where, with the Living Ones, mystical four,
Cherubim, Seraphim, bow and adore.

4
Then, when the earth was first poised in mid space,
Then, when the planets first sped on their race,
Then, when was ended the six days' employ,
f   Then all the sons of God shouted for joy.

5
mf   Still let them succour us ; still let them fight,
Lord of angelic hosts, battling for right ;
f   Till, where their anthems they ceaselessly pour,
We with the angels may bow and adore.

J. M. NEALE† Based on φωστῆρες τῆς αὐλου,
St. Joseph the Hymnographer

HYMN **289**   Kocher — 7 6 7 6   J. H. Knecht, 1752–1817

3

mf O happy band of pilgrims,
        If onward ye will tread
    With Jesus as your fellow
        To Jesus as your Head!

p The Cross that Jesus carried
        He carried as your due :
f The Crown that Jesus weareth
        He weareth it for you.

2

O happy if ye labour
    As Jesus did for men!
O happy if ye hunger
    As Jesus hungered then!

4

mf The faith by which ye see him,
        The hope in which ye yearn,
    The love that through all troubles
        To him alone will turn,

5

p The trials that beset you,
        The sorrows ye endure,
    The manifold temptations
        That death alone can cure.

6

mf What are they but his jewels
        Of right celestial worth?
    What are they but the ladder
        Set up to heaven on earth?

7

f O happy band of pilgrims,
        Look upward to the skies,
    Where such a light affliction
        Shall win so great a prize.

J. M. NEALE

General

Psalm 34

mf Through all the changing scenes of
  In trouble and in joy,   [life,
The praises of my God shall still
  My heart and tongue employ.

4

O make but trial of his love:
  Experience will decide
How blest are they, and only they,
  Who in his truth confide.

2

O magnify the Lord with me,
  With me exalt his name;
When in distress to him I called,
  He to my rescue came.

5

Fear him, ye saints, and you will then
  Have nothing else to fear;
Make you his service your delight,
  Your wants shall be his care.

3

The hosts of God encamp around
  The dwellings of the just;
Deliverance he affords to all
  Who on his succour trust.

6

f To Father, Son, and Holy Ghost,
  The God whom we adore,
Be glory, as it was, is now,
  And shall be evermore.

N. Tate and N. Brady
(*New Version*)

389

General

mf Oft in danger, oft in woe,
   Onward, Christians, onward go;
   Bear the toil, maintain the strife,
   Strengthened with the Bread of Life.

2

Onward, Christians, onward go,
   Join the war, and face the foe;
   Will ye flee in danger's hour?
   Know ye not your Captain's power?

3

Let not sorrow dim your eye;
   Soon shall every tear be dry:

   Let not fears your course impede;
f Great your strength, if great your
    need.

4

mf Let your drooping hearts be glad;
   March in heavenly armour clad;
   Fight, nor think the battle long:
f Soon shall victory wake your song.

5

Onward then in battle move;
   More than conquerors ye shall prove:
   Though opposed by many a foe,
   Christian soldiers, onward go.

H. KIRKE WHITE and others

Igjennem Nat og Trængsel

nf Through the night of doubt and
sorrow
Onward goes the pilgrim band,
Singing songs of expectation,
Marching to the Promised Land.
Clear before us through the darkness
Gleams and burns the guiding light;
Brother clasps the hand of brother,
Stepping fearless through the
night.

2

One the light of God's own presence
O'er his ransomed people shed,
Chasing far the gloom and terror,
Brightening all the path we tread:
One the object of our journey,
One the faith which never tires,
One the earnest looking forward,
One the hope our God inspires:

3*

f One the strain that lips of thousands
Lift as from the heart of one:
One the conflict, one the peril,
One the march in God begun:
One the gladness of rejoicing
On the far eternal shore,
Where the one almighty Father
Reigns in love for evermore.

4

mf Onward, therefore, pilgrim brothers,
Onward with the Cross our aid;
Bear its shame, and fight its battle,
Till we rest beneath its shade.
f Soon shall come the great awaking,
Soon the rending of the tomb;
Then the scattering of all shadows,
And the end of toil and gloom.

B. S. Ingemann
Tr. S. Baring-Gould

Alternative Tune, Marching, 182

HYMN **292**   SECOND TUNE

St. Oswald — 8 7 8 7   J. B. Dykes, 1823–76

The Descant may be sung by Trebles for the last four lines of verses 2 and 4, the main melody being sung in Unison

Igjennem Nat og Trængsel

mf Through the night of doubt and
  sorrow
  Onward goes the pilgrim band,
  Singing songs of expectation,
  Marching to the Promised Land.
  Clear before us through the darkness
  Gleams and burns the guiding light;
  Brother clasps the hand of brother,
  Stepping fearless through the night.

2
One the light of God's own presence
  O'er his ransomed people shed,
  Chasing far the gloom and terror,
  Brightening all the path we tread :
  One the object of our journey,
  One the faith which never tires,
  One the earnest looking forward,
  One the hope our God inspires :

3*
f One the strain that lips of thousands
  Lift as from the heart of one :
  One the conflict, one the peril,
  One the march in God begun :
  One the gladness of rejoicing
  On the far eternal shore,
  Where the one almighty Father
  Reigns in love for evermore.

4
mf Onward, therefore, pilgrim brothers,
  Onward with the Cross our aid ;
  Bear its shame, and fight its battle,
  Till we rest beneath its shade.
f Soon shall come the great awaking,
  Soon the rending of the tomb ;
  Then the scattering of all shadows,
  And the end of toil and gloom.

B. S. INGEMANN *Tr.* S. Baring-Gould

Hymn **293**   Bunyan — 6 5 6 5. 6 6 6 5   *Christen-schatz* (Basle, 1745)

Who would true valour see,
  Let him come hither;
One here will constant be,
  Come wind, come weather;
There's no discouragement
Shall make him once relent
His first avowed intent
  To be a pilgrim.

2
Whoso beset him round
  With dismal stories,
Do but themselves confound;
  His strength the more is.
No lion can him fright;
He'll with a giant fight,
But he will have the right
  To be a pilgrim.

3
No goblin nor foul fiend
  Can daunt his spirit;
He knows he at the end
  Shall life inherit.
Then, fancies, fly away;
He'll not fear what men say;
He'll labour night and day
  To be a pilgrim.

JOHN BUNYAN†

HYMN **294**   Ave virgo — 7 6 7 6. D   Medieval Melody as given by
J. Horn (1544)

Brothers, joining hand to hand
  In one bond united,
Pressing onward to that land
  Where all wrongs are righted :
Let your words and actions be⌣
  Worthy your vocation ;
Chosen of the Lord, and free,
  Heirs of Christ's salvation.

2
Christ, the Way, the Truth, the Life,
  Who hath gone before you
Through the turmoil and the strife,
  Holds his banner o'er you :

All who see the sacred sign
  Press towards heaven's portal,
Fired by hope that is divine,
  Love that is immortal.

3
They who follow fear no foe,
  Care not who assail them ;
Where the Master leads they go,
  He will never fail them.
Courage, brothers ! we are one,
  In the love that sought us ;
Soon the warfare shall be done,
  Through the grace he brought us.

J. A. WARNE

394

HYMN **295** Bewdley — 7 7 7 7   Sir F. A. G. Ouseley, 1825–89

mf   Children of the heavenly King,
As ye journey, sweetly sing;
Sing your Saviour's worthy praise,
Glorious in his works and ways.

2

We are travelling home to God
In the way the fathers trod;
They are happy now, and we⌣
Soon their happiness shall see.

3

f   Lift your eyes, ye sons of light!
Sion's city is in sight;
There our endless home shall be,
There our Lord we soon shall see.

4

Fear not, brethren! joyful stand
On the borders of your land;
Jesus Christ, your Father's Son,
Bids you undismayed go on.

5

p   Lord, obedient we would go,
Gladly leaving all below;
mf   Only thou our leader be,
f   And we still will follow thee.

J. CENNICK†

Alternative Tune, Innocents, 191

HYMN **296**

Pilgrimage — 8 7. 8 7. 4 7   Sir G. J. Elvey, 1816–93

A lower setting of this tune will be found at Hymn 457

Cwm Rhondda — 8 7. 8 7. 4 7   J. Hughes, 1873–1932

General

Arglwydd arwain trwy'r anialwch

mf Guide me, O thou great Redeemer,
Pilgrim through this barren land;
I am weak, but thou art mighty;
Hold me with thy powerful hand:
Bread of heaven,
Feed me now and evermore.

2
Open now the crystal fountain
Whence the healing stream doth flow;
Let the fiery cloudy pillar
Lead me all my journey through:
Strong deliverer,
f Be thou still my strength and shield.

3
p When I tread the verge of Jordan,
Bid my anxious fears subside;
f Death of death, and hell's destruction,
Land me safe on Canaan's side:
Songs and praises
I will ever give to thee.

W. WILLIAMS
Tr. P. and W. Williams‡

397

HYMN **297**   Ladywell — D.C.M.   W. H. Ferguson, 1872–1950

General

f Lift up your voice, ye Christian folk,
  To praise the Holy One,
  Who ransoms us from Satan's yoke
  Through Christ, his blessed Son.
mf Lo, we who were in grievous state
  By reason of our sin,
f Our heads look up, our fears abate,
  Our triumphs now begin.

2

p The mists hung cold, the night was black,
  About the way we trod;
  Our feet were stumbling from the track
  Which leads the soul to God.
mf But Christ, who broke from death's dark shroud,
  Hath sent his quickening ray :
f The sun breaks through the drifting cloud,
  And now 'tis glorious day.

3

Lift up your voice! with shout and song
 Extol his majesty,
Whose power hath made the feeble strong
 And caused the blind to see.
And when the sound of praise grows dim
 Still may our lives forth tell,
In all we do, our love of him
 Who doeth all things well.

P. H. B. LYON

HYMN **298**   FIRST TUNE

Alberta — 10 4. 10 4. 10 10   W. H. Harris

By permission of the Oxford University Press

SECOND TUNE

Lux benigna — 10 4. 10 4. 10 10   J. B. Dykes, 1823–

mf Lead, kindly Light, amid the encircling gloom,
        Lead thou me on;
p   The night is dark, and I am far from home;
        Lead thou me on.
mf Keep thou my feet; I do not ask to see
    The distant scene; one step enough for me.

2

I was not ever thus, nor prayed that thou
    Shouldst lead me on;
I loved to choose and see my path; but now
    Lead thou me on.
I loved the garish day, and, spite of fears,
Pride ruled my will : remember not past years.

3

So long thy power hath blest me, sure it still
    Will lead me on,
O'er moor and fen, o'er crag and torrent, till
    The night is gone.
And with the morn those angel faces smile,
Which I have loved long since, and lost a while.

CARDINAL J. H. NEWMAN

HYMN **298**   THIRD TUNE

Sandon — 10 4. 10 4. 10 10   C. H. Purday, 1799–1885

mf Lead, kindly Light, amid the encircling gloom,
        Lead thou me on;
p   The night is dark, and I am far from home;
        Lead thou me on.
mf Keep thou my feet; I do not ask to see⌣
        The distant scene; one step enough for me.

2

I was not ever thus, nor prayed that thou⌣
        Shouldst lead me on;
I loved to choose and see my path; but now⌣
        Lead thou me on.
I loved the garish day, and, spite of fears,
Pride ruled my will: remember not past years

3

So long thy power hath blest me, sure it still⌣
    Will lead me on,
O'er moor and fen, o'er crag and torrent, till⌣
    The night is gone,
And with the morn those angel faces smile,
Which I have loved long since, and lost a while.

CARDINAL J. H. NEWMAN

HYMN **299**   FIRST TUNE

Stracathro — C.M.   Melody by C. Hutcheson, 1792–1860
from *Christian Vespers*, Glasgow, 1832

Harmonized by Geoffrey Shaw

From *Enlarged Songs of Praise* by permission of the Oxford University Press

f O God of Bethel, by whose hand⌣
    Thy people still are fed,
Who through this weary pilgrimage
    Hast all our fathers led;

2

Our vows, our prayers, we now pre-
    sent
    Before thy throne of grace;
God of our fathers, be the God⌣
    Of their succeeding race.

3

p Through each perplexing path of
    life
    Our wandering footsteps guide;
Give us each day our daily bread,
    And raiment fit provide.

4

mf O spread thy covering wings around,
    Till all our wanderings cease,
And at our Father's loved abode
    Our souls arrive in peace.

P. DODDRIDGE

General

SECOND TUNE

Martyrdom — C.M.

H. Wilson, 1766–1824

A higher setting of this tune will be found at Hymn 314

mf   O God of Bethel, by whose hand⌣
    Thy people still are fed,
  Who through this weary pilgrimage
    Hast all our fathers led ;

2
  Our vows, our prayers, we now present
    Before thy throne of grace ;
  God of our fathers, be the God⌣
    Of their succeeding race.

3
p   Through each perplexing path of life
    Our wandering footsteps guide ;
  Give us each day our daily bread,
    And raiment fit provide.

4
mf   O spread thy covering wings around,
    Till all our wanderings cease,
  And at our Father's loved abode
    Our souls arrive in peace.

P. DODDRIDGE

404

HYMN **300**   Abridge — C.M.   I. Smith, *c.* 1735-1800

mf Be thou my guardian and my guide,
      And hear me when I call;
      Let not my slippery footsteps slide,
      And hold me lest I fall.

                    2
p   The world, the flesh, and Satan dwell
      Around the path I tread;
      O save me from the snares of hell,
      Thou quickener of the dead.

                    3
      And if I tempted am to sin,
      And outward things are strong,
      Do thou, O Lord, keep watch within,
      And save my soul from wrong.

                    4
mf Still let me ever watch and pray,
      And feel that I am frail;
      That if the tempter cross my way,
      Yet he may not prevail.

                              I. WILLIAMS

General

He that is down needs fear no fall,
  He that is low no pride;
He that is humble ever shall
  Have God to be his guide.

2
I am content with what I have,
  Little be it or much;
And, Lord, contentment still I crave,
  Because thou savest such.

3
Fullness to such a burden is
  That go on pilgrimage;
Here little, and hereafter bliss,
  Is best from age to age.

JOHN BUNYAN

HYMN **302** Totteridge — 6 6 8 4 Sir S. H. Nicholson, 1875–1947

Rise in the strength of God,
And face life's uphill way:
The steps which other feet have trod
You tread to-day.

2
Press onward, upward still,
To win your way at last,
With better hope and stronger will
Than in the past:

3
Life's work more nobly wrought,
Life's race more bravely run,
Life's daily conflict faced and fought,
Life's duty done.

ADA R. GREENAWAY

HYMN **303**   St. Ethelwald — S.M.   W. H. Monk, 1823–89

Soldiers of Christ, arise,
And put your armour on,   [plies,
Strong in the strength which God sup-
Through his eternal Son;

2
Strong in the Lord of Hosts,
And in his mighty power:
Who in the strength of Jesus trusts
Is more than conqueror.

3
Stand then in his great might,
With all his strength endued;
And take, to arm you for the fight,
The panoply of God.

4
From strength to strength go on,
Wrestle and fight and pray;
Tread all the powers of darkness down,
And win the well-fought day;

5
That, having all things done,
And all your conflicts past,
Ye may o'ercome, through Christ alone,
And stand entire at last.

C. WESLEY

Hymn 304　　　　　　FIRST TUNE

Duke Street — L.M.　　　　　Attributed to J. Hatton, *d.* 1793

SECOND TUNE

Pentecost — L.M.　　　　　W. Boyd, 1847–1928

f   Fight the good fight with all thy might!
Christ is thy strength, and Christ thy right;
Lay hold on life, and it shall be⌣
Thy joy and crown eternally.

2

Run the straight race through God's good grace,
Lift up thine eyes, and seek his face;
Life with its way before us lies;
Christ is the path, and Christ the prize.

3

mf   Cast care aside, lean on thy guide;
His boundless mercy will provide;
Trust, and thy trusting soul shall prove
Christ is its life, and Christ its love.

4

f   Faint not nor fear, his arms are near;
He changeth not, and thou art dear;
Only believe, and thou shalt see
That Christ is all in all to thee.

J. S. B. Monsell†

HYMN **305**   Crucis milites — 7 7 7 7   M. B. Foster, 1851–1922

f Soldiers of the Cross, arise!
　　Gird you with your armour bright:
　　Mighty are your enemies,
　　Hard the battle ye must fight.

2

mf O'er a faithless fallen world
　　Raise your banner in the sky;
　　Let it float there wide unfurled;
　　Bear it onward, lift it high.

3

　　'Mid the homes of want and woe,
　　Strangers to the living word,
f Let the Saviour's herald go,
　　Let the voice of hope be heard.

4

mf Where the shadows deepest lie,
　　Carry truth's unsullied ray;
　　Where are crimes of blackest dye,
　　There the saving sign display.

5

p To the weary and the worn
　　Tell of realms where sorrows cease;
　　To the outcast and forlorn
　　Speak of mercy and of peace.

6

mf Guard the helpless, seek the strayed;
　　Comfort troubles, banish grief;
　　In the might of God arrayed,
　　Scatter sin and unbelief.

7

f Be the banner still unfurled,
　　Still unsheathed the Spirit's sword,
　　Till the kingdoms of the world
　　Are the Kingdom of the Lord.

BISHOP W. WALSHAM HOW

General

5
Though few and small and weak your
   bands,
   Strong in your Captain's strength,
Go to the conquest of all lands :
   All must be his at length.

f Lift up your heads, ye gates of brass;
   Ye bars of iron, yield!
And let the King of Glory pass :
   The Cross is in the field.

2
That banner, brighter than the star
   That leads the train of night,
Shines on the march, and guides from
      far
   His servants to the fight.

6
The spoils at his victorious feet
   You shall rejoice to lay,
And lay yourselves as trophies meet,
   In his great judgement day.

3
mf A holy war those servants wage :
   In that mysterious strife
The powers of heaven and hell en-
      gage,
   For more than death or life.

7
f Then fear not, faint not, halt not
      now;
   In Jesus' name be strong!
To him shall all the nations bow,
   And sing the triumph song :

4
Ye armies of the living God,
   Sworn warriors of Christ's host,
Where hallowed footsteps never trod
   Take your appointed post.

8
Uplifted are the gates of brass,
   The bars of iron yield;
Behold the King of Glory pass :
   The Cross hath won the field!

J. MONTGOMERY†

411

HYMN **307**

Golden Grove — 7 6 7 6. D

Greville Cooke

Morning Light — 7 6 7 6. D

G. J. Webb, 1803–87

Stand up, stand up for Jesus,
 Ye soldiers of the Cross!
Lift high his royal banner,
 It must not suffer loss.
From victory unto victory
 His army he shall lead,
Till every foe is vanquished,
 And Christ is Lord indeed.

2*

f Stand up, stand up for Jesus!
 The solemn watchword hear;
If while ye sleep he suffers,
 Away with shame and fear.
Where'er ye meet with evil,
 Within you or without,
Charge for the God of battles,
 And put the foe to rout.

3

f Stand up, stand up for Jesus!
 The trumpet call obey;
Forth to the mighty conflict
 In this his glorious day.

Ye that are men now serve him
 Against unnumbered foes;
Let courage rise with danger
 And strength to strength oppose.

4

Stand up, stand up for Jesus!
 Stand in his strength alone;
The arm of flesh will fail you,
 Ye dare not trust your own.
f Put on the Gospel armour,
 Each piece put on with prayer;
When duty calls or danger
 Be never wanting there.

5

mf Stand up, stand up for Jesus!
 The strife will not be long;
This day the noise of battle,
 The next the victor's song.
f To him that overcometh
 A crown of life shall be;
He with the King of Glory
 Shall reign eternally.

G. DUFFIELD

413

HYMN **308**   FIRST TUNE

Sentinel — 7 7 7 3   Greville Cooke

SECOND TUNE

Vigilate — 7 7 7 3   W. H. Monk, 1823–8

mf 'Christian, seek not yet repose,'
    Hear thy guardian angel say;
   'Thou art in the midst of foes:
      Watch and pray!'

2
Principalities and powers,
    Mustering their unseen array,
Wait for thine unguarded hours:
      Watch and pray!

3
f Gird thy heavenly armour on,
    Wear it ever night and day;
   Ambushed lurks the evil one:
      Watch and pray!

4
Hear the victors who o'ercame;
    Still they mark each warrior's wa
All with one sweet voice exclaim:
      'Watch and pray!'

5

mf Hear, above all, hear thy Lord,
Him thou lovest to obey;
Hide within thy heart his word:
'Watch and pray!'

6

Watch, as if on that alone
Hung the issue of the day;
Pray, that help may be sent down:
Watch and pray!

CHARLOTTE ELLIOTT

HYMN **309**   Old Martyrs — C.M.   *Psalms* (Edinburgh, 1615)

nf O God of truth, whose living word
Upholds whate'er hath breath,
Look down on thy creation, Lord,
Enslaved by sin and death.

2

Set up thy standard, Lord, that we
Who claim a heavenly birth
May march with thee to smite the
lies
That vex thy ransomed earth.

3

f Ah, would we join that blest array,
And follow in the might
Of him, the Faithful and the True,
In raiment clean and white?

4

We fight for truth? we fight for God?
Poor slaves of lies and sin!
He who would fight for thee on earth
Must first be true within.

5

f Then, God of truth, for whom we
long,
Thou who wilt hear our prayer,
Do thine own battle in our hearts,
And slay the falsehood there.

6

Yea, come! Then, tried as in the fire,
From every lie set free,
Thy perfect truth shall dwell in us,
And we shall live in thee.

T. HUGHES

HYMN **310**   Doncaster — S.M.   S. Wesley, 1766–1837

> *f*   Put thou thy trust in God,
>   In duty's path go on;
>   Walk in his strength with faith and hope,
>   So shall thy work be done.

> 2
> *mf*   Commit thy ways to him,
>   Thy works into his hands,
>   And rest on his unchanging word,
>   Who heaven and earth commands.

> 3
>   Though years on years roll on,
>   His covenant shall endure;
> *f*   Though clouds and darkness hide his path,
>   The promised grace is sure.

> 4
> *mf*   Give to the winds thy fears;
>   Hope, and be undismayed:
>   God hears thy sighs and counts thy tears;
> *f*   God shall lift up thy head.

> 5
> *mf*   Through waves and clouds and storms
>   His power will clear thy way:
> *f*   Wait thou his time; the darkest night
>   Shall end in brightest day.

> 6
> *mf*   Leave to his sovereign sway
>   To choose and to command;
>   So shalt thou, wondering, own his way,
>   How wise, how strong his hand.

J. WESLEY and others
Cento from *Befiehl du deine Wege*, P. Gerha

HYMN **311** Mannheim — 8 7. 8 7. 8 7   F. Filitz, 1804–76

mf Lead us, heavenly Father, lead us
    O'er the world's tempestuous sea;
    Guard us, guide us, keep us, feed us,
    For we have no help but thee;
    Yet possessing every blessing,
    If our God our Father be.

2

p Saviour, breathe forgiveness o'er us:
    All our weakness thou dost know;
    Thou didst tread this earth before us,
    Thou didst feel its keenest woe;
    Lone and dreary, faint and weary,
    Through the desert thou didst go.

3

mf Spirit of our God, descending,
    Fill our hearts with heavenly joy,
    Love with every passion blending,
    Pleasure that can never cloy:
    Thus provided, pardoned, guided,
    Nothing can our peace destroy.

J. EDMESTON

HYMN **312** Tempest — 6 4 6 4. D   J. B. König, 1691–1758

By permission of Schott & Co., Ltd.

ζοφερᾶς τρικυμίας

f Fierce was the wild billow,
    Dark was the night;
Oars laboured heavily,
    Foam glimmered white;
Trembled the mariners,
    Peril was nigh:
Then said the God of God,
p   'Peace! It is I.'

2
f Ridge of the mountain-wave,
    Lower thy crest!
Wail of the hurricane,
    Be thou at rest!
Sorrow can never be,
    Darkness must fly,
Where saith the Light of Light,
p   'Peace! It is I.'

3
mf Jesus, deliverer,
    Nigh to us be;
Soothe thou my voyaging
    Over life's sea:
f Thou, when the storm of death ⏝
    Roars, sweeping by,
p Whisper, O Truth of Truth,
    'Peace! It is I.'

ST. ANATOLIUS *Tr.* J. M. Neale†

418

HYMN **313**   St. Aëlred — 8 8 8 3   J. B. Dykes, 1823–76

mf   Fierce raged the tempest o'er the deep,
      Watch did thine anxious servants keep,
p   But thou wast wrapped in guileless sleep,
                        Calm and still.

2

mf   'Save, Lord, we perish,' was their cry,
      'O save us in our agony!'
      Thy word above the storm rose high,
                        'Peace, be still.'

3

      The wild winds hushed; the angry deep⌣
      Sank, like a little child, to sleep;
      The sullen billows ceased to leap,
                        At thy will.

4

      So, when our life is clouded o'er,
      And storm-winds drift us from the shore,
      Say, lest we sink to rise no more,
          p   'Peace, be still.'

                        G. THRING

General

A lower setting of this tune will be found at Hymn 299

Psalm 42

mf   As pants the hart for cooling streams
     When heated in the chase,
     So longs my soul, O God, for thee,
     And thy refreshing grace.

2

For thee, my God, the living God,
     My thirsty soul doth pine :
O when shall I behold thy face,
     Thou majesty divine?

3

p   Why restless, why cast down, my soul?
f   Hope still, and thou shalt sing⌣
The praise of him who is thy God,
     Thy health's eternal spring.

4

To Father, Son, and Holy Ghost,
     The God whom we adore,
Be glory, as it was, is now,
     And shall be evermore.

N. Tate and N. Brady
(*New Version*)

420

General

2

f Up to the throne on high,
   In loyal love and trust,
 We, children of an hour,
 Lift voices from the dust.

mf Suffer us not to stray
   From thee, our God, our guide,
 Whatever trials come,
 Whatever ills betide.

3

Grant us in mercy, Lord,
  The gifts thou deemest best,
Help for the daily task,
And for our spirits rest.

4

f Strong in the power of faith,
   From doubt and care set free,
 We tread the appointed path
 That brings us home to thee.

5

Bid empty terror cease;
  Neath thy o'ershadowing might
Uphold our hearts in hope,
And lead us into light.

E. H. BLAKENEY

Alternative Tune, Eden, 327

HYMN **316**   Chapel Royal — 8 8 6. 8 8 6   W. Boyce, 1710–79

Supreme motor cordium

mf Great mover of all hearts, whose hand‿
 Doth all the secret springs command
  Of human thought and will,
 Thou, since the world was made, dost bless‿
 Thy saints with fruits of holiness,
  Their order to fulfil.

2

 Faith, hope, and love here weave one chain;
 But love alone shall then remain
  When this short day is gone :
f O Love, O Truth, O endless Light,
 When shall we see thy sabbath bright
  With all our labours done?

3

p We sow 'mid perils here and tears ;
 There the glad hand the harvest bears,
  Which here in grief hath sown :
mf Great Three in One, the increase give ;
 Thy gifts of grace, by which we live,
  With heavenly glory crown.

C. COFFIN *Tr.* I. Williams

HYMN **317**   St. Hugh — C.M.   E. J. Hopkins, 1818–1901

Lord, teach us how to pray aright
    With reverence and with fear;
Though dust and ashes in thy sight,
    We may, we must, draw near.

2
We perish if we cease from prayer :
    O grant us power to pray;
And, when to meet thee we prepare,
    Lord, meet us by the way.

3
God of all grace, we bring to thee
    A broken, contrite heart;
Give what thine eye delights to see,
    Truth in the inward part;

4
Faith in the only Sacrifice
    That can for sin atone,
To cast our hopes, to fix our eyes,
    On Christ, on Christ alone;

5
Patience to watch and wait and weep,
    Though mercy long delay;
Courage our fainting souls to keep,
    And trust thee though thou slay.

6
Give these, and then thy will be done;
    Thus, strengthened with all might,
We, through thy Spirit and thy Son,
    Shall pray, and pray aright.

                    J. MONTGOMERY†

General

HYMN **318** St. Etheldreda — C.M.   Bishop T. Turton, 1780–1864

mf Shepherd divine, our wants relieve
    In this our evil day;
  To all thy tempted followers give
    The power to watch and pray.

2
Long as our fiery trials last,
    Long as the cross we bear,
O let our souls on thee be cast
    In never-ceasing prayer.

3
The Spirit's interceding grace
    Give us in faith to claim;
To wrestle till we see thy face,
    And know thy hidden Name.

4
Till thou thy perfect love impart,
    Till thou thyself bestow,
Be this the cry of every heart,
    'I will not let thee go.'

5
I will not let thee go, unless
    Thou tell thy Name to me;
With all thy great salvation bless,
    And make me all like thee.

6
f Then let me on the mountain-top
    Behold thy open face;
Where faith in sight is swallowed up,
    And prayer in endless praise.

C. WESLEY†

NOTE. *The latter part of this hymn makes reference to Jacob's encounter with the angel* (*Gen.* 32. 24–30)

HYMN **319**   FIRST TUNE

Song 13 — 7 7 7 7   Orlando Gibbons, 1583–1625

General

SECOND TUNE

£ast Peckham — 7 7 7 7   G. C. E. Ryley, 1866–1947

UNISON

By permission of the Royal School of Church Music

mf Come, my soul, thy suit prepare:
Jesus loves to answer prayer;
He himself has bid thee pray,
Therefore will not say thee nay.

2

Thou art coming to a King:
Large petitions with thee bring;
For his grace and power are such
None can ever ask too much.

3

p With my burden I begin:
Lord, remove this load of sin;
Let thy Blood, for sinners spilt,
Set my conscience free from guilt.

4

Lord, I come to thee for rest;
Take possession of my breast;
There thy blood-bought right main-
And without a rival reign.   [tain,

5

mf While I am a pilgrim here,
Let thy love my spirit cheer;
Be my guide, my guard, my friend,
Lead me to my journey's end.

J. NEWTON†

425

HYMN **320**   Bedford — C.M.   W. Wheale, 1690–1727

O help us, Lord! each hour of need
   Thy heavenly succour give;
Help us in thought and word and deed
   Each hour on earth we live.

2
O help us, when our spirits bleed
   With contrite anguish sore;
And when our hearts are cold and dead,
   O help us, Lord, the more.

3
O help us, through the prayer of faith
   More firmly to believe;
For still the more the servant hath,
   The more shall he receive.

4
O help us, Jesu, from on high;
   We know no help but thee:
O help us so to live and die
   As thine in heaven to be.

H. H. MILMAN

Alternative Tune, Nun danket all, 347

HYMN **321**   St. Raphael — 8 7. 8 7. 4 7   E. J. Hopkins, 1818–1901

mf Jesus, Lord of life and glory,
  Bend from heaven thy gracious ear;
While our waiting souls adore thee,
  Friend of helpless sinners, hear :
    By thy mercy,
    O deliver us, good Lord.

2

mf From the depths of nature's blindness,
  From the hardening power of sin,
From all malice and unkindness,
  From the pride that lurks within :
    By thy mercy,
    O deliver us, good Lord.

3

When temptation sorely presses,
  In the day of Satan's power,
In our times of deep distresses,
  In each dark and trying hour :
    By thy mercy,
    O deliver us, good Lord.

4

mf When the world around is smiling,
  In the time of wealth and ease,
Earthly joys our hearts beguiling,
  In the day of health and peace :
p   By thy mercy,
    O deliver us, good Lord.

5

In the weary hours of sickness,
  In the times of grief and pain,
When we feel our mortal weakness,
  When all human help is vain :
    By thy mercy,
    O deliver us, good Lord.

6

In the solemn hour of dying,
  In the aweful judgement day,
mf May our souls, on thee relying,
  Find thee still our Rock and stay :
p   By thy mercy,
    O deliver us, good Lord.

J. J. CUMMINS†

HYMN **322**   St. Bride — S.M.   S. Howard, 1710–82

Psalm 130

p   Out of the deep I call
      To thee, O Lord, to thee;
      Before thy throne of grace I fall:
      Be merciful to me.

2

Out of the deep I cry,
The woeful deep of sin,
Of evil done in days gone by,
Of evil now within.

3

Out of the deep of fear,
And dread of coming shame,
From morning watch till night is near
I plead the precious name.

4

mf   Lord, there is mercy now,
       As ever was, with thee;
       Before thy throne of grace I bow:
p   Be merciful to me.

SIR H. W. BAKER

Hymn **323**   Derry — 8 8 8 6   J. B. Dykes, 1823-76

Forsaken once, and thrice denied,
The risen Lord gave pardon free,
Stood once again at Peter's side,
   And asked him, 'Lov'st thou me?'

2
How many times with faithless word
Have we denied his holy name,
How oft forsaken our dear Lord,
   And shrunk when trial came!

3
Saint Peter, when the cock crew clear,
Went out, and wept his broken faith:
Strong as a rock through strife and fear,
   He served his Lord till death.

4
How oft his cowardice of heart
We have without his love sincere,
The sin without the sorrow's smart,
   The shame without the tear!

5
O oft forsaken, oft denied,
Forgive our shame, wash out our sin;
Look on us from thy Father's side
   And let that sweet look win.

6
Hear when we call thee from the deep,
Still walk beside us on the shore,
Give hands to work, and eyes to weep,
   And hearts to love thee more.

Mrs. C. F. Alexander

General

Remission — 6 6. 6 6. 6 6   L. J. Blake

SECOND TUNE

Waltham — 6 6. 6 6. 6 6   W. H. Monk, 1823–8

p Not for our sins alone
   Thy mercy, Lord, we sue;
Let fall thy pitying glance
   On our devotions too,
What we have done for thee,
   And what we think to do.

2

mf The holiest hours we spend
   In prayer upon our knees,
The times when most we deem
   Our songs of praise will please,
Thou searcher of all hearts,
p   Forgiveness pour on these.

3

mf And all the gifts we bring,
   And all the vows we make,
And all the acts of love
   We plan for thy dear sake,
p Into thy pardoning thought,
   O God of mercy, take.

4

mf And most, when we, thy flock,
   Before thine altar bend,
And strange, bewildering thoughts
   With those sweet moments blend,
p By him whose Death we plead,
   Good Lord, thy help extend.

5

mf Bow down thine ear and hear!
   Open thine eyes and see!
Our very love is shame,
   And we must come to thee
To make it of thy grace
   What thou wouldst have it be.

                                    H. TWELLS

431

General

FIRST TUNE

Song 67 — C.M.

Melody from E. Prys, *Psalms*, 1621
Bass by Orlando Gibbons, 1583–1625

A lower setting of this tune will be found at Hymn 571

SECOND TUNE

Stockton — C.M.

T. Wright, 1763–1829

O for a heart to praise my God,
  A heart from sin set free;
A heart that's sprinkled with the Blood
  So freely shed for me:

2
A heart resigned, submissive, meek,
  My great Redeemer's throne;
Where only Christ is heard to speak,
  Where Jesus reigns alone:

3
A humble, lowly, contrite heart,
  Believing, true, and clean,
Which neither life nor death can part
  From him that dwells within:

4
A heart in every thought renewed,
  And full of love divine;
Perfect and right and pure and good—
  A copy, Lord, of thine!

432

5

Thy nature, gracious Lord, impart,
Come quickly from above;
Write thy new name upon my heart,
Thy new best name of Love.

C. Wesley†

Hymn **326**   Caithness — C.M.   *Scottish Psalter,* 1635

By permission of the English Hymnal Company, Ltd.

O for a closer walk with God,
A calm and heavenly frame;
A light to shine upon the road
That leads me to the Lamb!

2

What peaceful hours I once enjoyed!
How sweet their memory still!
But they have left an aching void
The world can never fill.

3

Return, O holy Dove, return,
Sweet messenger of rest:
I hate the sins that made thee mourn,
And drove thee from my breast.

4

The dearest idol I have known,
Whate'er that idol be,
Help me to tear it from thy throne,
And worship only thee.

5

So shall my walk be close with God,
Calm and serene my frame;
So purer light shall mark the road
That leads me to the Lamb.

W. Cowper

HYMN **327** Eden — 6 6 6 6   O. M. Feilden, 1837–1924

Lord, be thy word my rule,
    In it may I rejoice;
Thy glory be my aim,
    Thy holy will my choice;

2
Thy promises my hope,
    Thy providence my guard,
Thine arm my strong support,
    Thyself my great reward.

BISHOP CHR. WORDSWORTH

HYMN **328**   Galway — S.M.   E. Miller, 1731-1807

A charge to keep I have,
A God to glorify,
A never-dying soul to save,
And fit it for the sky.

2
To serve the present age,
My calling to fulfil,
O may it all my powers engage
To do my Master's will.

3
Arm me with jealous care,
As in thy sight to live;
And O, thy servant, Lord, prepare
A good account to give.

4
Help me to watch and pray,
And on thyself rely;
And let me ne'er my trust betray,
But press to realms on high.

C. WESLEY

HYMN **329** FIRST TUNE

Hereford — L.M. S. S. Wesley, 1810–76

SECOND TUNE

St. Gregory — L.M. *Darmstadt Gesangbuch,* 169

A higher setting of this tune will be found at Hymn 83

O thou who camest from above
  The fire celestial to impart,
Kindle a flame of sacred love
  On the mean altar of my heart.

2

There let it for thy glory burn
  With inextinguishable blaze,
And trembling to its source return
  In humble prayer and fervent praise.

3

Jesus, confirm my heart's desire
  To work and speak and think for thee;
Still let me guard the holy fire
  And still stir up the gift in me.

4

Still let me prove thy perfect will,
  My acts of faith and love repeat;
Till death thy endless mercies seal,
  And make the sacrifice complete.

C. WESLEY†

HYMN **330** Newington — 7 7 7 7 Archbishop W. D. Maclagan, 1826–1910

Thine for ever! God of love,
Hear us from thy throne above;
Thine for ever may we be
Here and in eternity.

2

Thine for ever! Lord of life,
Shield us through our earthly strife;
Thou the Life, the Truth, the Way,
Guide us to the realms of day.

3

Thine for ever! O how blest
They who find in thee their rest!
Saviour, guardian, heavenly friend,
O defend us to the end.

4*

Thine for ever! Shepherd, keep
Us thy frail and trembling sheep;
Safe alone beneath thy care,
Let us all thy goodness share.

5

Thine for ever! thou our guide,
All our wants by thee supplied,
All our sins by thee forgiven,
Lead us, Lord, from earth to heaven.

MRS. M. F. MAUDE

HYMN **331**   Wolvercote — 7 6 7 6. D   W. H. Ferguson, 1872–1950

General

O Jesus, I have promised
　To serve thee to the end;
Be thou for ever near me,
　My Master and my Friend;
I shall not fear the battle
　If thou art by my side,
Nor wander from the pathway
　If thou wilt be my guide.

2*

O let me feel thee near me:
　The world is ever near;
I see the sights that dazzle,
　The tempting sounds I hear;
My foes are ever near me,
　Around me and within;
But, Jesus, draw thou nearer,
　And shield my soul from sin.

3

O let me hear thee speaking
　In accents clear and still,
Above the storms of passion,
　The murmurs of self-will;
O speak to reassure me,
　To hasten or control;
O speak, and make me listen,
　Thou guardian of my soul.

4

O Jesus, thou hast promised
　To all who follow thee,
That where thou art in glory
　There shall thy servant be;
And, Jesus, I have promised
　To serve thee to the end:
O give me grace to follow,
　My Master and my Friend.

5

O let me see thy foot-marks,
　And in them plant mine own;
My hope to follow duly
　Is in thy strength alone:
O guide me, call me, draw me,
　Uphold me to the end;
And then in heaven receive me,
　My Saviour and my Friend.

J. E. BODE

Alternative Tune, Thornbury, 256

General

FIRST TUNE

Poplar — Irregular

Bishop T. B. Strong, 1861–1944

1 God be in my head, And in my un - der - stand - ing;

2 God be in my eyes, And in my look ing;

3 God be in my mouth, And in my speak - ing;

4 God be in my heart, And in my think - ing;

5 God be at my end, And at my de - part - ing.

By permission of the Oxford University Press

Pynson's *Horae,* 1514

General

Lytlington — Irregular   Sir S. H. Nicholson, 1875–1947

1 God be in my head, And in my un - der - stand - ing;

2 God be in my eyes, And in my look - ing;

3 God be in my mouth, And in my speak - ing;

4 God be in my heart, And in my think - ing;

5 God be at my end, And at my de - part - ing.

By permission of the Royal School of Church Music

Pynson's *Horae*, 1514

441

HYMN **333** Breslau — L.M.   *Geistliche Gesänge* (Leipzig, 1625)

A lower setting of this tune will be found at Hymn 460

Take up thy cross, the Saviour said,
If thou wouldst my disciple be;
Deny thyself, the world forsake,
And humbly follow after me.

2
Take up thy cross! let not its weight
Fill thy weak spirit with alarm:
His strength shall bear thy spirit up,
And brace thy heart, and nerve thine arm.

3
Take up thy cross, nor heed the shame,
Nor let thy foolish pride rebel:
Thy Lord for thee the Cross endured,
To save thy soul from death and hell.

4
Take up thy cross then in his strength,
And calmly every danger brave;
'Twill guide thee to a better home,
And lead to victory o'er the grave.

5
Take up thy cross, and follow Christ,
Nor think till death to lay it down;
For only he who bears the cross
May hope to wear the glorious crown.

6
To thee, great Lord, the One in Three,
All praise for evermore ascend:
O grant us in our home to see
The heavenly life that knows no end.

C. W. EVEREST‡

HYMN **334**   FIRST TUNE

Windsor — C.M.   W. Damon, *Psalms*, 1591

Lord, as to thy dear Cross we flee,
    And plead to be forgiven,
So let thy life our pattern be,
    And form our souls for heaven.

2

Help us, through good report and ill,
    Our daily cross to bear;
Like thee, to do our Father's will,
    Our brethren's griefs to share.

3

Let grace our selfishness expel,
    Our earthliness refine,
And kindness in our bosoms dwell
    As free and true as thine.

4

If joy shall at thy bidding fly,
    And grief's dark day come on,
We in our turn would meekly cry,
    'Father, thy will be done.'

5

Kept peaceful in the midst of strife,
    Forgiving and forgiven,
O may we lead the pilgrim's life,
    And follow thee to heaven.

                    J. H. GURNEY

HYMN **334**   SECOND TUNE

Westminster New — C.M.   J. Nares, 1715–83

Lord, as to thy dear Cross we flee,
And plead to be forgiven,
So let thy life our pattern be,
And form our souls for heaven.

2
Help us, through good report and ill,
Our daily cross to bear;
Like thee, to do our Father's will,
Our brethren's griefs to share.

3
Let grace our selfishness expel,
Our earthliness refine,
And kindness in our bosoms dwell
As free and true as thine.

4
If joy shall at thy bidding fly,
And grief's dark day come on,
We in our turn would meekly cry,
'Father, thy will be done.'

5
Kept peaceful in the midst of strife,
Forgiving and forgiven,
O may we lead the pilgrim's life,
And follow thee to heaven.

J. H. GURNEY

HYMN **335**   Franconia — S.M.   *Harmonischer Liederschatz,* 1738

Blest are the pure in heart,
For they shall see our God;
The secret of the Lord is theirs,
Their soul is Christ's abode.

2

The Lord, who left the heavens
Our life and peace to bring,
To dwell in lowliness with men,
Their pattern and their King;

3

Still to the lowly soul
He doth himself impart,
And for his dwelling and his throne
Chooseth the pure in heart.

4

Lord, we thy presence seek;
May ours this blessing be;
Give us a pure and lowly heart,
A temple meet for thee.

J. KEBLE and others

445

HYMN 336   Song 34 — L.M.   Orlando Gibbons, 1583–1625

Forth in thy name, O Lord, I go,
   My daily labour to pursue;
Thee, only thee, resolved to know,
   In all I think or speak or do.

2
The task thy wisdom hath assigned
   O let me cheerfully fulfil;
In all my works thy presence find,
   And prove thy good and perfect will.

3
Thee may I set at my right hand,
   Whose eyes my inmost substance see,
And labour on at thy command,
   And offer all my works to thee.

4
Give me to bear thy easy yoke,
   And every moment watch and pray,
And still to things eternal look,
   And hasten to thy glorious day;

5
For thee delightfully employ
   Whate'er thy bounteous grace hath given,
And run my course with even joy,
   And closely walk with thee to heaven.

C. WESLEY†

446

HYMN **337** Sandys — S.M.   Sandys' *Christmas Carols*, 1833

Teach me, my God and King,
In all things thee to see;
And what I do in anything
To do it as for thee.

2
A man that looks on glass,
On it may stay his eye;
Or, if he pleaseth, through it pass,
And then the heaven espy.

3
All may of thee partake;
Nothing can be so mean
Which, with this tincture, *For thy sake*,
Will not grow bright and clean.

4
A servant with this clause
Makes drudgery divine;
Who sweeps a room, as for thy laws,
Makes that and the action fine.

5
This is the famous stone
That turneth all to gold;
For that which God doth touch and own
Cannot for less be told.

GEORGE HERBERT

447

HYMN **338**   Holyrood — S.M.   J. Watson, 1816–80

mf Fair waved the golden corn
  In Canaan's pleasant land,
  When full of joy, some shining morn,
  Went forth the reaper-band.

2

f To God so good and great
  Their cheerful thanks they pour;
  Then carry to his Temple-gate
  The choicest of their store.

3

mf Like Israel, Lord, we give‿
  Our earliest fruits to thee,
  And pray that, long as we shall live,
  We may thy children be.

4

  Thine is our youthful prime,
  And life and all its powers:
  Be with us in our morning time,
  And bless our evening hours.

5

  In wisdom let us grow,
  As years and strength are given,
f That we may serve thy Church below,
  And join thy saints in heaven.

J. H. GURNEY

Alternative Tune, St. Helena, 531

HYMN **339**   Qui laborat orat — 4 10 10. 10 4   Sir H. P. Allen, 1869–1946

Come, labour on!
Who dares stand idle on the harvest plain,
While all around him waves the golden grain?
And to each servant does the Master say,
    'Go, work to-day!'

2
Come, labour on!
Away with gloomy doubts and faithless fear!
No arm so weak but may do service here;
By feeblest agents can our God fulfil
    His righteous will.

3
Come, labour on!
No time for rest, till glows the western sky,
Till the long shadows o'er our pathway lie,
And a glad sound comes with the setting sun,
    'Servants, well done!'

4
Come, labour on!
The toil is pleasant, the reward is sure;
Blessèd are those who to the end endure:
How full their joy, how deep their rest, shall be,
    O Lord, with thee!

JANE L. BORTHWICK

HYMN **340**   Hamburg — 7 6 8 6. D   J. W. Franck, *c.* 1641–88

O God, before whose altar
   The stars like tapers burn,
At whose inscrutable decree
   The planets wheel and turn,
Though earth and sea and heaven
   Unite thy praise to sing,
Man in his weakness yet may give
   A worthier offering.

2

Those who give up life's bounty
   To serve a race to be,
Whose bones lie white along the trail
   Which leads the world to thee;
Those who when fears beset them
   Stand fast and fight and die,
Their unconsidered lives go up
   Like incense to the sky.

3

All those oppressed or lonely
   Or long at strife with pain,
Who face the darkness undismayed
   And turn their loss to gain,
Those who with love and meekness
   Outlast the years of wrong,
Their silent courage pleads to heaven
   More eloquent than song.

4

O Lord, be ours the glory
   Beyond all earthly fame,
Like those to conquer for thy sake
   Despair and doubt and shame;
Till through a world made noble,
   Through lands from sin set free,
The armies of the living God
   Shall march to victory

P. H. B. LYON

HYMN **341**   Magda — 10 10 10 10   R. Vaughan Williams

By permission of the Oxford University Press

'Lift up your hearts!' We lift them, Lord, to thee;
Here at thy feet none other may we see :
'Lift up your hearts!' E'en so, with one accord,
We lift them up, we lift them to the Lord.

2

Above the level of the former years,
The mire of sin, the slough of guilty fears,
The mist of doubt, the blight of love's decay,
O Lord of Light, lift all our hearts to-day!

3*

Above the swamps of subterfuge and shame,
The deeds, the thoughts, that honour may not name,
The halting tongue that dares not tell the whole,
O Lord of Truth, lift every Christian soul!

4

Lift every gift that thou thyself hast given :
Low lies the best till lifted up to heaven;
Low lie the bounding heart, the teeming brain,
Till, sent from God, they mount to God again.

5
Then, as the trumpet-call in after years,
'Lift up your hearts !' rings pealing in our ears,
Still shall those hearts respond with full accord,
'We lift them up, we lift them to the Lord !'

H. MONTAGU BUTLER

HYMNS OF PERSONAL DEVOTION

HYMN **342**   Cheshire — C.M.   Este, *Psalms,* 1592

Lord, it belongs not to my care
  Whether I die or live:
To love and serve thee is my share,
  And this thy grace must give.

2
Christ leads me through no darker rooms
  Than he went through before;
He that unto God's Kingdom comes
  Must enter by this door.

3
Come, Lord, when grace hath made me
  Thy blessèd face to see;   [meet
For if thy work on earth be sweet,
  What will thy glory be !

4
Then I shall end my sad complaints
  And weary, sinful days,
And join with the triumphant saints
  That sing my Saviour's praise.

5
My knowledge of that life is small,
  The eye of faith is dim;
But 'tis enough that Christ knows all,
  And I shall be with him.

R. BAXTER†

Alternative Tune, St. Hugh, 317

453

HYMN **343** Wrestling Jacob — 8 8. 8 8. 8 8 S. S. Wesley, 1810–76

3

mf Come, O thou Traveller unknown,
　　Whom still I hold, but cannot see;
　My company before is gone,
　　And I am left alone with thee;
　With thee all night I mean to stay,
　And wrestle till the break of day.

mf In vain thou strugglest to get free;
　　I never will unloose my hold.
　Art thou the Man that died for me?
　　The secret of thy love unfold:
　Wrestling, I will not let thee go,
　Till I thy Name, thy nature know.

2

p I need not tell thee who I am,
　　My misery or sin declare;
　Thyself hast called me by my name;
　　Look on thy hands, and read it
　　　there!
　But who, I ask thee, who art thou?
　Tell me thy Name, and tell me now.

4

　Yield to me now, for I am weak,
　　But confident in self-despair;
　Speak to my heart, in blessings speak,
　　Be conquered by my instant
　　　prayer. [move
　Speak, or thou never hence shal
　And tell me if thy Name is Love?

454

General

5

f   'Tis Love! 'tis Love! thou diedst for me!
I hear thy whisper in my heart!
The morning breaks, the shadows flee;
Pure universal Love thou art;
To me, to all, thy mercies move;
Thy nature and thy Name is Love.

C. WESLEY†

NOTE. *This hymn is based on the story of Jacob's encounter with the angel in Gen.* 32. 24–30

Alternative Tune, Emmaus, 585

HYMN **344**   FIRST TUNE

Tunbridge — 7 7 7 7   J. Clarke, *c.* 1659–1707

mf Hark, my soul! it is the Lord;
'Tis thy Saviour, hear his word;
Jesus speaks, and speaks to thee,
p 'Say, poor sinner, lov'st thou me?

2

mf 'I delivered thee when bound,
And, when wounded, healed thy wound;
Sought thee wandering, set thee right,
Turned thy darkness into light.

3

'Can a woman's tender care
Cease towards the child she bare?
Yes, she may forgetful be,
Yet will I remember thee.

4

f   'Mine is an unchanging love,
Higher than the heights above,
Deeper than the depths beneath,
Free and faithful, strong as death.

5

'Thou shalt see my glory soon,
When the work of grace is done;
Partner of my throne shalt be:
p Say, poor sinner, lov'st thou me?'

6

mf Lord, it is my chief complaint
That my love is weak and faint;
f Yet I love thee, and adore;
O for grace to love thee more!

W. COWPER

HYMN **344**   SECOND TUNE

St. Bees — 7 7 7 7   J. B. Dykes, 1823-76

3

mf Hark, my soul! it is the Lord;
  'Tis thy Saviour, hear his word;
  Jesus speaks, and speaks to thee,
p 'Say, poor sinner, lov'st thou me?

'Can a woman's tender care
Cease towards the child she bare?
Yes, she may forgetful be,
Yet will I remember thee.

2

mf 'I delivered thee when bound,
  And, when wounded, healed thy
    wound;
  Sought thee wandering, set thee right,
  Turned thy darkness into light.

4

f 'Mine is an unchanging love,
Higher than the heights above,
Deeper than the depths beneath,
Free and faithful, strong as death.

5

  'Thou shalt see my glory soon,
  When the work of grace is done;
  Partner of my throne shalt be:
p Say, poor sinner, lov'st thou me?'

6

mf Lord, it is my chief complaint
  That my love is weak and faint;
f Yet I love thee, and adore;
  O for grace to love thee more!

W. COWPER

HYMN 345 Bangor — C.M.   W. Tans'ur, *Harmony of Zion*, 1735

mf Approach, my soul, the mercy-seat,
Where Jesus answers prayer;
There humbly fall before his feet,
For none can perish there.

2
p Thy promise is my only plea,
With this I venture nigh:
Thou callest burdened souls to thee,
And such, O Lord, am I.

3
Bowed down beneath a load of sin,
By Satan sorely pressed,
By war without and fears within,
I come to thee for rest.

4
Be thou my shield and hiding-place,
That, sheltered near thy side,
I may my fierce accuser face,
And tell him thou hast died.

5
mf O wondrous love, to bleed and die,
To bear the Cross and shame,
That guilty sinners, such as I,
Might plead thy gracious name!

J. NEWTON

Alternative Tune, Bedford, 320

457

HYMN **346**   Nearer Home — D.S.M.   I. B. Woodbury, 1819–58
(arranged by Sir A. Sullivan)

VERSE 2, LINES 5 AND 6

† Ah! then my spi - rit   faints   To   reach   the   land   I   love,

·For ever with the Lord!'
   Amen; so let it be:
Life from the dead is in that word,
   'Tis immortality.
Here in the body pent,
   Absent from him I roam,
Yet nightly pitch my moving tent
   A day's march nearer home.

2
My Father's house on high,
   Home of my soul, how near
At times to faith's foreseeing eye
   Thy golden gates appear!
†Ah, then my spirit faints
   To reach the land I love,
The bright inheritance of saints,
   Jerusalem above.

3
'For ever with the Lord!'
   Father, if 'tis thy will,
The promise of that faithful word
   Even here to me fulfil.
Be thou at my right hand,
   Then can I never fail;
Uphold thou me, and I shall stand,
   Fight, and I must prevail.

4
So when my latest breath
   Shall rend the veil in twain,
By death I shall escape from death,
   And life eternal gain.
Knowing as I am known,
   How shall I love that word,
And oft repeat before the throne,
   'For ever with the Lord!'

J. MONTGOMERY

HYMN 347 Nun danket all — C.M. *Praxis pietatis melica*, 1653

Jesus, these eyes have never seen
That radiant form of thine;
The veil of sense hangs dark between
Thy blessèd face and mine.

2
I see thee not, I hear thee not,
Yet art thou oft with me;
And earth hath ne'er so dear a spot
As where I meet with thee.

3
Yet, though I have not seen, and still
Must rest in faith alone,
I love thee, dearest Lord, and will,
Unseen, but not unknown.

4
When death these mortal eyes shall seal
And still this throbbing heart,
The rending veil shall thee reveal
All glorious as thou art.

R. PALMER

p   Art thou weary, art thou languid,
        Art thou sore distrest?
 mf 'Come to me,' saith One, 'and coming
   p   Be at rest!'

               2
      Hath he marks to lead me to him,
        If he be my guide?
      'In his feet and hands are wound-prints,
           And his side.'

               3
 mf Hath he diadem as Monarch
        That his brow adorns?
   p   'Yea, a crown, in very surety,
           But of thorns.'

               4
 mf If I find him, if I follow,
        What his guerdon here?
   p   'Many a sorrow, many a labour,
           Many a tear.'

               5
 mf If I still hold closely to him,
        What hath he at last?
   f   'Sorrow vanquished, labour ended,
           Jordan past.'

               6
 mf If I ask him to receive me,
        Will he say me nay?
   f   'Not till earth, and not till heaven, .
           Pass away.'

               7
 mf Finding, following, keeping, struggling,
        Is he sure to bless?
   f   'Angels, martyrs, prophets, virgins,
           Answer, Yes!'

               J. M. NEALE†

HYMN **349**   Misericordia — 8 8 8 6   H. Smart, 1813–79

4

p Just as I am, without one plea
But that thy Blood was shed for me,
And that thou bidst me come to thee,
O Lamb of God, I come.

mf Just as I am, thou wilt receive,
Wilt welcome, pardon, cleanse, re-
    lieve :
Because thy promise I believe,
O Lamb of God, I come.

2

Just as I am, though tossed about
With many a conflict, many a doubt,
Fightings and fears within, without,
O Lamb of God, I come.

5

Just as I am (thy love unknown
Has broken every barrier down),
f Now to be thine, yea, thine alone,
O Lamb of God, I come.

3

Just as I am, poor, wretched, blind;
Sight, riches, healing of the mind,
Yea, all I need, in thee to find,
O Lamb of God, I come.

6

mf Just as I am, of that free love‿
The breadth, length, depth, an
    height to prove,
f Here for a season, then above,
O Lamb of God, I come.

CHARLOTTE ELLIOT

Alternative Tune, Saffron Walden, 120

HYMN **350**   Come unto Me — 7 6 7 6. D   J. B. Dykes, 1823–7

General

NOTE. *It is suggested that the first two lines of each verse should be sung by Tenors and Basses only, but if necessary they may be sung in octaves by all the voices*

f 'Come unto me, ye weary,
    And I will give you rest.'
O blessèd voice of Jesus,
    Which comes to hearts opprest!
It tells of benediction,
    Of pardon, grace, and peace,
Of joy that hath no ending,
    Of love which cannot cease.

2

'Come unto me, ye wanderers,
    And I will give you light.'
O loving voice of Jesus,
    Which comes to cheer the night!
Our hearts were filled with sadness,
    And we had lost our way;
But he has brought us gladness
    And songs at break of day.

3

mf 'Come unto me, ye fainting,
    And I will give you life.'
O cheering voice of Jesus,
    Which comes to aid our strife!
The foe is stern and eager,
    The fight is fierce and long;
f But he has made us mighty,
    And stronger than the strong.

4

mf 'And whosoever cometh,
    I will not cast him out.'
f O welcome voice of Jesus,
    Which drives away our doubt!
Which calls us very sinners,
    Unworthy though we be
Of love so free and boundless,
    To come, dear Lord, to thee.

W. CHATTERTON DIX

HYMN **351**   Vox dilecti — D.C.M.   J. B. Dykes, 1823–76

mf I heard the voice of Jesus say,
    'Come unto me and rest;
    Lay down, thou weary one, lay down
    Thy head upon my breast:'
 f I came to Jesus as I was,
    Weary and worn and sad;
    I found in him a resting-place,
    And he has made me glad.

2

mf I heard the voice of Jesus say,
    'Behold, I freely give⌣
    The living water, thirsty one;
    Stoop down and drink and live :'
f *I came to Jesus, and I drank⌣
    Of that life-giving stream;
    My thirst was quenched, my soul revived,
    And now I live in him.

3

mf I heard the voice of Jesus say,
    'I am this dark world's Light;
    Look unto me, thy morn shall rise,
    And all thy day be bright :'
f *I looked to Jesus, and I found
    In him my Star, my Sun;
    And in that Light of life I'll walk
    Till travelling days are done.

* VERSES 2 AND 3, LINES 5 AND 6

2 I   came to Je - sus, and I drank
3 I   looked to Je - sus, and I found

2 Of that life - giv - ing stream.
3 In him my Star, my Sun.

H. BONAR

465

HYMN **352**   Horbury — 6 4 6 4. 6 6 4   J. B. Dykes, 1823–76

3
mf There let my way appear
         Steps unto heaven,
All that thou sendest me
         In mercy given;
Angels to beckon me
Nearer, my God, to thee,
         Nearer to thee.

mf Nearer, my God, to thee,
         Nearer to thee!
E'en though it be a cross
         That raiseth me;
Still all my song shall be,
'Nearer, my God, to thee,
         Nearer to thee!'

2
p Though, like the wanderer,
         The sun gone down,
Darkness comes over me,
         My rest a stone;
Yet in my dreams I'd be
Nearer, my God, to thee,
         Nearer to thee.

4
f Then, with my waking thoughts
         Bright with thy praise,
Out of my stony griefs
         Beth-el I'll raise;
So by my woes to be
Nearer, my God, to thee,
         Nearer to thee.

MRS. S. F. ADAMS†

NOTE *This hymn is based on the story of Jacob's dream in Gen. 28. 11–19*

HYMN **353** Pearsall — 7 6 7 6. D   R. L. Pearsall, 1795–1856

I could not do without thee,
O Saviour of the lost,
Whose precious Blood redeemed me
At such tremendous cost:
Thy righteousness, thy pardon,
Thy precious Blood, must be⌣
My only hope and comfort,
My glory and my plea.

2
I could not do without thee,
I cannot stand alone,
I have no strength or goodness,
No wisdom of my own;
But thou, belovèd Saviour,
Art all in all to me,
And weakness will be power
If leaning hard on thee.

3
I could not do without thee,
O Jesus, Saviour dear;
E'en when my eyes are holden,
I know that thou art near:
How dreary and how lonely
This changeful life would be
Without the sweet communion,
The secret rest, with thee!

4
I could not do without thee,
For years are fleeting fast,
And soon in solemn loneness
The river must be passed;
But thou wilt never leave me,
And, though the waves roll high,
I know thou wilt be near me,
And whisper, 'It is I.'

FRANCES R. HAVERGAL

HYMN **354**   Pilgrims — 11 10. 11 10. 9 11   H. Smart, 1813–79

mf Hark! hark, my soul! angelic songs are swelling
    O'er earth's green fields and ocean's wave-beat shore:
    How sweet the truth those blessèd strains are telling
    Of that new life when sin shall be no more!
p   Angels of Jesus, angels of light,
    Singing to welcome the pilgrims of the night!

2

mf Onward we go, for still we hear them singing,
p   'Come, weary souls, for Jesus bids you come;'
mf And through the dark, its echoes sweetly ringing,
    The music of the Gospel leads us home.
p   Angels of Jesus, angels of light,
    Singing to welcome the pilgrims of the night!

3*

Far, far away, like bells at evening pealing,
    The voice of Jesus sounds o'er land and sea,
And laden souls, by thousands meekly stealing,
    Kind Shepherd, turn their weary steps to thee.
p   Angels of Jesus, angels of light,
    Singing to welcome the pilgrims of the night!

4

mf Rest comes at length: though life be long and dreary,
    The day must dawn, and darksome night be past;
    Faith's journey ends in welcome to the weary,
    And heaven, the heart's true home, will come at last.
p   Angels of Jesus, angels of light,
    Singing to welcome the pilgrims of the night!

5

f   Angels, sing on, your faithful watches keeping,
    Sing us sweet fragments of the songs above;
    Till morning's joy shall end the night of weeping,
    And life's long shadows break in cloudless love.
p   Angels of Jesus, angels of light,
    Singing to welcome the pilgrims of the night!

F. W. FABER†

HYMN **355**   St. Catherine — 7 6 7 6. D   R. F. Dale, 1845-1919

p O Jesu, thou art standing
  Outside the fast-closed door,
  In lowly patience waiting
  To pass the threshold o'er :
mf Shame on us, Christian brethren,
  His name and sign who bear,
  O shame, thrice shame upon us
p   To keep him standing there!

2

O Jesu, thou art knocking;
  And lo, that hand is scarred,
  And thorns thy brow encircle,
  And tears thy face have marred :

mf O love that passeth knowledge,
  So patiently to wait!
  O sin that hath no equal
  So fast to bar the gate!

3

p O Jesu, thou art pleading
  In accents meek and low,
  'I died for you, my children,
  And will ye treat me so?'
mf O Lord, with shame and sorrow
  We open now the door :
  Dear Saviour, enter, enter,
  And leave us nevermore.

BISHOP W. WALSHAM HOW

HYMN **356** Ibstone — 6 6 6 6   Maria Tiddeman, 1837–1911

mf Thy way, not mine, O Lord,
    However dark it be;
    Lead me by thine own hand,
    Choose out the path for me.

2
Smooth let it be or rough,
    It will be still the best;
    Winding or straight, it leads⌣
    Right onward to thy rest.

3
I dare not choose my lot;
    I would not if I might:
    Choose thou for me, my God,
    So shall I walk aright.

4
The Kingdom that I seek⌣
    Is thine; so let the way⌣
    That leads to it be thine,
    Else I must surely stray.

5
p   Take thou my cup, and it⌣
    With joy or sorrow fill,
    As best to thee may seem;
    Choose thou my good and ill.

6
Choose thou for me my friends,
    My sickness or my health;
    Choose thou my cares for me,
    My poverty or wealth.

7
mf   Not mine, not mine, the choice
    In things or great or small;
    Be thou my guide, my strength,
    My wisdom, and my all.

H. BONAR

HYMN 357   FIRST TUNE

Ins Feld geh — 8 8 8 4   *Geistliche Volkslieder* (Paderborn, 1856)

4
If thou shouldst call me to resign
What most I prize, it ne'er was mine;
I only yield thee what is thine:
    Thy will be done!

My God, my Father, while I stray,
Far from my home, on life's rough way,
O teach me from my heart to say,
    'Thy will be done!'

2
Though dark my path, and sad my lot,
Let me be still and murmur not,
Or breathe the prayer divinely taught,
    'Thy will be done!'

5
Let but my fainting heart be blest
With thy sweet Spirit for its guest,
My God, to thee I leave the rest:
    Thy will be done!

3
What though in lonely grief I sigh
For friends beloved no longer nigh,
Submissive would I still reply,
    'Thy will be done!'

6
Renew my will from day to day,
Blend it with thine, and take away
All that now makes it hard to say,
    'Thy will be done!'

CHARLOTTE ELLIOTT

Troyte's Chant No. 1 — 8 8 8 4   A. H. Dyke Troyte, 1811-57

My God, my Father, while I stray,
Far from my home, on life's rough way,
O teach me from my héart to say,
   'Thy will be done!'

2
Though dark my path, and sád my lot,
Let me be still and múrmur not,
Or breathe the prayer divínely taught,
   'Thy will be done!'

3
What though in lonely gríef I sigh
For friends beloved no lónger nigh,
Submissive would I stíll reply,
   'Thy will be done!'

4
If thou shouldst call me tó resign
What most I prize, it ne'ér was mine;
I only yield thee whát is thine:
   Thy will be done!

5
Let but my fainting héart be blest
With thy sweet Spirit fór its guest,
My God, to thee I léave the rest:
   Thy will be done!

6
Renew my will from dáy to day,
Blend it with thine, and táke away
All that now makes it hárd to say,
   'Thy will be done!'

      CHARLOTTE ELLIOTT

General

HYMN 358

FIRST TUNE

Song 46 — 10 10

Orlando Gibbons, 1583–1625

SECOND TUNE

Pax tecum — 10 10

G. T. Caldbeck (1877)

mf Peace, perfect peace, in this dark world of sin?
p   The Blood of Jesus whispers peace within.

2
mf Peace, perfect peace, by thronging duties pressed?
p   To do the will of Jesus, this is rest.

3
mf Peace, perfect peace, with sorrows surging round?
p   On Jesus' bosom naught but calm is found.

4
mf Peace, perfect peace, with loved ones far away?
p   In Jesus' keeping we are safe and they.

5
mf Peace, perfect peace, our future all unknown?
f   Jesus we know, and he is on the throne.

6
p   Peace, perfect peace, death shadowing us and ours?
f   Jesus has vanquished death and all its powers.

7
mf It is enough : earth's struggles soon shall cease,
     And Jesus call us to heaven's perfect peace.

BISHOP E. H. BICKERSTETH

474

mf   O Love that wilt not let me go,
     I rest my weary soul in thee :
     I give thee back the life I owe,
     That in thine ocean depths its flow⌣
       May richer, fuller, be.

2

p   O Light that followest all my way,
     I yield my flickering torch to thee :
mf   My heart restores its borrowed ray,
     That in thy sunshine's blaze its day⌣
       May brighter, fairer be.

3

p   O Joy that seekest me through pain,
     I cannot close my heart to thee :
mf   I trace the rainbow through the rain,
     And feel the promise is not vain
       That morn shall tearless be.

4

     O Cross that liftest up my head,
     I dare not ask to fly from thee :
     I lay in dust life's glory dead,
f   And from the ground there blossoms red
       Life that shall endless be.

G. MATHESON

General

HYMN 360   North Coates — 6 5 6 5   T. R. Matthews, 1826–1910

p   O my Saviour, lifted
    From the earth for me,
    Draw me, in thy mercy,
    Nearer unto thee.

2
Lift my earth-bound longings,
    Fix them, Lord, above;
    Draw me with the magnet
    Of thy mighty love.

3
mf Lord, thine arms are stretching
    Ever far and wide,

To enfold thy children
    To thy loving side.

4
And I come, O Jesus :
    Dare I turn away?
f   No, thy love hath conquered,
    And I come to-day;

5
mf Bringing all my burdens,
    Sorrow, sin, and care,
At thy feet I lay them,
    And I leave them there.

              BISHOP W. WALSHAM HOW

HYMN 361   Consecration — 7 7 7 7   W. H. Havergal, 1793–1870

Take my life, and let it be
Consecrated, Lord, to thee;
Take my moments and my days,
Let them flow in ceaseless praise.

2
Take my hands, and let them move
At the impulse of thy love.
Take my feet, and let them be
Swift and beautiful for thee.

3
Take my voice, and let me sing
Always, only, for my King;
Take my lips, and let them be
Filled with messages from thee.

4
Take my silver and my gold;
Not a mite would I withhold.
Take my intellect, and use
Every power as thou shalt choose.

5
Take my will, and make it thine:
It shall be no longer mine.
Take my heart: it is thine own;
It shall be thy royal throne.

6
Take my love; my Lord, I pour
At thy feet its treasure-store.
Take myself, and I will be
Ever, only, all for thee.

FRANCES R. HAVERGAL

HYMN **362** Carlisle — S.M.   C. Lockhart, 1745–1815

Slow

A higher setting of this tune will be found at Hymn 374

Revive thy work, O Lord!
Thy mighty arm make bare;
Speak with the voice that wakes the dead,
And make thy people hear.

2
Revive thy work, O Lord!
Disturb this sleep of death;
Quicken the smouldering embers now
By thine almighty breath.

3
Revive thy work, O Lord!
Create soul-thirst for thee:

And hungering for the Bread of Life
O may our spirits be.

4
Revive thy work, O Lord!
Exalt thy precious name;
And by the Holy Ghost our love
For thee and thine inflame.

5
Revive thy work, O Lord!
Give Pentecostal showers;
The glory shall be all thine own,
The blessing, Lord, be ours.

A. MIDLANE

HYMN **363** Margaret — Irregular T. R. Matthews, 1826–1910

mf   Thou didst | leave thy throne and thy | kingly crown,
     When thou | camest to earth for me;
    But in | Bethlehem's home was there | found no room
     For thy | holy Nativity:
       O come to my heart, Lord Jesus;
       There is room in my heart for thee.

2

f   Heaven's | arches rang when the | angels sang,
     Pro- | claiming thy royal degree;
p   But in | lowly birth didst thou | come to earth,
     And in | great humility:
       O come to my heart, Lord Jesus;
       There is room in my heart for thee.

3

mf   The | foxes found rest, and the | bird had its nest
     In the | shade of the cedar tree;
p   But thy | couch was the sod, O thou | Son of God,
     In the | desert of Galilee:
       O come to my heart, Lord Jesus;
       There is room in my heart for thee.

4

mf   Thou | camest, O Lord, with the | living word
     That should | set thy people free;
p   But with | mocking scorn and with | crown of thorn
     They | bore thee to Calvary:
       O come to my heart, Lord Jesus;
       There is room in my heart for thee.

5

f   When the | heavens shall ring, and the | angels sing,
     At thy | coming to victory,
    Let thy | voice call me home, saying, | 'Yet there is room,
     There is | room at my side for thee:'
       O come to my heart, Lord Jesus;
       There is room in my heart for thee.

EMILY E. S. ELLIOTT

HYMN **364** Gott will's machen — 8 7 8 7   J. L. Steiner, 1688–1761

Souls of men! why will ye scatter
Like a crowd of frightened sheep?
Foolish hearts! why will ye wander
From a love so true and deep?

2
Was there ever kindest shepherd
Half so gentle, half so sweet,
As the Saviour who would have us
Come and gather round his feet?

3

There's a wideness in God's mercy
  Like the wideness of the sea;
There's a kindness in his justice
  Which is more than liberty.

4

There is no place where earth's sorrows
  Are more felt than up in heaven;
There is no place where earth's failings
  Have such kindly judgement given.

5

There is plentiful redemption
  In the Blood that has been shed;
There is joy for all the members
  In the sorrows of the Head.

6

For the love of God is broader
  Than the measures of man's mind;
And the heart of the Eternal
  Is most wonderfully kind.

7

Pining souls! come nearer Jesus,
  And oh, come not doubting thus,
But with faith that trusts more bravely
  His huge tenderness for us.

8

If our love were but more simple,
  We should take him at his word;
And our lives would be all sunshine
  In the sweetness of our Lord.

F. W. FABER

HYMN **365**   Praise, my soul — 8 7. 8 7. 8 7   Sir J. GOSS, 1800-80

UNISON

1 Praise, my soul, the King of hea - ven, To his feet thy tri-bute bring;

Ran-somed, healed, re - stored, for - giv - en, Who like me his praise should sing?

Al-le - lu - ia! Al - le - lu - ia! Praise the ev - er - last - ing King.

General

2 Praise him for his grace and fa - vour To our fa-thers in dis - tress;

Praise him still the same as ev - er, Slow to chide, and swift to bless:

Al - le - lu - ia! Al - le - lu - ia! Glo - rious in his faith-ful - ness.

TREBLES

3 Fa-ther-like, he tends and spares us, Well our fee - ble frame he knows;

483

In his hands he gen-tly bears us, Res-cues us from all our foes:

Al-le-lu-ia! Al-le-lu-ia! Wide-ly as his mer-cy flows.

UNISON

4 An-gels, help us to a-dore him; Ye be-hold him

face to face; Sun and moon, bow down be - fore him,

Dwell-ers all in time and space: Al - le - lu - ia!

Al - le - lu - ia! Praise with us the God of grace.

H. F. LYTE†

HYMN **366**　　　　　　FIRST TUNE

Saving health — 8 7 8 7. 8 8 7　　　　*Etlich Christliche Lyeder,* 1524

HYMN **366**   SECOND TUNE

Luther -- 8 7 8 7. 8 8 7   M. Luther, 1483-1545

Sei Lob und Ehr' dem höchsten Gut

Sing praise to God who reigns above,
   The God of all creation,
The God of power, the God of love,
   The God of our salvation;
With healing balm my soul he fills,
And every faithless murmur stills :
   To God all praise and glory.

2
The Lord is never far away,
   But, through all grief distressing,
An ever-present help and stay,
   Our peace and joy and blessing;

As with a mother's tender hand,
He leads his own, his chosen band :
   To God all praise and glory.

3
Thus all my gladsome way along
   I sing aloud thy praises,
That men may hear the grateful song
   My voice unwearied raises.
Be joyful in the Lord, my heart;
Both soul and body bear your part :
   To God all praise and glory.

J. J. SCHÜTZ *Tr*. Frances E. Cox

Alternative Tune, Laus Deo (Bach), 422

HYMN **367**

Salve cordis gaudium — 7 4 7 4. 7 4 7 4. 4

J. R. Ahle, 1625–73
Harmony by J. S. Bach, 1685–1750

Al - - - - le - lu - ia.

f　King of glory, King of peace,
　　I will love thee;
　And, that love may never cease,
　　I will move thee.
　Thou hast granted my request,
　　Thou hast heard me;
　Thou didst note my working breast,
　　Thou hast spared me. Alleluia!

2

　Wherefore with my utmost art
　　I will sing thee,
　And the cream of all my heart
　　I will bring thee.
mf　Though my sins against me cried,
　　Thou didst clear me,
　And alone, when they replied,
　　Thou didst hear me. Alleluia!

3

f　Seven whole days, not one in seven,
　　I will praise thee;
　In my heart, though not in heaven,
　　I can raise thee.
mf　Small it is, in this poor sort
　　To enrol thee:
f　E'en eternity's too short
　　To extol thee. Alleluia!

GEORGE HERBERT

HYMN 367   SECOND TUNE

Gwalchmai — 7 4 7 4. D   J. D. Jones, 1827–70

f   King of glory, King of peace,
     I will love thee;
And, that love may never cease,
     I will move thee.
Thou hast granted my request,
     Thou hast heard me;
Thou didst note my working breast,
     Thou hast spared me.

2

Wherefore with my utmost art
     I will sing thee,
And the cream of all my heart
     I will bring thee.
mf Though my sins against me cried,
     Thou didst clear me,
And alone, when they replied,
     Thou didst hear me.

3

f   Seven whole days, not one in seven,
     I will praise thee;
In my heart, though not in heaven,
     I can raise thee.
mf Small it is, in this poor sort
     To enrol thee:
f   E'en eternity's too short
     To extol thee.

GEORGE HERBERT

HYMN **368** Austria — 8 7 8 7. D   F. J. Haydn, 1732–1809

A lower setting of this tune will be found at Hymn 257

Psalm 148

Praise the Lord! ye heavens, adore him;
   Praise him, angels, in the height;
Sun and moon, rejoice before him,
   Praise him, all ye stars and light.
Praise the Lord! for he hath spoken;
   Worlds his mighty voice obeyed:
Laws, which never shall be broken,
   For their guidance he hath made.

2

Praise the Lord! for he is glorious;
   Never shall his promise fail:
God hath made his saints victorious
   Sin and death shall not prevail.
Praise the God of our salvation;
   Hosts on high, his power proclaim;
Heaven and earth and all creation,
   Laud and magnify his name!

Foundling Hospital Collection, 1ɪ

HYMN **369**   Northampton — 7 7 7 7   C. J. King, 1859–1934

mf Songs of praise the angels sang,
     Heaven with Alleluias rang,
     When creation was begun,
     When God spake and it was done.

2

Songs of praise awoke the morn
When the Prince of Peace was born;
f   Songs of praise arose when he‿
     Captive led captivity.

3

p   Heaven and earth must pass away;
     Songs of praise shall crown that day:
f   God will make new heavens and earth;
     Songs of praise shall hail their birth.

4

p   And will man alone be dumb
     Till that glorious Kingdom come?
f   No, the Church delights to raise‿
     Psalms and hymns and songs of praise.

5

mf Saints below, with heart and voice,
     Still in songs of praise rejoice;
     Learning here, by faith and love,
     Songs of praise to sing above.

[UNISON]   6

f   Hymns of glory, songs of praise,
     Father, unto thee we raise,
     Jesu, glory unto thee,
     With the Spirit, ever be.

                    J. MONTGOMERY and Compilers

Alternative Tune, Culbach, 73

493

HYMN **370**   Old 100th — L.M.   L. Bourgeois, *c.* 1500–61

A lower setting of this tune will be found at Hymn 621, and an Alternative Version at Hymn 166

Psalm 100

mf Before Jehovah's awful throne,
   Ye nations, bow with sacred joy;
   Know that the Lord is God alone:
   He can create, and he destroy.

2

   His sovereign power, without our
      aid,
   Made us of clay, and formed us
      men;
   And, when like wandering sheep we
      strayed,
   He brought us to his fold again.

3

f We'll crowd thy gates with thankful
      songs,
   High as the heavens our voices raise;
   And earth, with her ten thousand
      tongues,
   Shall fill thy courts with sounding
      praise.

4

   Wide as the world is thy command,
   Vast as eternity thy love;
   Firm as a rock thy truth shall stand,
   When rolling years shall cease to
      move.

                                   I. WATTS‡

HYMN **371**   Darwall's 148th — 6 6 6 6. 4 4 4 4   J. Darwall, 1731–8

DESCANT

4 My soul, bear thou thy part, Tri - umph in God a - bove,

General

And with a well - tuned heart Sing thou the songs of love. Let

all thy days Till life shall end, What-e'er he send, Be filled with praise.

The Descant may be sung by Trebles for verse 4, the main melody being sung in Unison

Ye holy angels bright,
  Who wait at God's right hand,
Or through the realms of light
  Fly at your Lord's command,
    Assist our song,
    For else the theme
    Too high doth seem
  For mortal tongue.

2
f Ye blessèd souls at rest,
  Who ran this earthly race,
And now, from sin released,
  Behold the Saviour's face,
    His praises sound,
    As in his light
    With sweet delight
  Ye do abound.

3
Ye saints who toil below,
  Adore your heavenly King,
And onward as ye go
  Some joyful anthem sing;
    Take what he gives
    And praise him still,
    Through good and ill,
  Who ever lives.

[UNISON] ### 4
f My soul, bear thou thy part,
  Triumph in God above,
And with a well-tuned heart
  Sing thou the songs of love.
    Let all thy days
    Till life shall end,
    Whate'er he send,
  Be filled with praise.

R. BAXTER and J. H. GURNEY

HYMN **372**   St. Denio — 11 11 11 11   Welsh Hymn Melody

Immortal, invisible, God only wise,
In light inaccessible hid from our eyes,
Most blessèd, most glorious, the Ancient of Days,
Almighty, victorious, thy great name we praise.

2
Unresting, unhasting, and silent as light,
Nor wanting, nor wasting, thou rulest in might;
Thy justice like mountains high soaring above
Thy clouds which are fountains of goodness and love.

3
To all life thou givest, to both great and small;
In all life thou livest, the true life of all;
We blossom and flourish as leaves on the tree,
And wither and perish; but naught changeth thee.

4
Great Father of glory, pure Father of light,
Thine angels adore thee, all veiling their sight;
All laud we would render : O help us to see‿
'Tis only the splendour of light hideth thee.

W. CHALMERS SMITH

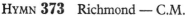

HYMN **373** Richmond — C.M.   T. Haweis, 1734–1820

Fill thou my life, O Lord my God,
　In every part with praise,
That my whole being may proclaim
　Thy being and thy ways.

2
Not for the lip of praise alone,
　Nor e'en the praising heart,
I ask, but for a life made up⌣
　Of praise in every part:

3
Praise in the common things of life,
　Its goings out and in;
Praise in each duty and each deed,
　However small and mean.

4
Fill every part of me with praise:
　Let all my being speak⌣
Of thee and of thy love, O Lord,
　Poor though I be and weak.

5*
So shalt thou, Lord, receive from me
　The praise and glory due;
And so shall I begin on earth
　The song for ever new.

6*
So shall each fear, each fret, each care,
　Be turnèd into song;
And every winding of the way
　The echo shall prolong.

[UNISON]　7
So shall no part of day or night
　Unblest or common be;
But all my life, in every step,
　Be fellowship with thee.

H. BONAR†

497

HYMN **374** Carlisle — S.M. C. Lockhart, 1745–1815

Slow

A lower setting of this tune will be found at Hymn 362

Stand up, and bless the Lord,
Ye people of his choice;
Stand up, and bless the Lord your God
With heart and soul and voice.

2
Though high above all praise,
Above all blessing high,
Who would not fear his holy name,
And laud and magnify?

3
O for the living flame
From his own altar brought,
To touch our lips, our mind inspire,
And wing to heaven our thought!

4
God is our strength and song,
And his salvation ours;
Then be his love in Christ proclaimed
With all our ransomed powers.

5
Stand up, and bless the Lord,
The Lord your God adore;
Stand up, and bless his glorious name
Henceforth for evermore.

J. MONTGOMERY

498

HYMN **375**   Luckington — 10 4. 6 6. 6 6. 10 4   B. Harwood, 1859-1949

2

.et all the world in every corner sing,
  My God and King!
The heavens are not too high,
His praise may thither fly:
The earth is not too low,
His praises there may grow.
.et all the world in every corner sing,
  My God and King!

Let all the world in every corner sing,
  My God and King!
The Church with psalms must shout,
No door can keep them out;
But above all the heart
Must bear the longest part.
Let all the world in every corner sing,
  My God and King!

GEORGE HERBERT

General

Laudate Dominum — 10 10 11 11   Sir C. H. H. Parry, 1848–1918

Based on Psalm 150

f O praise ye the Lord!
  Praise him in the height;
  Rejoice in his word,
  Ye angels of light;
Ye heavens adore him
By whom ye were made,
And worship before him,
  In brightness arrayed.

2

mf O praise ye the Lord!
  Praise him upon earth,
  In tuneful accord,
  Ye sons of new birth;

f Praise him who hath brought you
  His grace from above,
Praise him who hath taught you
  To sing of his love.

3

O praise ye the Lord,
  All things that give sound;
Each jubilant chord
  Re-echo around;
Loud organs, his glory
  Forth tell in deep tone,
mf And, sweet harp, the story
  Of what he hath done.

500

General

4 O praise ye the Lord! Thanks - giv - ing and song   To him be out - poured   All a - ges a - long: For love in cre -

501

HYMN **376** (*first tune—continued*)

SIR H. W. BAKER

Gauntlett — 10 10 11 11   H. J. Gauntlett, 1805–76

Based on Psalm 150

f O praise ye the Lord!
  Praise him in the height;
  Rejoice in his word,
  Ye angels of light;
  Ye heavens adore him
    By whom ye were made,
  And worship before him,
    In brightness arrayed.

2
mf O praise ye the Lord!
  Praise him upon earth,
  In tuneful accord,
  Ye sons of new birth;
f Praise him who hath brought you
    His grace from above,
  Praise him who hath taught you
    To sing of his love.

3
  O praise ye the Lord,
    All things that give sound;
  Each jubilant chord
    Re-echo around;
  Loud organs, his glory
    Forth tell in deep tone,
mf And, sweet harp, the story
    Of what he hath done.

4
f O praise ye the Lord!
    Thanksgiving and song
  To him be outpoured
    All ages along:
  For love in creation,
    For heaven restored,
  For grace of salvation,
    O praise ye the Lord!

Sir H. W. Baker

General

Psalm 136

f Let us, with a gladsome mind,
Praise the Lord, for he is kind :
   For his mercies ay endure,
   Ever faithful, ever sure.

2
Let us blaze his name abroad,
For of gods he is the God :
   For his mercies ay endure,
   Ever faithful, ever sure.

3
He with all-commanding might
Filled the new-made world with light :
   For his mercies ay endure,
   Ever faithful, ever sure.

4
mf He the golden-tressèd sun
Caused all day his course to run :
f   For his mercies ay endure,
   Ever faithful, ever sure.

5
p And the hornèd moon at night
'Mid her spangled sisters bright :
f   For his mercies ay endure,
   Ever faithful, ever sure.

6
mf All things living he doth feed,
His full hand supplies their need :
f   For his mercies ay endure,
   Ever faithful, ever sure.

7
Let us, with a gladsome mind,
Praise the Lord, for he is kind :
   For his mercies ay endure,
   Ever faithful, ever sure.

JOHN MILTON‡

HYMN **378** Harvest — 10 10 7 C. J. Frost, 1843–1922

Thanksgiving for the Church's work overseas

mf Lord of the Harvest, it is right and meet
That we should lay our first-fruits at thy feet
　　　With joyful Alleluia.

2
Sweet is the soul's thanksgiving after prayer;
Sweet is the worship that with heaven we share,
　　　Who sing the Alleluia.

3
Lowly we prayed, and thou didst hear on high,
Didst lift our hearts and change our suppliant cry
　　　To festal Alleluia.

4
So sing we now in tune with that great song,
That all the age of ages shall pro- [long,
　　　The endless Alleluia.

5*
To thee, O Lord of Harvest, who hast heard,
And to thy white-robed reapers given the word,
　　　We sing our Alleluia.

6*
O Christ, who in the wide world's ghostly sea
Hast bid the net be cast anew, to thee﹏
　　　We sing our Alleluia.

7*
To thee, eternal Spirit, who again
Hast moved with life upon the slum-brous main,
　　　We sing our Alleluia.

8
Yea, for sweet hope new-born, blest work begun,
Sing Alleluia to the Three in One,
　　　Adoring Alleluia.

9
f　'Glory to God!' the Church in patience cries;
'Glory to God!' the Church at rest replies,
　　　With endless Alleluia.

S. J. STONE

Alternative Tune, St. Sebastian, 283

General

Nun danket alle Gott

f Now thank we all our God,
 With heart and hands and voices,
  Who wondrous things hath done,
  In whom his world rejoices;
   Who from our mother's arms
   Hath blessed us on our way
  With countless gifts of love,
  And still is ours to-day.

2

mf O may this bounteous God
 Through all our life be near us,
  With ever joyful hearts
  And blessèd peace to cheer us;

And keep us in his grace,
 And guide us when perplexed,
 And free us from all ills
 In this world and the next.

[UNISON]   **3**
f All praise and thanks to God
 The Father now be given,
  The Son, and him who reigns
 With them in highest heaven,
  The one eternal God,
   Whom earth and heaven adore,
  For thus it was, is now,
  And shall be evermore.

M. RINKART *Tr.* Catherine Winkworth

506

HYMN **380**   Old 124th — 10 10 10 10 10   Melody in *Genevan Psalter*, 1551

By permission of the English Hymnal Company, Ltd.

Psalm 145

We would extol thee, ever-blessèd Lord;
Thy holy name for ever be adored;
Each day we live to thee our psalm we raise:
Thou, God and King, art worthy of our praise,
Great and unsearchable in all thy ways.

2
Age shall to age pass on the endless song,
Telling the wonders which to thee belong,
Thy mighty acts with joy and fear relate;
Laud we thy glory while on thee we wait,
Glad in the knowledge of thy love so great.

3
Thou, Lord, art gracious, merciful to all,
Nigh to thy children when on thee they call;
Slow unto anger, pitiful and kind,
Thou to compassion ever art inclined:
We love thee with our heart and strength and mind.

NICHOL GRIEVE

Verse 1 *may be repeated at the end*

Psalm 148

Praise the Lord of heaven, praise him in the height;
Praise him, all ye angels, praise him, stars and light;
Praise him, skies and waters, which above the skies,
When his word commanded, stablished did arise.

2

Praise the Lord, ye fountains of the deeps and seas,
Rocks and hills and mountains, cedars and all trees;
Praise him, clouds and vapours, snow and hail and fire,
Stormy wind fulfilling only his desire.

3

Praise him, fowls and cattle, princes and all kings;
Praise him, men and maidens, all created things;
For the name of God is excellent alone :
On the earth his footstool, over heaven his throne.

T. B. BROWNE

HYMN **382** Praxis pietatis — 14 14. 4 7 8   P. Sohren's edition of *Praxis pietatis melica*, 1668

Lobe den Herren

Praise to the Lord, the Almighty, the
King of creation;
O my soul, praise him, for he is thy
health and salvation:
 All ye who hear,
 Now to his temple draw near,
Joining in glad adoration.

2
Praise to the Lord, who o'er all things
so wondrously reigneth,
f Shieldeth thee gently from harm, or
when fainting sustaineth:
 Hast thou not seen⌣
 How thy heart's wishes have
 been⌣
Granted in what he ordaineth?

3
f Praise to the Lord, who doth prosper
thy work and defend thee;
Surely his goodness and mercy shall
daily attend thee:
 Ponder anew
 What the Almighty can do,
If to the end he befriend thee.

4
Praise to the Lord! O let all that is
in me adore him!
All that hath life and breath, come
now with praises before him!
 Let the Amen
 Sound from his people again:
Gladly for ay we adore him.

J. NEANDER
Tr. Catherine Winkworth‡

HOLY COMMUNION

Hymn 383   FIRST TUNE

Pange lingua — 8 7. 8 7. 8 7   Mode iii

PART I

Pange, lingua, gloriosi Corporis mysterium

1 Now, my tongue, the mys-tery tell - ing / Of the glo - rious Bo - dy sing,
2 Given for us, and con - de - scend-ing / To be born for us be - low,
3 That last night, at sup-per ly - ing, / 'Mid the Twelve, his cho - sen band,
4 Word made flesh, true bread he mak - eth / By his word his Flesh to be,

1 And the Blood, all price ex - cell - ing, / Which the Gen-tiles' Lord and King,
2 He, with men in con - verse blend-ing, / Dwelt the seed of truth to sow,
3 Je - sus, with the law com - ply - ing, / Keeps the feast its rites de-mand;
4 Wine his Blood; which who - so tak - eth / Must from carn - al thoughts be free:

1 In a Vir - gin's womb once dwell-ing, / Shed for this world's ran-som-ing.
2 Till he closed with won - drous end - ing / His most pa - tient life of woe.
3 Then, more pre - cious food sup - ply - ing, / Gives him - self with his own hand.
4 Faith a - lone, though sight for - sak - eth, / Shows true hearts the mys - ter - y.

510

Holy Communion

Tantum ergo

5 There-fore we, be - fore him bend - ing, This great Sa -cra - ment re - vere:
6 Glo - ry let us give and bless - ing To the Fa-ther and the Son,

5 Types and sha - dows have their end - ing, For the new - er rite is here;
6 Hon - our, might, and praise ad - dress-ing, While e - ter - nal a - ges run;

Faith, our out-ward sense be - friend-ing, Makes our in - ward vi - sion clear.
Ev - er too his love con - fess - ing, Who, from Both, with Both is One.

The Sarum form of this melody will be found at Hymn 97

511

Holy Communion

Tantum ergo — 8 7. 8 7. 8 7　　　　　　　French Melody

512

Holy Communion

PART 1

Pange, lingua, gloriosi Corporis mysterium

mf Now, my tongue, the mystery telling
 Of the glorious Body sing,
 And the Blood, all price excelling,
 Which the Gentiles' Lord and King,
p In a Virgin's womb once dwelling,
 Shed for this world's ransoming.

2

mf Given for us, and condescending
 To be born for us below,
 He, with men in converse blending,
 Dwelt the seed of truth to sow,
p Till he closed with wondrous ending
 His most patient life of woe.

3

mf That last night, at supper lying,
 'Mid the Twelve, his chosen band,
 Jesus, with the law complying,
 Keeps the feast its rites demand;
 Then, more precious food supplying,
 Gives himself with his own hand.

4

p Word made flesh, true bread he maketh
 By his word his Flesh to be,
 Wine his Blood; which whoso taketh
 Must from carnal thoughts be free:
mf Faith alone, though sight forsaketh,
 Shows true hearts the mystery.

PART 2

Tantum ergo

5

p Therefore we, before him bending,
 This great Sacrament revere:
 Types and shadows have their ending,
 For the newer rite is here;
mf Faith, our outward sense befriending,
 Makes our inward vision clear.

6

f Glory let us give and blessing
 To the Father and the Son,
 Honour, might, and praise addressing,
 While eternal ages run;
 Ever too his love confessing,
 Who, from Both, with Both is One.

St. Thomas Aquinas
Tr. E. Caswall, J. M. Neale and others

513

HYMN **384**   FIRST TUNE

Verbum supernum prodiens — L.M.   Mode viii

PART 1 — **Verbum supernum prodiens**   PART 2 — **O salutaris**

1 The heaven - ly Word, pro - ceed - ing forth Yet leav - ing
2 By false dis - ci - ple to be given To foe - men
3 He gave him - self in eith - er kind, His pre - cious
4 By birth their fel - low - man was he, Their meat, when

PART 2
5 O sav - ing Vic - tim, ope - ning wide⌣ The gate of
6 All praise and thanks to thee as - cend For ev - er -

1 not the Fa - ther's side, Ac - com - plish - ing his work
2 for his life a - thirst, Him - self, the ve - ry Bread
3 Flesh, his pre - cious Blood; In love's own ful - ness thus
4 sit - ting at the board; He died, their ran - som - er

PART 2
5 heaven to man be - low, Our foes press on from ev -
6 more, blest One in Three; O grant us life that shall

1 on earth Had reached at length life's e - ven - tide.
2 of Heaven, He gave to his dis - ci - ples first.
3 de - signed Of the whole man to be the food.
4 to be; He ev - er reigns, their great re - ward.

PART 2
5 ery side: Thine aid sup - ply, thy strength be - stow.
6 not end In our true na - tive land with thee.

HYMN **384**   SECOND TUNE

Das walt' Gott — L.M.   D. Vetter (1713)

Harmony from J. S. Bach, 1685–1750

PART 1

Verbum supernum prodiens

uf The heavenly Word, proceeding
forth
Yet leaving not the Father's side,
Accomplishing his work on earth
Had reached at length life's even-
tide.

2

uf By false disciple to be given
To foemen for his life athirst,
Himself, the very Bread of heaven,
He gave to his disciples first.

3

He gave himself in either kind,
His precious Flesh, his precious
Blood;
In love's own fulness thus designed
Of the whole man to be the food.

4

p By birth their fellow-man was he,
Their meat, when sitting at the
board;
He died, their ransomer to be;
f   He ever reigns, their great reward.

PART 2

O salutaris

5

O saving Victim, opening wide
The gate of heaven to man below,
Our foes press on from every side:
Thine aid supply, thy strength be-
stow.

6

f All praise and thanks to thee ascend
For evermore, blest One in
Three;
O grant us life that shall not end
In our true native land with thee.

St. Thomas Aquinas
Tr. J. M. Neale, E. Caswall, and others

515

HYMN **385**　　　　　FIRST TUNE

Adoro te devote — 10 10 10 10　　　　　Mode v

Adoro te devote, latens Deitas

1 Thee we a - dore, O hid - den Sa - viour, thee, Who in thy
2 O blest mem - or - ial of our dy - ing Lord, Who liv - ing
3 Foun-tain of good-ness, Je - su, Lord and God, Cleanse us, un -
4 O Christ, whom now be-neath a veil we see, May what we

1 Sa - cra-ment dost deign to be; Both flesh and spi - rit at thy
2 Bread to men doth here af - ford! O may our souls for ev - er
3 clean, with thy most clean-sing Blood; In - crease our faith and love, that
4 thirst for soon our por - tion be: To gaze on thee un - veiled, and

1 Pre - sence fail, Yet here thy Pre - sence we de-vout - ly hail.
2 feed on thee, And thou, O Christ, for ev - er pre - cious be.
3 we may know. The hope and peace which from thy Pre - sence flow.
4 see thy face, The vi - sion of thy glo - ry and thy grace.

Holy Communion

SECOND TUNE

Leamington — 10 10 10 10   Sir S. H. Nicholson, 1875-1947

By permission of the Faith Press, Ltd.

Adoro te devote, latens Deitas

Thee we adore, O hidden Saviour, thee,
Who in thy Sacrament dost deign to be;
Both flesh and spirit at thy Presence fail,
Yet here thy Presence we devoutly hail.

2
O blest memorial of our dying Lord,
Who living Bread to men doth here afford!
O may our souls for ever feed on thee,
And thou, O Christ, for ever precious be.

3
Fountain of goodness, Jesu, Lord and God,
Cleanse us, unclean, with thy most cleansing Blood;
Increase our faith and love, that we may know
The hope and peace which from thy Presence flow

4
O Christ, whom now beneath a veil we see,
May what we thirst for soon our portion be :
To gaze on thee unveiled, and see thy face,
The vision of thy glory and thy grace.

St. Thomas Aquinas
Tr. Bishop J. R. Woodford†

517

Holy Communion

FIRST TUNE

St. Sechnall — 10 10 10 10

Irish Traditional Melody

Slowly. May be sung in Unison

SECOND TUNE

Elberton — 10 10

B. Harwood, 1859-1949

518

Holy Communion

Sancti, venite, Christi Corpus sumite

p Draw nigh and take the Body of the Lord,
And drink the holy Blood for you outpoured.

2
Saved by that Body and that holy Blood,
With souls refreshed, we render thanks to God.

3
Salvation's giver, Christ the only Son,
By his dear Cross and Blood the victory won.

4
Offered was he for greatest and for least,
Himself the Victim, and himself the Priest.

5*
Victims were offered by the law of old,
Which in a type this heavenly mystery told.

6*
mf He, Lord of life, and Saviour of our race,
Hath given to his saints a wondrous grace.

7
p Approach ye then with faithful hearts sincere,
And take the safeguard of salvation here.

8
mf He that his saints in this world rules and shields
To all believers life eternal yields;

9
He feeds the hungry with the Bread of heaven,
And living streams to those who thirst are given.

10*
p Alpha and Omega, to whom shall bow
All nations at the Doom, is with us now.

7th cent. *Tr.* J. M. NEALE
and Compilers (1904)

NOTE. Alpha and Omega, *the first and last letters of the Greek
alphabet, are used in the book of Revelation as a title of Jesus Christ,
who, as the Word of God, is the beginning and the end of all creation*

Alternative Tune, Song 46, 358

Holy Communion

HYMN **387**   FIRST TUNE

Jesu, dulcedo cordium — L.M.   Mode ii

Jesu, dulcedo cordium

1 Je - su,   thou   joy   of   lov - ing   hearts!
2 Thy   truth   un - changed   hath   ev - er   stood;
3 We   taste   thee,   O   thou   liv - ing   Bread,
4 Our   rest - less   spi - rits   yearn   for   thee,
5 O   Je - su,   ev - er   with   us   stay;

1 Thou fount   of   life, thou Light   of   men!   From   the   best   bliss
2 Thou sav - est   those that   on   thee   call;   To   them   that   seek
3 And long   to   feast up - on   thee   still;   We   drink   of   thee,
4 Where - 'er   our   change-ful   lot   is   cast,   Glad   when thy   gra -
5 Make all   our   mo - ments calm   and bright;   Chase   the   dark   night

1 that earth   im - parts   We   turn   un - filled   to   thee   a - gain.
2 thee thou   art good,   To   them   that   find   thee   all   in   all.
3 the foun - tain - head,   And   thirst   our   souls from   thee   to   fill.
4 cious smile   we   see,   Blest when   our   faith   can   hold   thee fast.
5 of   sin   a - way;   Shed   o'er   the   world   thy   ho - ly   light.

HYMN 387   SECOND TUNE

Ealing — L.M.   Sir H. Oakeley, 1830–1903

Jesu, dulcedo cordium

Jesu, thou joy of loving hearts!
Thou fount of life, thou Light of men!
From the best bliss that earth imparts
We turn unfilled to thee again.

2
Thy truth unchanged hath ever stood;
Thou savest those that on thee call;
To them that seek thee thou art good,
To them that find thee all in all.

3
We taste thee, O thou living Bread,
And long to feast upon thee still;
We drink of thee, the fountain-head,
And thirst our souls from thee to fill.

4
Our restless spirits yearn for thee,
Where'er our changeful lot is cast,
Glad when thy gracious smile we see,
Blest when our faith can hold thee fast

5
O Jesu, ever with us stay;
Make all our moments calm and bright;
Chase the dark night of sin away;
Shed o'er the world thy holy light.

Cento from *Jesu dulcis memoria*
Tr. R. PALMER

Alternative Tune, St. Bernard (Monk), 188

HYMN **388**

FIRST TUNE

Eia, Jesu adorande — 8 7. 8 7. 8 7

Mode iii

Eia, Jesu adorande

1 O Lord Je - sus, I a - dore thee For the bread of worth un - told
2 Make thou of my soul an or - chard Quick-ened in - to fruit - ful - ness;
PART 2
3 Ah, Lord Je - sus, go not from me, Stay, ah, stay with me, my Lord;
4 Would that I could keep thee al - ways In mine in - most heart to be,

1 Free - ly given in thy Com-mun - ion, Won - der - ful a thou-sand-fold,
2 Come, O come, life - giv - ing Man - na, Mak - ing glad my wil - der - ness:
PART 2
3 Make me shrink from what-so - ev - er Will not with thy name ac - cord;
4 Thou and on - ly thou sug-gest - ing Ev - ery thought and wish in me;

1 Given to - day in lov - ing boun - ty More than my poor heart can hold.
2 Sweet - er far than an - y sweet-ness Tongue can taste, or words ex - press.
PART 2
3 Act through me in ev - ery ac - tion, Speak through me in ev - ery word.
4 All my soul, with sing - ing, of - fered For a sa - cri - fice to thee.

HYMN 388   SECOND TUNE

St. Thomas — 8 7. 8 7. 8 7   Traditional Melody (18th cent.)

A lower setting of this tune will be found at Hymn 536

Eia, Jesu adorande

PART 1

O Lord Jesus, I adore thee
  For the bread of worth untold
Freely given in thy Communion,
  Wonderful a thousandfold,
Given to-day in loving bounty
  More than my poor heart can hold.

2

Make thou of my soul an orchard
  Quickened into fruitfulness;
Come, O come, life-giving Manna,
  Making glad my wilderness:
Sweeter far than any sweetness
  Tongue can taste, or words express.

PART 2

3

Ah, Lord Jesus, go not from me,
  Stay, ah, stay with me, my Lord;
Make me shrink from whatsoever
  Will not with thy name accord;
Act through me in every action,
  Speak through me in every word.

4

Would that I could keep thee always
  In mine inmost heart to be,
Thou and only thou suggesting
  Every thought and wish in me;
All my soul, with singing, offered
  For a sacrifice to thee.

JOHN MAUBURN
Tr. J. M. C. Crum

Holy Communion

FIRST TUNE

Magdalen College — 8 8 6. 8 8 6 W. Hayes, 1706–77

SECOND TUNE

Manna — 8 8 6. 8 8 6 J. G. Schicht, 1753–1823

Holy Communion

O esca viatorum

O Food that weary pilgrims love,
O Bread of angel-hosts above,
    O Manna of the saints,
The hungry soul would feed on thee;
Ne'er may the heart unsolaced be
    Which for thy sweetness faints.

2
O fount of love, O cleansing tide,
Which from the Saviour's piercèd side
    And sacred heart dost flow,
Be ours to drink of thy pure rill,
Which only can our spirits fill,
    And all our need bestow.

3
Lord Jesu, whom, by power divine
Now hidden 'neath the outward sign,
    We worship and adore,
Grant, when the veil away is rolled,
With open face we may behold
    Thyself for evermore.

17th cent. *Tr.* COMPILERS

Holy Communion

HARMONIZED VERSION FOR UNACCOMPANIED SINGING

Holy Communion

σιγησάτω πᾶσα σάρξ

p   Let all mortal flesh keep silence
     And with fear and trembling stand;
     Ponder nothing earthly-minded,
     For with blessing in his hand
mf   Christ our God to earth descendeth,
     Our full homage to demand.

2

King of Kings, yet born of Mary,
     As of old on earth he stood,
Lord of Lords, in human vesture—
     In the Body and the Blood—
He will give to all the faithful
     His own self for heavenly food.

3

f   Rank on rank the host of heaven
     Spreads its vanguard on the way,
As the Light of Light descendeth
     From the realms of endless day,
That the powers of hell may vanish
     As the darkness clears away.

4

mf ˙ At his feet the six-winged seraphs,
     Cherubim with sleepless eye,
Veil their faces to the Presence,
     As with ceaseless voice they cry,
f   Alleluia, Alleluia,
     Alleluia! Lord most high.

Liturgy of St. James
Tr. G. MOULTRIE

Holy Communion

οἱ τὰ χερουβὶμ μυστικῶς εἰκονίζοντες

UNISON

1 Here, while the cher - u - bim with - in the veil A - dore the blest,
2 So let all earth - ly cares be cast a - side, That we may wel -

1 life - giv - ing Trin - i - ty, We, in earth's wor - ship
2 come him who draw - eth nigh, The King of Glo - ry

1 ech - o - ing their part, Hymn the Thrice-Ho -ly in their com - pa - ny.
2 en - ter - ing his courts, Girt by the hid - den arm - ies of the sky.

AFTER THE SECOND VERSE ONLY

HARMONY

Al - le - lu - ia! Al - le - lu - ia! Al - le - lu - ia!

6th cent. *Tr.* C. S. Phillips

528

Holy Communion

Slow

AFTER THE LAST VERSE ONLY

VOICES

ff Al - le - lu - ia,   Al - le - lu - ia,   Al - le - lu - ia.

σιγησάτω πᾶσα σάρξ

mf Not a thought of earthly things!
Every head in awe be bended:
Christ our God, the King of Kings,
Comes by angel troops attended.

2

mf Forth he comes, a Victim he
For the wide world's need avail-
ing,

And his people's food to be,
With himself their souls regaling.

3

Cherubim with watchful eyes,
Seraphim their brows concealing,
f Powers and Principalities,
Cry aloud, like thunder pealing,
Alleluia!

Liturgy of St. James Tr. A. J. MASON

HYMN **393**   Schmücke dich — 8 8 8 8. D   J. Crüger, 1598-1662

Holy Communion

PART 1

Schmücke dich

f Deck thyself, my soul, with gladness,
Leave the gloomy haunts of sadness;
Come into the daylight's splendour,
There with joy thy praises render
Unto him whose grace unbounded
Hath this wondrous banquet founded:
High o'er all the heavens he reigneth,
Yet to dwell with thee he deigneth.

2

p Now I sink before thee lowly,
Filled with joy most deep and holy,
As with trembling awe and wonder
On thy mighty works I ponder:
How, by mystery surrounded,
Depth no man hath ever sounded,
None may dare to pierce unbidden
Secrets that with thee are hidden.

PART 2

3

mf Sun, who all my life dost brighten,
Light, who dost my soul enlighten,
Joy, the sweetest man e'er knoweth,
Fount, whence all my being floweth,
At thy feet I cry, my Maker,
Let me be a fit partaker
Of this blessèd food from heaven,
For our good, thy glory, given.

4

Jesus, Bread of Life, I pray thee,
Let me gladly here obey thee;
Never to my hurt invited,
Be thy love with love requited:
From this banquet let me measure,
Lord, how vast and deep its treasure;
Through the gifts thou here dost give me,
As thy guest in heaven receive me.

J. FRANCK
Tr. Catherine Winkworth

Holy Communion

HYMN 394   FIRST TUNE

Gweedore — 6 6 6 6. 8 8   S. S. Wesley, 1810–76

SECOND TUNE

Author of Life — 6 6 6 6. 8 8   Sir J. Stainer, 1840–1901

532

Holy Communion

Author of life divine,
 Who hast a table spread,
 Furnished with mystic Wine
 And everlasting Bread,
mf Preserve the life thyself hast given,
 And feed and train us up for heaven.

2

p Our needy souls sustain
 With fresh supplies of love,
 Till all thy life we gain,
 And all thy fulness prove,
mf And, strengthened by thy perfect grace,
 Behold without a veil thy face.

J. WESLEY

HYMN **395**   Das neugeborne Kindelein — 8 8. 8 8. 8 8   M. Vulpius,
c. 1560-1616

Harmony by J. S. Bach, 1685-1750

O thou, before the world began
Ordained a Sacrifice for man,
And by the eternal Spirit made
An Offering in the sinner's stead;
Our everlasting Priest art thou,
Pleading thy Death for sinners now.

2
Thy Offering still continues new
Before the righteous Father's view;
Thyself the Lamb for ever slain,
Thy Priesthood doth unchanged remain;
Thy years, O God, can never fail,
Nor thy blest work within the veil.

3
O that our faith may never move,
But stand unshaken as thy love!
Sure evidence of things unseen,
Now let it pass the years between,
And view thee bleeding on the Tree,
My Lord, my God, who dies for me.

C. WESLEY and others

Alternative Tune, Surrey, 179

Holy Communion

FIRST TUNE

Swanmore — L.M.   A. K. Blackall

SECOND TUNE

Rockingham — L.M.   Adapted by E. Miller, 1731-1807

Holy Communion

A lower setting of this tune will be found at Hymn 490

mf My God, and is thy table spread,
    And doth thy cup with love o'erflow?
Thither be all thy children led,
    And let them all thy sweetness know.

2

Hail, sacred feast which Jesus makes,
    Rich banquet of his Flesh and Blood!
Thrice happy he who here partakes
    That sacred stream, that heavenly food.

3

p Why are its bounties all in vain
    Before unwilling hearts displayed?
Was not for them the Victim slain?
    Are they forbid the children's Bread?

4

mf O let thy table honoured be,
    And furnished well with joyful guests;
And may each soul salvation see,
    That here its sacred pledges tastes.

P. DODDRIDGE†

537

Holy Communion

FIRST TUNE

Song 24 — 10 10. 10 10. 10 10   Orlando Gibbons, 1583–1625

SECOND TUNE

Unde et memores — 10 10. 10 10. 10 10   W. H. Monk, 1823–89

p And now, O Father, mindful of the love
    That bought us, once for all, on Calvary's Tree,
And having with us him that pleads above,
    We here present, we here spread forth to thee
mf That only Offering perfect in thine eyes,
    The one true, pure, immortal Sacrifice.

2

p Look, Father, look on his anointed face,
    And only look on us as found in him;
Look not on our misusings of thy grace,
    Our prayer so languid, and our faith so dim:
mf For lo, between our sins and their reward
    We set the Passion of thy Son our Lord.

3

p And then for those, our dearest and our best,
    By this prevailing Presence we appeal:
mf O fold them closer to thy mercy's breast,
    O do thine utmost for their souls' true weal;
From tainting mischief keep them white and clear,
And crown thy gifts with strength to persevere.

4

p And so we come: O draw us to thy feet,
    Most patient Saviour, who canst love us still;
mf And by this food, so aweful and so sweet,
    Deliver us from every touch of ill:
f In thine own service make us glad and free,
    And grant us never more to part with thee.

W. BRIGHT

HYMN **398**   Albano — C.M.   V. Novello, 1781–1861

4

mf Once, only once, and once for all,   *p* So he who once atonement wrought,
    His precious life he gave;   Our Priest of endless power,
    Before the Cross our spirits fall,   Presents himself for those he bought‿
    And own it strong to save.   In that dark noontide hour.

2   5
    'One Offering, single and complete,'   *mf* His Manhood pleads where now it
    With lips and heart we say;   On heaven's eternal throne,   [lives
    But what he never can repeat   And where in mystic rite he gives‿
    He shows forth day by day.   Its Presence to his own.

3   6
    For, as the priest of Aaron's line   And so we show thy Death, O Lord,
    Within the Holiest stood,   Till thou again appear;   [board,
    And sprinkled all the mercy-shrine   And feel, when we approach thy
    With sacrificial blood;   We have an altar here.

7
f   All glory to the Father be,
    All glory to the Son,
    All glory, Holy Ghost, to thee,
    While endless ages run.

W. BRIGHT

HYMN **399**   FIRST TUNE

Alleluia — 8 7 8 7. D   S. S. Wesley, 1810–76

3

Alleluia! Bread of angels,
  Thou on earth our food, our stay;
Alleluia! here the sinful⌣
  Flee to thee from day to day:
Intercessor, Friend of sinners,
  Earth's Redeemer, plead for me,
Where the songs of all the sinless
  Sweep across the crystal sea.

Alleluia! sing to Jesus!
  His the sceptre, his the throne;
Alleluia! his the triumph,
  His the victory alone:
Hark! the songs of peaceful Sion
  Thunder like a mighty flood;
Jesus out of every nation
  Hath redeemed us by his Blood.

2

mf Alleluia! not as orphans⌣
  Are we left in sorrow now;
Alleluia! he is near us,
  Faith believes, nor questions how:
Though the cloud from sight re-
    ceived him,
  When the forty days were o'er,
Shall our hearts forget his promise,
  'I am with you evermore'?

4

Alleluia! King eternal,
  Thee the Lord of Lords we own;
Alleluia! born of Mary,
  Earth thy footstool, heaven thy
    throne:
Thou within the veil hast entered,
  Robed in flesh, our great High Priest;
Thou on earth both Priest and Victim
  In the Eucharistic feast.

W. CHATTERTON DIX

The first verse may be repeated at the end

HYMN **399** SECOND TUNE

Hyfrydol — 8 7 8 7. D R. H. Prichard, 1811–87

Holy Communion

f Alleluia! sing to Jesus!
  His the sceptre, his the throne;
Alleluia! his the triumph,
  His the victory alone:
Hark! the songs of peaceful Sion
  Thunder like a mighty flood;
Jesus out of every nation
  Hath redeemed us by his Blood.

2

mf Alleluia! not as orphans
  Are we left in sorrow now;
Alleluia! he is near us,
  Faith believes, nor questions how:
Though the cloud from sight received him,
  When the forty days were o'er,
Shall our hearts forget his promise,
  'I am with you evermore'?

3

Alleluia! Bread of angels,
  Thou on earth our food, our stay;
Alleluia! here the sinful
  Flee to thee from day to day:
Intercessor, Friend of sinners,
  Earth's Redeemer, plead for me,
Where the songs of all the sinless
  Sweep across the crystal sea.

4

Alleluia! King eternal,
  Thee the Lord of Lords we own;
Alleluia! born of Mary,
  Earth thy footstool, heaven thy throne:
Thou within the veil hast entered,
  Robed in flesh, our great High Priest;
Thou on earth both Priest and Victim
  In the Eucharistic feast.

W. CHATTERTON DIX

The first verse may be repeated at the end

Holy Communion

f Lord, enthroned in heavenly splen-
    dour,
  First-begotten from the dead,
  Thou alone, our strong defender,
  Liftest up thy people's head.
    Alleluia!
  Jesu, true and living Bread.

2

mf Here our humblest homage pay we,
  Here in loving reverence bow;
  Here for faith's discernment pray we,
  Lest we fail to know thee now.
f   Alleluia!
  Thou art here, we ask not how.

3

p Though the lowliest form doth veil
  As of old in Bethlehem,   [thee
  Here as there thine angels hail thee,
  Branch and Flower of Jesse's Stem
f   Alleluia!
  We in worship join with them.

4

mf Paschal Lamb, thine Offering, fin-
  ished,
  Once for all when thou wast slain,
  In its fulness undiminished
  Shall for evermore remain,
f   Alleluia!
  Cleansing souls from every stain.

5

Life-imparting heavenly Manna,
Stricken Rock with streaming side,
Heaven and earth with loud Hosanna
Worship thee, the Lamb who died,
Alleluia!
Risen, ascended, glorified!

G. H. Bourne

Holy Communion

We pray thee, heavenly Father,
  To hear us in thy love,
And pour upon thy children
  The unction from above;
That so in love abiding,
  From all defilement free,
We may in pureness offer
  Our Eucharist to thee.

2
Be thou our guide and helper,
  O Jesu Christ, we pray;
So may we well approach thee,
  If thou wilt be the Way:
Thou, very Truth, hast promised
  To help us in our strife,
Food of the weary pilgrim,
  Eternal source of Life.

3
And thou, Creator Spirit,
  Look on us, we are thine;
Renew in us thy graces,
  Upon our darkness shine;
That, with thy benediction
  Upon our souls outpoured,
We may receive in gladness
  The Body of the Lord.

4
O Trinity of Persons!
  O Unity most high!
On thee alone relying
  Thy servants would draw nigh:
Unworthy in our weakness,
  On thee our hope is stayed,
And blessed by thy forgiveness
  We will not be afraid.

V. S. S. COLES

Holy Communion

mf O thou, who at thy Eucharist didst pray
    That all thy Church might be for ever one,
p Grant us at every Eucharist to say
    With longing heart and soul, 'Thy will be done:'
    O may we all one Bread, one Body be,
    Through this blest Sacrament of unity.

2

mf For all thy Church, O Lord, we intercede;
    Make thou our sad divisions soon to cease;
    Draw us the nearer each to each, we plead,
    By drawing all to thee, O Prince of Peace:
    Thus may we all one Bread, one Body be,
p Through this blest Sacrament of unity.

3

We pray thee too for wanderers from thy fold;
    O bring them back, Good Shepherd of the sheep,
Back to the faith which saints believed of old,
    Back to the Church which still that faith doth keep:
Soon may we all one Bread, one Body be,
Through this blest Sacrament of unity.

4

mf So, Lord, at length when sacraments shall cease,
    May we be one with all thy Church above,
One with thy saints in one unbroken peace,
    One with thy saints in one unbounded love:
More blessèd still, in peace and love to be
p One with the Trinity in Unity.

W. H. TURTON

Holy Communion

f We hail thy Presence glorious,
　　O Christ our great High Priest,
O'er sin and death victorious,
　　At thy thanksgiving feast :
As thou art interceding
　　For us in heaven above,
Thy Church on earth is pleading
　　Thy perfect work of love.

2

mf Through thee in every nation
　　Thine own their hearts upraise,
Offering one pure Oblation,
　　One Sacrifice of praise :
With thee in blest communion
　　The living and the dead
Are joined in closest union,
　　One Body with one Head.

3

O Living Bread from heaven,
　　Jesu, our Saviour good,
Who thine own self hast given
　　To be our souls' true food ;
For us thy body broken
　　Hung on the Cross of shame :
This Bread its hallowed token
　　We break in thy dear name.

4

O stream of love unending,
　　Poured from the one true Vine,
With our weak nature blending
　　The strength of life divine ;
Our thankful faith confessing
　　In thy life-blood outpoured,
We drink this Cup of blessing
　　And praise thy name, O Lord.

5
May we thy word believing
  Thee through thy gifts receive,
That, thou within us living,
  We all to God may live;

Draw us from earth to heaven
  Till sin and sorrow cease,
Forgiving and forgiven,
  In love and joy and peace.

BISHOP R. G. PARSONS

HYMN **404**   Stonor — 11 10 11 10   S. Watson

O joy of God, that comest in the morning,
  For thee, unsunned, we wait and eastward gaze,
Lift on our dark the splendours of thy dawning,
  Flood all our being in the feast of praise.

2
O life of God, for whom our spirits hunger,
  Except we eat and drink indeed of thee,
With love and faith renewed and hope grown younger
  Send us out hence thy saving health to see.

3
O peace of God, that passest understanding,
  Guard thou our heart through every fretting day:
In him who is our Peace, our wills commanding,
  Direct our path and perfect all our way.

BISHOP C. H. BOUTFLOWER

Holy Communion

HYMN **405** St. Mark — L.M. W. Crowfoot, 1724–83
From Crisp's *Divine Harmony*, 1755

At the Offertory

f Almighty Father, Lord most high,
　　Who madest all, who fillest all,
　　Thy name we praise and magnify,
　　For all our needs on thee we call.

2

mf We offer to thee of thine own
　　Ourselves and all that we can bring,
　　In Bread and Cup before thee shown,
　　Our universal offering.

3

　　All that we have we bring to thee,
　　Yet all is naught when all is done,
　　Save that in it thy love can see
　　The Sacrifice of thy dear Son.

4

　　By his command in Bread and Cup
　　His Body and his Blood we plead:
p What on the Cross he offered up
　　Is here our Sacrifice indeed.

5

mf For all thy gifts of life and grace,
　　Here we thy servants humbly pray
　　That thou would'st look upon the face
　　Of thine anointed Son to-day.

V. S. S. COLES

550

Holy Communion

HYMN **406**   Gott des Himmels — 8 7. 8 7. 7 7   H. Albert, 1604–5ı

At the Offertory

1
Lord, accept the alms we offer,
  Tokens of our love to thee;
Out of grateful hearts we render
  This our act of charity;
Even though full well we know
All we have to thee we owe.

2
Use them, Father, to thy glory,
  Teach us fully how to give,
For his sake who leaving heaven
  Gave us all that we might live:
All we have could not suffice
To repay his Sacrifice.

3
Now the priest upon the altar
  Doth present the bread and wine,
To become, in wondrous manner,
  For our souls the food divine:
Soul and body by thee fed,
Praise we give for daily bread.

4
With our alms and our oblations
  Take, O Lord, our prayers of love;
Make thy Church in fullest concord
  Serve as one, below, above;
And in fellowship complete
Reach at last thy mercy-seat.

S. N. SEDGWICK

Holy Communion

FIRST TUNE

Ave verum Corpus natum — Irregular   Mode v

Ave verum Corpus natum

1 {Hail, true Bo-dy, born of Ma-ry, By a won-drous Vir-gin-birth!
  {Thou who on the Cross wast of-fered To re-deem the sons of earth;

2 {Thou whose side be-came a foun-tain Pour-ing forth thy pre-cious Blood,
  {Give us now, and at our dy-ing, Thine own self to be our food.

O sweet-est Je - su, O gra-cious Je - su,

O Je - su, bless - èd Ma - ry's Son.

Holy Communion

Standish — Irregular   J. Dykes Bower

Slow and sustained. May be sung in Unison

AFTER THE SECOND VERSE:

O sweet-est Je - su, O gra-cious Je - su, O Je - su,

bless-èd Ma - ry's Son.

At the Communion

Ave verum Corpus natum

Hail, true Body, born of Mary,
 By a wondrous Virgin-birth!
Thou who on the Cross wast offered
 To redeem the sons of earth;

2
Thou whose side became a fountain
 Pouring forth thy precious Blood,
Give us now, and at our dying,
 Thine own self to be our food.

O sweetest Jesu, O gracious Jesu,
O Jesu, blessèd Mary's Son.

14th cent. *Tr.* H. N. OxENHAM‡

Holy Communion

HYMN **408** Liebster Jesu — 7 8. 7 8. 8 8   J. R. Ahle, 1625-73

Harmony by J. S. Bach, 1685-1750

At the Communion

Liebster Jesu, wir sind hier

2

mf Dearest Jesu, we are here,
    At thy call, thy Presence owning;
    Pleading now in holy fear
      That great Sacrifice atoning:
p   Word incarnate, much in wonder
    On this mystery deep we ponder.

mf Jesu, strong to save—the same‿
    Yesterday, to-day, for ever—
    Make us fear and love thy name,
      Serving thee with best endeavour
f   In this life, O ne'er forsake us,
    But to bliss hereafter take us.

T. CLAUSNITZER
Tr. G. R. Woodward

554

Holy Communion

FIRST TUNE

Genevan Psalm cxviii — 9 8 9 8. D   L. Bourgeois, *Genevan Psalter*, 1543

1 *p* Bread of the world in mer - cy bro - ken, Wine of the soul in mer - cy shed,

mf By whom the words of life were spo-ken, And in whose Death our sins are dead;

2 *p* Look on the heart by sor-row bro - ken, Look on the tears by sin-ners shed;

mf And be thy feast to us the to - ken That by thy grace our souls are fed.

BISHOP R. HEBER

Holy Communion

SECOND TUNE

Emmanuel — 9 8 9 8

German 'Courante,' *c.* 1675

Harmony from J. S. Bach, 1685–1750

At the Communion

p Bread of the world in mercy broken,
   Wine of the soul in mercy shed,
mf By whom the words of life were spoken,
   And in whose Death our sins are dead;

2

p Look on the heart by sorrow broken,
   Look on the tears by sinners shed;
mf And be thy feast to us the token
   That by thy grace our souls are fed.

BISHOP R. HEBER

Holy Communion

Sicilian Melody

At the Communion

O most mer - ci - ful! O most boun - ti - ful!

God the Fa - ther Al - migh - ty,

By the Re - deem - er's Sweet in - ter - ces - sion,

Hear us, help us, when we cry.

BISHOP R. HEBER

557

HYMN 411 FIRST TUNE

Nicht so traurig — 7 7. 7 7. 7 7 J. S. Bach. 1685–1750

SECOND TUNE

Bread of Heaven — 7 7. 7 7. 7 7 Archbishop W. D. Maclagan
1826–191

At the Communion

mf Bread of heaven, on thee we feed,
For thy Flesh is meat indeed;
Ever may our souls be fed
With this true and living Bread;
Day by day with strength supplied
Through the life of him who died.

2

Vine of heaven, thy Blood supplies⏝
This blest Cup of Sacrifice;
p   Lord, thy wounds our healing give,
To thy Cross we look and live:
mf Jesus, may we ever be⏝
Grafted, rooted, built in thee.

J. Conder‡

Holy Communion

ALTERNATIVE VERSION

(Melody in the Tenor part)

Harmonized by T. Ravenscroft (1621)

The Alternative Version may be used for verses 2 and 4

Holy Communion

At the Communion

p O God, unseen yet ever near,
    Thy Presence may we feel;
And, thus inspired with holy fear,
    Before thine altar kneel.

2

mf Here may thy faithful people know
    The blessings of thy love,
The streams that through the desert flow,
    The manna from above.

3

We come, obedient to thy word,
    To feast on heavenly food;
Our meat the Body of the Lord,
    Our drink his precious Blood.

4

Thus may we all thy word obey,
    For we, O God, are thine;
And go rejoicing on our way,
    Renewed with strength divine.

E. OSLER

Alternative Tune, Irish, 263

Holy Communion

B. Luard Selby, 1853–1919

A lower setting of this tune will be found at Hymn 89

At the Communion

p   I hunger and I thirst:
    Jesu, my manna be;
    Ye living waters, burst⌣
    Out of the rock for me.

2
Thou bruised and broken Bread,
    My life-long wants supply;
    As living souls are fed,
    O feed me, or I die.

3
mf   Thou true life-giving Vine,
    Let me thy sweetness prove;
    Renew my life with thine,
    Refresh my soul with love.

4
p   Rough paths my feet have trod
    Since first their course began:
    Feed me, thou Bread of God;
    Help me, thou Son of Man.

5
For still the desert lies
    My thirsting soul before:
mf   O living waters, rise⌣
    Within me evermore.

J. S. B. MONSELL

Holy Communion

HYMN **414**   Farley Castle — 10 10 10 10   H. Lawes, 1596–1662

At the Communion

mf Here, O my Lord, I see thee face to face;
    Here faith would touch and handle things unseen;
    Here grasp with firmer hand the eternal grace,
    And all my weariness upon thee lean.

2

Here would I feed upon the Bread of God;
    Here drink with thee the royal Wine of heaven;
    Here would I lay aside each earthly load;
    Here taste afresh the calm of sin forgiven.

3

p   I have no help but thine; nor do I need
    Another arm save thine to lean upon:
mf It is enough, my Lord, enough indeed,
    My strength is in thy might, thy might alone.

H. Bonar

563

Holy Communion

At the Communion

Faithful Shepherd, feed me
  In the pastures green;
Faithful Shepherd, lead me
  Where thy steps are seen.

2
Hold me fast, and guide me
  In the narrow way;
So, with thee beside me,
  I shall never stray.

3
Daily bring me nearer⌣
  To the heavenly shore;
Make my faith grow clearer,
  May I love thee more.

4
Hallow every pleasure,
  Every gift and pain;
Be thyself my treasure,
  Though none else I gain.

5
Day by day prepare me
  As thou seest best,
Then let angels bear me⌣
  To thy promised rest.

T. B. POLLOCK

Holy Communion

May be sung in Unison

By permission of the English Hymnal Company, Ltd.

At the Communion

Wherefore, O Father, we thy humble servants
Here bring before thee Christ thy well-belovèd,
All perfect Offering, Sacrifice immortal,
    Spotless Oblation.

2

See now thy children, making intercession
Through him our Saviour, Son of God incarnate,
For all thy people, living and departed,
    Pleading before thee.

W. H. H. JERVOIS

565

Holy Communion

After Communion

ἀπὸ δόξης εἰς δόξαν πορευόμενοι

From glory to glory advancing, we praise thee, O Lord;
Thy name with the Father and Spirit be ever adored.

2

From strength unto strength we go forward on Sion's highway,
To appear before God in the city of infinite day.

3

Thanksgiving, and glory and worship, and blessing and love,
One heart and one song have the saints upon earth and above.

4

Evermore, O Lord, to thy servants thy presence be nigh;
Ever fit us by service on earth for thy service on high.

Liturgy of St. James
Tr. C. W. HUMPHREYS

Holy Communion

Bournemouth — 6 5 6 5   Sir C. H. H. Parry, 1848–1918

SECOND TUNE

Eucharisticus — 6 5 6 5   Sir J. Stainer, 1840–1901

After Communion

p Jesu, gentlest Saviour,
  Thou art in us now :
mf Fill us with thy goodness,
  Till our hearts o'erflow.

2
p Multiply our graces,
  Chiefly love and fear,
mf And, dear Lord, the chiefest,
  Grace to persevere.

3*
Nature cannot hold thee,
  Heaven is all too strait
For thine endless glory
  And thy royal state.

4*
Yet the hearts of children
  Hold what worlds cannot,
And the God of wonders
  Loves the lowly spot.

5
O how can we thank thee
  For a gift like this,
Gift that truly maketh
  Heaven's eternal bliss?

6
p Ah, when wilt thou always
  Make our hearts thy home?
mf We must wait for heaven ;
  Then the day will come.

F. W. FABER

567

HYMN **419**   O Jesu Christ — L.M.   P. Reinigius (1587)

After Communion

O Jesu, sode Jesu, dig

mf O Jesu, blessèd Lord, to thee
My heartfelt thanks for ever be,
Who hast so lovingly bestowed
On me thy Body and thy Blood.

2

f Break forth, my soul, for joy, and say,
'What wealth is come to me to-day!
mf My Saviour dwells within me now;
How blest am I! how good art thou!'

T. KINGO
Tr. A. J. Mason

HYMN **420** Brockham — L.M.   J. Clarke, *c.* 1659–1707

A higher setting of this tune will be found at Hymn 45

   f   How glorious is the life above
       Which in this ordinance we taste,
    That fulness of celestial love,
       That joy which shall for ever last!

2
  mf That heavenly life in Christ concealed
       These earthen vessels could not bear;
    The part which now we find revealed
       No tongue of angels can declare.

3
   f   The light of life eternal darts⌣
       Into our souls a dazzling ray;
    A drop of heaven o'erflows our hearts,
       And floods with joy the house of clay.

4
    Sure pledge of ecstasies unknown
       Shall this divine Communion be:
    The ray shall rise into a sun,
       The drop shall swell into a sea.

                      C. WESLEY†

Holy Communion

VERSES 2 AND 3 SHOULD BEGIN THUS:

f   Hosanna in the highest
To our exalted Saviour,
   Who left behind
   For all mankind
These tokens of his favour:
mf His bleeding love and mercy,
His all-redeeming Passion;
f   Who here displays,
   And gives the grace
Which brings us our salvation.

2

Louder than gathered waters,
Or bursting peals of thunder,
   We lift our voice
   And speak our joys,
And shout our loving wonder.
Shout, all our elder brethren,
While we record the story
   Of him that came
   And suffered shame,
To carry us to glory.

3

mf Angels in fixed amazement
Around our altars hover,
   With eager gaze
   Adore the grace
Of our eternal Lover:
Himself and all his fulness
Who gives to the believer;
f   And by this Bread
   Whoe'er are fed
Shall live with God for ever.

C. WESLEY

HYMN **422**   Laus Deo — 8 7 8 7. 8 8 7   J. S. Bach, 1685–1750
From G. C. Schemelli's *Gesang-Buch*, 1736

Thee, living Christ, our eyes behold
 Amid thy Church appearing,
All girt about thy breast with gold
And bright apparel wearing;
Thy countenance is burning light,
A sun that shineth in his might:
 Lord Christ, we see thy glory.

2

Thy glorious feet have sought and
 Thy sons of every nation; [found
Thine everlasting voice doth sound
 The call of our salvation;

Thine eyes of flame do search and scan
The whole outspreading realm of man:
 Lord Christ, we see thy glory.

3

O risen Christ, who art alive,
 Amid thy Church abiding,
Who dost thy Blood and Body give
 New life and strength providing,
We join in heavenly company
To sing thy praise triumphantly:
 For we have seen thy glory.

BISHOP E. R. MORGAN

NOTE. *This hymn is based on the vision of the Glorified Christ in Rev.* 1. 12–16

572

Holy Communion

*Hymn Melody of the
Bohemian Brethren,* 1566

2

Let us employ all notes of joy
  And praise that never endeth
To God above, whose mighty love⌣
  Our hearts and minds defendeth;
Who by his grace, in every place,
To all who need, and duly plead,
  His power and presence lendeth.

For, ere he died, the Crucified⌣
  Wrought things eternal for us
By bread and wine, which Love divine⌣
  Hath given to assure us:
O taste and see; find him to be
Our great reward, our living Lord
  Most willing to restore us.

3

The word he spoke, the bread he broke
  Shall fill our lives with glory,
If we are true and loving too
  And for our sins are sorry:
O do his will, and praise him still,
And still proclaim his glorious name
  And deathless Gospel story.

ADAM FOX

The following hymns are suitable:

494 Hands that have been handling.
622 Praise, O Sion, praise thy Master.

HOLY BAPTISM

HYMN **424**   St. Stephen — C.M.   W. Jones, 1726-1800

A higher setting of this tune will be found at Hymn 52

mf   In token that thou shalt not fear⌣
    Christ crucified to own,
We print the cross upon thee here,
    And stamp thee his alone.

2

In token that thou shalt not blush⌣
    To glory in his name,
We blazon here upon thy front
    His glory and his shame.

3

In token that thou shalt not flinch⌣
    Christ's quarrel to maintain,
But 'neath his banner manfully
    Firm at thy post remain ;

4

In token that thou too shalt tread⌣
    The path he travelled by,
Endure the cross, despise the shame,
    And sit thee down on high ;

5

f   Thus outwardly and visibly⌣
    We seal thee for his own ;
And may the brow that wears his Cross
    Hereafter share his crown.

H. ALFORD

Holy Baptism

HYMN **425** The Child Jesus — 8 8 8 8. 8

Melody by S. Scheidt,
1587–1654

Ach lieber Herre, Jesu Christ

Lord Jesu Christ, our Lord most dear,
As thou wast once an infant here,
So give this child of thine, we pray,
Thy grace and blessing day by day:
O holy Jesu, Lord divine.

2

As in thy heavenly kingdom, Lord,
All things obey thy sacred word,
Do thou thy mighty succour give,
And shield this child by morn and eve:
O holy Jesu, Lord divine.

3

Their watch let angels round *him* keep
Where'er *he* be, awake, asleep;
Thy holy Cross now let *him* bear,
That *he* thy crown with saints may wear:
O holy Jesu, Lord divine.

H. von Laufenberg
Tr. Catherine Winkworth‡

575

Holy Baptism

A higher setting of this tune will be found at Hymn 317

O Father, for this little life
　Entrusted from above,
Ere yet *he* face earth's sin and strife,
　We supplicate thy love.

2
As Hannah to the Temple gate
　Her dearest treasure bore,
So, Lord, to thee we consecrate
　This child for evermore.

3
Thy faithful soldier, may *he* fight
　With falsehood, sin, and shame,
And losing all to win the right
　Confess thy holy name.

4
Thy faithful servant, may *he* learn
　To love and labour still,
And with a flaming spirit burn
　To know and do thy will.

5
O Saviour, all *he* is is thine,
　And all *he* yet may be :
O shelter *him* with love divine,
　And draw *him* near to thee.

6
For thou, O Lord, art all our life,
　In thee all struggles end :
Through all the sorrow and the strife
　Our Maker and our Friend.

BISHOP GILBERT WHITE

576

Holy Baptism

HYMN **427**   Hawkhurst — L.M.   H. J. Gauntlett, 1805–76

A higher setting of this tune will be found at Hymn 232

O loving Father, to thy care
  We give again this child of thine,
Baptized and blessed with faithful prayer
  And sealed with Love's victorious sign.

2
As Christ, thy Son, did not refuse
  The homage of the children's cry,
So teach *him* childhood's gifts to use
  Thy name to praise and magnify.

3
Through youth and age, through shine and shade,
  Grant *him* to run *his* earthly race,
Forgetting not that man was made
  To show thy glory and thy grace:

4
A loving child, a faithful friend,
  A light in doubt and darkness given
To point the path that knows no end
  Save in the fuller light of heaven;

5
Till, at the last, before thy throne
  He lays *his* earthly armour down,
His task of loving service done,
  And, in thy mercy, takes *his* crown.

C. A. ALINGTON

Holy Baptism

HYMN **428**   Christe sanctorum — 11 11 11 5   La Feillée, *Méthode*, 1782

May be sung in Unison

To thee, O Father, lamp of all the living,
We offer now this life of thine own giving:
Humbly we pray thee, through this earth's endeavour
    Light *his* steps ever.

2
Jesus, thyself a baby once from heaven,
To thee this little pilgrim here is given:
Within the mercy of thy fold befriend *him*;
    Thy love attend *him*.

3
Spirit of Comfort, fountain ever welling,
This infant's heart take now to be thy dwelling;
So may *he* live, grace, pity, truth confessing,
    Thy peace possessing.

4
Gather *him*, Holy Trinity, for ever
Into the wisdom of thy strength, that never
In life's dark shadow-lands thy love may leave *him*:
    Thine own receive *him*.

RONALD, LORD GORELL

578

FOR THE YOUNG

HYMN **429** Keine Schönheit hat die Welt — 7 7 7 7 Melody in
G. Joseph's *Seelenlust*, 1657

Harmonized by C. Wood, 1866–1926

By permission of Schott & Co., Ltd.

Morning

Through the night thy angels kept⏝
Watch beside me while I slept;
Now the dark has passed away,
Thank thee, Lord, for this new day.

2
North and south and east and west
May thy holy name be blest;
Everywhere beneath the sun,
As in heaven, thy will be done.

3
Give me food that I may live;
Every naughtiness forgive;
Keep all evil things away
From thy little child this day.

W. CANTON

579

For the Young

Morning

A work hath Christ for thee to do :
He bore the Cross, he laboured too.
He marks thine every deed and word :
Be true this day to Christ thy Lord.

2

A way hath Christ for thee to go,
The royal way he trod below :
Fear not, for he is at thy side,
Thy heart to cheer, thy steps to guide.

3

Then bravely forth his praise to tell,
With song on lip, to serve him well.
Life this new dawn begins anew :
For Jesus' sake be true, be true.

E. D. Sedding

For the Young

By permission of J. Curwen & Sons, Ltd.

Evening

p Now the day is over,
   Night is drawing nigh,
Shadows of the evening
   Steal across the sky.

2
Now the darkness gathers,
   Stars begin to peep,
Birds and beasts and flowers
   Soon will be asleep.

3
mf Jesu, give the weary
   Calm and sweet repose;
p With thy tenderest blessing
   May mine eyelids close.

4
mf Grant to little children
   Visions bright of thee;
Guard the sailors tossing
   On the deep blue sea.

5
p Comfort every sufferer
   Watching late in pain;
Those who plan some evil
   From their sin restrain.

6
Through the long night watches
   May thine angels spread
Their white wings above me,
   Watching round my bed.

7
mf When the morning wakens,
   Then may I arise
Pure and fresh and sinless
   In thy holy eyes.

8
f Glory to the Father,
   Glory to the Son,
And to thee, blest Spirit,
   Whilst all ages run.

S. BARING-GOULD

581

For the Young

HYMN 432 Irby — 8 7. 8 7. 7 7 H. J. Gauntlett, 1805–76

* *In verses 2 and 4 these minims are sung as two crotchets*

Suitable for Christmas

mf Once in royal David's city
Stood a lowly cattle shed,
Where a mother laid her baby
In a manger for his bed :
Mary was that Mother mild,
Jesus Christ her little Child.

582

2

He came down to earth from heaven
Who is God and Lord of all,
p   And his shelter was a stable,
And his cradle was a stall;
With the poor and mean and lowly
Lived on earth our Saviour holy.

3

mf And through all his wondrous childhood
He would honour and obey,
Love and watch the lowly Maiden,
In whose gentle arms he lay:
Christian children all must be
Mild, obedient, good as he.

4

For he is our childhood's pattern,
Day by day like us he grew,
p   He was little, weak, and helpless,
Tears and smiles like us he knew;
mf And he feeleth for our sadness,
And he shareth in our gladness.

5

f   And our eyes at last shall see him,
Through his own redeeming love,
For that Child so dear and gentle
Is our Lord in heaven above;
And he leads his children on
To the place where he is gone.

6

mf Not in that poor lowly stable,
With the oxen standing by,
We shall see him; but in heaven,
f   Set at God's right hand on high;
Where like stars his children crowned
All in white shall wait around.

Mrs. C. F. Alexander

For the Young

FIRST TUNE

Glenfinlas — 6 5 6 5   K. G. Finlay

SECOND TUNE

Newland — 6 5 6 5   J. Armstrong, 1840–1928

584

For the Young

mf Do no sinful action,
    Speak no angry word :
    Ye belong to Jesus,
      Children of the Lord.

2

Christ is kind and gentle,
    Christ is pure and true ;
    And his little children
      Must be holy too.

3

p There's a wicked spirit
    Watching round you still,
    And he tries to tempt you
      To all harm and ill.

4

mf But ye must not hear him,
    Though 'tis hard for you
    To resist the evil,
      And the good to do.

5

For ye promised truly,
    In your infant days,
    To renounce him wholly,
      And forsake his ways.

6

Ye are new-born Christians,
    Ye must learn to fight
    With the bad within you,
      And to do the right.

7

Christ is your own Master,
    He is good and true,
    And his little children
      Must be holy too.

MRS. C. F. ALEXANDER

For the Young

Suitable for Lent

We have a King who came to earth
   To win the world for God,
And we, the children of the King,
   Must follow where he trod.

2
The banner that our King unfurled
   Was love to every man,
So we must try to show that love
   In all the ways we can.

3
The enemies he came to fight
   Are selfishness and sin :
Then who would be a traitor now
   And let his foemen in?

4
He bids us keep our bodies pure,
   For 'tis the pure and clean‿
Can see the glory of the King,
   And tell what they have seen.

5
We are a little company,
   But we are pledged to bring‿
Pure holy lives, kind joyful hearts,
   And bring them to the King.

MARGARET CROPPER

For the Young

Suitable for Passiontide

mf It is a thing most wonderful,
Almost too wonderful to be,
That God's own Son should come from heaven,
And die to save a child like me.

2
And yet I know that it is true:
He chose a poor and humble lot,
p And wept and toiled and mourned and died
For love of those who loved him not.

3
mf I cannot tell how he could love
A child so weak and full of sin;
His love must be most wonderful,
If he could die my love to win.

4
p I sometimes think about the Cross,
And shut my eyes, and try to see͜
The cruel nails and crown of thorns,
And Jesus crucified for me.

5
But even could I see him die,
I could but see a little part
mf Of that great love which, like a fire,
Is always burning in his heart.

6
It is most wonderful to know
His love for me so free and sure;
p But 'tis more wonderful to see
My love for him so faint and poor.

7
mf And yet I want to love thee, Lord!
O light the flame within my heart,
f And I will love thee more and more,
Until I see thee as thou art.

BISHOP W. WALSHAM HOW

587

For the Young

Suitable for Passiontide

O dearest Lord, thy sacred head
  With thorns was pierced for me;
O pour thy blessing on my head
  That I may think for thee.

2

O dearest Lord, thy sacred hands
  With nails were pierced for me;
O shed thy blessing on my hands
  That they may work for thee.

3

O dearest Lord, thy sacred feet
  With nails were pierced for me;
O pour thy blessing on my feet
  That they may follow thee.

4

O dearest Lord, thy sacred heart
  With spear was pierced for me;
O pour thy Spirit in my heart
  That I may live for thee.

H. E. Hardy (Father Andrew)

Hymn **437**   Infantium laudes — 7 6 7 6. 7 6 7 6. 11   Sir C. H. H. Parry,
                                                  1848–1918

For the Young

Ho - san - na, Ho - san - na to Je - sus

Suitable for Palm Sunday

When, his salvation bringing,
    To Zion Jesus came,
The children all stood singing
    Hosanna to his name;
Nor did their zeal offend him,
    But, as he rode along,
He let them still attend him,
    And listened to their song:
        Hosanna to Jesus they sang.

2

And since the Lord retaineth
    His love for children still,
Though now as King he reigneth
    On Zion's heavenly hill,

We'll flock around his banner,
    Who sits upon the throne,
And cry aloud 'Hosanna'
    To David's royal Son:
        Hosanna to Jesus we'll sing.

3

For should we fail proclaiming
    Our great Redeemer's praise,
The stones, our silence shaming,
    Would their Hosannas raise.
But shall we only render
    The tribute of our words?
No, while our hearts are tender,
    They, too, shall be the Lord's:
        Hosanna to Jesus, our King!

J. KING

For the Young

Easter

Good Joseph had a garden,
  Close by that sad green hill
Where Jesus died a bitter death
  To save mankind from ill.

2
One evening in that garden,
  Their faces dark with gloom,
They laid the Saviour's body
  Within good Joseph's tomb.

3
There came the holy women
  With spices and with tears;
The angels tried to comfort them,
  But could not calm their fears.

4
Came Mary to that garden
  And sobbed with heart forlorn;
She thought she heard the gardener ask
  'Whom seekest thou this morn?'

5
She heard her own name spoken,
  And then she lost her care:
All in his strength and beauty
  The risen Lord stood fair!

6
Good Joseph had a garden;
  Amid its trees so tall
The Lord Christ stood on Easter Day:
  He lives to save us all.

7
And as he rose at Easter
  He is alive for ay,
The very same Lord Jesus Christ
  Who hears us sing to-day.

8
Go tell the Lord Christ's message,
  The Easter triumph sing,
Till all his waiting children know
  That Jesus is their King.

ALDA M. MILNER-BARRY

For the Young

HYMN **439** St. James — C.M. R. Courteville (1697)

A lower setting of this tune will be found at Hymn 557

Ascension

The golden gates are lifted up,
The doors are opened wide,
The King of Glory is gone up
Unto his Father's side.

2
And ever on our earthly path
A gleam of glory lies,
A light still breaks behind the cloud
That veils thee from our eyes.

3
Lift up our hearts, lift up our minds,
And let thy grace be given,
That, while we linger yet below,
Our treasure be in heaven;

4
That, where thou art at God's right hand,
Our hope, our love may be:
Dwell in us now, that we may dwell
For evermore in thee.

MRS. C. F. ALEXANDER

For the Young

HYMN **440** London New — C.M. *Psalms* (Edinburgh, 1635)

Suitable for Whitsuntide

mf Thou Wind of God, whose coming stirred
    A world as yet unmade,
    And things, which were not, woke and heard
    And answered and obeyed;

2
    By thee the lives that live and move
    In earth and sea began,
    And human thought and human love
    Lit up the heart of man;

3
p Until thou camest, Holy One,
    In Jesus' heart to dwell,
  That man, in him, might be a son
    And please the Father well.

4
mf O thou, who from the Father art,
    Upon our spirits move,
f Until the children's thankful heart
    Reflects the Father's love.

J. M. C. CRUM

HYMN **441** Radwell — 11 11 11 11 H. P. Chadwyck-Heal

For the Young

Suitable for Dedication

O Father, we thank thee for Jesus thy Son,
For all that for us by his death he hath won,
His rising at Easter, his reign on thy throne,
His gift of the Spirit to make us thine own.

2

All praise to thee, Lord, for evangelists brave,
The witness by word and by life that they gave,
The Church of our fathers, the home of us all,
Her sturdy grey towers and steeples so tall.

3

All praise for the masons who built them so true
With axe and with chisel, the best that they knew;
All praise for the craftsmen who carved with a will,
The nave and the chancel with glory to fill.

4

How surely they painted, those guildsmen of old,
The screen with its martyrs aglimmer with gold!
How fair shone their windows which let the sun through,
And flecked the white pillars with crimson and blue!

5

Then ring out, ye belfries, from hill and from plain,
And thunder, ye organs, in deep-toned refrain:
Praise God, priest and people, for blessings outpoured
On Britain, our homeland. Yes, praise ye the Lord!

E. D. SEDDING

NOTE. *Most of the above hymns, while being specially suitable for the seasons indicated, may sung throughout the year*

For the Young

Royal Oak — 7 6 7 6 with refrain   Adapted from an English traditional
melody by Martin Shaw

1 All things bright and beau-ti-ful, All crea-tures great and small,

All things wise and won-der-ful, The Lord God made them all.

2 Each lit-tle flower that o-pens, Each lit-tle bird that sings, He

NOTE. *The pause (⌢) is for the last time only*

594

For the Young

made their glow-ing col-ours, He made their ti-ny wings.

f All things bright and beautiful,
　　All creatures great and small,
　　All things wise and wonderful,
　　The Lord God made them all.

2
mf Each little flower that opens,
　　Each little bird that sings,
　　He made their glowing colours,
　　He made their tiny wings.
f 　　All things bright, etc.

3
mf The purple-headed mountain,
　　The river running by,
　　The sunset, and the morning
　　That brightens up the sky :
f 　　All things bright, etc.

4
mf The cold wind in the winter,
　　The pleasant summer sun,
　　The ripe fruits in the garden,
　　He made them every one.
f 　　All things bright, etc.

5*
mf The tall trees in the greenwood,
　　The meadows where we play,
　　The rushes by the water
　　We gather every day :
f 　　All things bright, etc.

6
mf He gave us eyes to see them,
　　And lips that we might tell
　　How great is God Almighty,
　　Who has made all things well.
f 　　All things bright, etc.

Mrs. C. F. Alexander

595

For the Young

All things bright and beautiful — 7 6 7 6 with refrain

W. H. Monk,
1823–89

VERSE 1, AND THE REFRAIN AFTER VERSES 2, 3, 4, 5, 6

1 All things bright and beau - ti - ful, All crea - tures great and small,

Fine.

All things wise and won - der - ful, The Lord God made them all.

VERSES 2, 3, 4, 5, 6

D.C.

Org.

For the Young

f All things bright and beautiful,
   All creatures great and small,
   All things wise and wonderful,
      The Lord God made them all.

2

mf Each little flower that opens,
    Each little bird that sings,
    He made their glowing colours,
    He made their tiny wings.
f   All things bright, etc.

3

mf The purple-headed mountain,
    The river running by,
    The sunset, and the morning
    That brightens up the sky :
f   All things bright, etc.

4

mf The cold wind in the winter,
    The pleasant summer sun,
    The ripe fruits in the garden,
    He made them every one.
f   All things bright, etc.

5*

mf The tall trees in the greenwood,
    The meadows where we play,
    The rushes by the water
    We gather every day :
f   All things bright, etc.

6

mf He gave us eyes to see them,
    And lips that we might tell
    How great is God Almighty,
    Who has made all things well.
f   All things bright, etc.

MRS. C. F. ALEXANDER

For the Young

HYMN **443** St. Leonard — C.M.　　　　　　　　　H. Smart, 1813-79

Lord, I would own thy tender care,
And all thy love to me;
The food I eat, the clothes I wear,
Are all bestowed by thee.

2

'Tis thou preservest me from death
And dangers every hour;
I cannot draw another breath
Unless thou give me power.

3

Kind angels guard me every night,
As round my bed they stay;
Nor am I absent from thy sight
In darkness or by day.

4

My health and friends and parents dear
To me by God are given;
I have not any blessing here
But what is sent from heaven.

5

Such goodness, Lord, and constant care
I never can repay;
But may it be my daily prayer,
To love thee and obey.

JANE TAYLOR

Alternative Tune, Stracathro, 299

598

For the Young

mf Loving Shepherd of thy sheep,
Keep thy lamb, in safety keep;
Nothing can thy power withstand,
None can pluck me from thy hand.

2

p Loving Saviour, thou didst give‿
Thine own life that we might live,
And the hands outstretched to bless
Bear the cruel nails' impress.

3

f I would praise thee every day,
Gladly all thy will obey,
Like thy blessèd ones above
Happy in thy precious love.

4

mf Loving Shepherd, ever near,
Teach thy lamb thy voice to hear;
Suffer not my steps to stray
From the straight and narrow way.

5

Where thou leadest I would go,
Walking in thy steps below,
f Till before my Father's throne
I shall know as I am known.

JANE E. LEESON

For the Young

FIRST TUNE

Mernle — 7 6 7 6. D

D. P. Symonds

By permission of the Royal School of Church Music

600

For the Young

I love to hear the story
  Which angel voices tell,
How once the King of Glory
  Came down on earth to dwell.
I am both weak and sinful,
  But this I surely know,
The Lord came down to save me,
  Because he loved me so.
    I love to hear the story
      Which angel voices tell,
    How once the King of Glory
      Came down on earth to dwell.

2

I'm glad my blessèd Saviour
  Was once a child like me,
To show how pure and holy
  His little ones might be;
And if I try to follow
  His footsteps here below,
He never will forget me,
  Because he loves me so.
    I love to hear the story
      Which angel voices tell,
    How once the King of Glory
      Came down on earth to dwell.

3

To tell his love and mercy
  My sweetest songs I'll raise;
And though I cannot see him,
  I know he hears my praise;
For he himself has promised
  That even I may go
To sing among his angels,
  Because he loves me so.
    I love to hear the story
      Which angel voices tell,
    How once the King of Glory
      Came down on earth to dwell.

Mrs. E. Miller†

For the Young

I love to hear the story — 7 6 7 6. D   H. J. Gauntlett, 1805–76

I love to hear the sto-ry Which an-gel voi-ces tell,

How once the King of Glo-ry Came down on earth to dwell.

Fine.

I am both weak and sin-ful, But this I sure-ly know,

D.C.

The Lord came down to save me, Be-cause he loved me so.

602

For the Young

I love to hear the story
　Which angel voices tell,
How once the King of Glory
　Came down on earth to dwell.
I am both weak and sinful,
　But this I surely know,
The Lord came down to save me,
　Because he loved me so.
　　I love to hear the story
　　　Which angel voices tell,
　　How once the King of Glory
　　　Came down on earth to dwell.

2
I'm glad my blessèd Saviour
　Was once a child like me,
To show how pure and holy
　His little ones might be;
And if I try to follow
　His footsteps here below,
He never will forget me,
　Because he loves me so.
　　I love to hear the story
　　　Which angel voices tell,
　　How once the King of Glory
　　　Came down on earth to dwell

3
To tell his love and mercy
　My sweetest songs I'll raise;
And though I cannot see him,
　I know he hears my praise;
For he himself has promised
　That even I may go
To sing among his angels,
　Because he loves me so.
　　I love to hear the story
　　　Which angel voices tell,
　　How once the King of Glory
　　　Came down on earth to dwell.

Mrs. E. Miller†

HYMN **446** Valley — C.M. G. H. Knight

mf Sing to the Lord the children's hymn,
   His gentle love declare,
Who bends amid the seraphim
   To hear the children's prayer.

2

p He at a mother's breast was fed,
   Though God's own Son was he;
He learnt the first small words he said
   At a meek mother's knee.

3

Close to his loving heart he pressed
   The children of the earth;
He lifted up his hands and blessed
   The babes of human birth.

4

mf Lo, from the stars his face will turn
   On us with glances mild;
The angels of his presence yearn
   To bless the little child.

5

Keep us, O Jesus, Lord, for thee,
   That so, by thy dear grace,
We, children of the font, may see
   Our heavenly Father's face

R. S. HAWKER

For the Young

Hymn **447**   Pastor bonus — 6 5 6 5. D   Sir J. Stainer, 1840–1901

f Christ, who once amongst us
    As a child did dwell,
    Is the children's Saviour,
    And he loves us well;
mf If we keep our promise
    Made him at the font,
f He will be our Shepherd,
    And we shall not want.

3
    Though we may not see him
    For a little while,
    We shall know he holds us,
    Often feel his smile;
p Death will be to slumber
    In that sweet embrace,
f And we shall awaken
    To behold his face.

2
mf There it was they laid us
    In those tender arms,
    Where the lambs are carried
    Safe from all alarms;
    If we trust his promise,
    He will let us rest,
    In his arms for ever,
    Leaning on his breast.

4
mf He will be our Shepherd,
    After as before,
    By still heavenly waters
    Lead us evermore;
    Make us lie in pastures
    Beautiful and green,
    Where none thirst or hunger,
    And no tears are seen.

5
p Jesus, our Good Shepherd,
    Laying down thy life,
    Lest thy sheep should perish
    In the cruel strife,
mf Help us to remember
    All thy love and care,
f Trust in thee, and love thee
    Always, everywhere.

W. St. Hill Bourne

HYMN **448**   Solothurn — L.M.   Swiss Traditional Melody

   mf Around the throne of God a band‿
        Of glorious angels ever stand ;
   f   Bright things they see, sweet harps they hold,
        And on their heads are crowns of gold.

2

   mf Some wait around him, ready still
        To sing his praise and do his will ;
        And some, when he commands them, go‿
        To guard his servants here below.

3

        Lord, give thy angels every day
        Command to guide us on our way,
        And bid them every evening keep‿
        Their watch around us while we sleep.

4

        So shall no wicked thing draw near,
        To do us harm or cause us fear ;
   f   And we shall dwell, when life is past,
        With angels round thy throne at last.

                       J. M. NEALE†

For the Young

D. W. Dearle (1926)

By permission of the Proprietors of the Church and School Hymnal

O, David was a shepherd lad,
  And guarded well the sheep;
By night and day, good times or bad,
  His watch he used to keep.
But David's less than David's Son,
  Though a Shepherd too is he;
Through all the world his pastures run,
  And of his flock are we.

2

O, David was a shepherd lad,
  And more he dared to do:
Goliath all in armour clad
  With sling and stone he slew.

But David's Son, more daring yet,
  Put weapons all away;
All evil things with goodness met,
  And stronger was than they.

3

O, David was a shepherd lad,
  And a kingdom he attained;
And gold and glory great he had,
  And forty years he reigned.
But David's Son is rich in love,
  And reigns eternally;
For King he is in heaven above,
  And on the earth shall be.

C. Erskine Clarke

For the Young

By permission of the Oxford University Press

mf O Christ, whom we may love and know
And follow to the end,
We who are friends together come
To thee our heavenly Friend.

2
Thou who didst share our daily toil
To make us good and free,
Help us to share thy fiery love
And shining purity.

3
Give us thy love, that loves us all
And dared the glorious Cross,
That we may love to share and know
Each other's joy and loss.

4
Give us thy purity to shield
Our souls in each dark place,
f To give us wings to rise to thee,
And power to see thy face.

MARGARET CROPPER

608

For the Young

HYMN **451**   Simplicity — 7 7 7 7   Sir J. Stainer, 1840–1901

For young children

PART I

Gentle Jesus, meek and mild,
Look upon a little child;
Pity my simplicity,
Suffer me to come to thee.

2
Fain I would to thee be brought:
Dearest God, forbid it not;
Give me, blessed Lord, a place
In the kingdom of thy grace.

3
Hide me, from all evil hide,
Self and stubbornness and pride;
Hold me fast in thine embrace,
Let me see thy smiling face.

PART 2

4
Lamb of God, I look to thee;
Thou shalt my example be:
Thou art gentle, meek, and mild,
Thou wast once a little child.

5
Fain I would be as thou art;
Give me thy obedient heart.
Thou art pitiful and kind;
Let me have thy loving mind.

6
Let me, above all, fulfil
God my heavenly Father's will,
Never his good Spirit grieve,
Only to his glory live.

PART 3

Thou didst live to God alone;
Thou didst never seek thine own;
Thou thyself didst never please:
God was all thy happiness.

8
Loving Jesus, gentle Lamb,
In thy gracious hands I am:
Make me, Saviour, what thou art;
Live thyself within my heart.

9
I shall then show forth thy praise,
Serve thee all my happy days;
Then the world shall always see
Christ, the holy Child, in me.

C. WESLEY

For the Young

There's a Friend for lit - tle chil - dren A - bove the bright blue sky, A Friend who ne - ver chan - ges, Whose love will ne - ver die: Our earth - ly friends may fail us, And change with chang - ing years; This Friend is al - ways wor - thy Of that dear name he bears.

For the Young

mf There's a Friend for little children
　　Above the bright blue sky,
　　A Friend who never changes,
　　Whose love will never die:
p 　Our earthly friends may fail us,
　　And change with changing years;
f 　This Friend is always worthy
　　Of that dear name he bears.

2*

mf There's a rest for little children
　　Above the bright blue sky,
　　Who love the blessèd Saviour,
　　And to the Father cry:
p 　A rest from every turmoil,
　　From sin and sorrow free,
　　Where every little pilgrim
　　Shall rest eternally.

3

mf There's a home for little children
　　Above the bright blue sky,
f 　Where Jesus reigns in glory,
　　A home of peace and joy:
mf No home on earth is like it,
　　Nor can with it compare;
f 　For every one is happy,
　　Nor could be happier, there.

4*

　　There's a crown for little children
　　Above the bright blue sky,
mf And all who look for Jesus
　　Shall wear it by and by:
f 　A crown of brightest glory,
　　Which he will then bestow
mf On those who found his favour
　　And loved his name below.

5

f 　There's a song for little children
　　Above the bright blue sky,
　　A song that will not weary,
　　Though sung continually:
mf 　A song which even angels
　　Can never, never sing;
　　They know not Christ as Saviour,
　　But worship him as King.

6

f 　There's a robe for little children
　　Above the bright blue sky;
　　And a harp of sweetest music,
　　And palms of victory.
　　All, all above is treasured,
　　And found in Christ alone:
p 　Lord, grant thy little children
　　To know thee as their own.

A. MIDLANE

For the Young

f   Hosanna we sing, like the children dear,
In the olden days when the Lord lived here;
mf   He blessed little children, and smiled on them,
While they chanted his praise in Jerusalem.

2

f   Alleluia we sing, like the children bright
With their harps of gold and their raiment white,
As they follow their Shepherd with loving eyes
Through the beautiful valleys of Paradise.

3

Hosanna we sing, for he bends his ear,
And rejoices the hymns of his own to hear;
mf   We know that his heart will never wax cold
To the lambs that he feeds in his earthly fold.

For the Young

4

f   Alleluia we sing in the church we love,
Alleluia resounds in the Church above;
To thy little ones, Lord, may such grace be given,
That we lose not our part in the song of heaven.

G. S. Hodges

HYMN **454** Lyne — 7 7 7 7   *Magdalen Hospital Hymns, c.* 1762

In our work and in our play,
    Jesus, be thou ever near,
Guarding, guiding, all the day,
    Keeping in thy holy fear.

2

Thou didst toil, O royal Child,
    In the far-off Holy Land,
Blessing labour undefiled,
    Pure and honest, of the hand.

3

Thou wilt bless our play-hour too,
    If we ask thy succour strong;
Watch o'er all we say and do,
    Hold us back from guilt and wrong.

4

O, how happy thus to spend
    Work and play-time in his sight,
Till the rest which shall not end,
    Till the day which knows not night!

W. Chatterton Dix

For the Young

D. E. Hopkins

National

Let us thank the Christ for all who did their duty,
Famous men of old and great of heart in fight;
Who fought their way and laboured for their day,
And strove to make our England
A happy, lovely England,
Happy in his praise and lovely in his light.

For the Young

2

Now they thank the Christ who called them to be captains;
Now they sing his praise in everlasting light;
And still they pray, they pray the Lord to-day
That he would make our England
A happy, lovely England,
Happy in his praise and lovely in his light.

3

Let us pray the Christ that he would make us soldiers
Truer in his ways and braver in his fight;
That we, as they, may loyally obey,
And help to make our England
A happy, lovely England,
Happy in his praise and lovely in his light.

J. M. C. Crum

Hymn 456   Quem pastores — 8 8 8 7   German Medieval Melody

A closing prayer

Jesus, kind above all other,
Gentle Child of gentle Mother,
In the stable born our Brother,
    Whom the angel hosts adore:

2

Jesus, cradled in a manger,
Keep us free from sin and danger,
And to all, both friend and stranger,
    Give thy blessing evermore.

J. M. Neale†
Based on Adam of St. Victor

FOR SCHOOL AND COLLEGE USE

A higher setting of this tune will be found at Hymn 296

Beginning of Term

Lord, behold us with thy blessing
  Once again assembled here :
Onward be our footsteps pressing
  In thy love and faith and fear ;
    Still protect us‿
  By thy presence ever near.

2
For thy mercy we adore thee,
  For this rest upon our way ;
Lord, again we bow before thee,
  Speed our labours day by day ;
    Mind and spirit‿
  With thy choicest gifts array.

3
Keep the spell of home affection
  Still alive in every heart ;
May its power, with mild direction,
  Draw our love from self apart,
    Till thy children‿
  Feel that thou their Father art.

4
Break temptation's fatal power,
  Shielding all with guardian care,
Safe in every careless hour,
  Safe from sloth and sensual snare ;
    Thou, our Saviour,
  Still our failing strength repair.

H. J. Buckoll

616

For School and College Use

End of Term

Lord, dismiss us with thy blessing,
  Thanks for mercies past receive;
Pardon all, their faults confessing;
  Time that's lost may all retrieve;
    May thy children⌣
  Ne'er again thy Spirit grieve.

2

Bless thou all our days of leisure,
  Help us selfish lures to flee;
Sanctify our every pleasure;
  Pure and blameless may it be;
    May our gladness⌣
  Draw us evermore to thee.

3

By thy kindly influence cherish
  All the good we here have gained;
May all taint of evil perish
  By thy mightier power restrained;
    Seek we ever⌣
  Knowledge pure and love unfeigned.

4

Let thy Father-hand be shielding
  All who here shall meet no more;
May their seed-time past be yielding
  Year by year a richer store;
    Those returning⌣
  Make more faithful than before.

H. J. Buckoll

617

CONFIRMATION

HYMN **459** St. Peter — C.M. A. R. Reinagle, 1799–1877

A lower setting of this tune will be found at Hymn 13

mf My God, accept my heart this day,
 And make it always thine,
 That I from thee no more may stray,
 No more from thee decline.

2

p Before the Cross of him who died,
 Behold, I prostrate fall;
 Let every sin be crucified,
 And Christ be all in all.

3

mf Anoint me with thy heavenly grace,
 And seal me for thine own;
f That I may see thy glorious face,
 And worship near thy throne.

4

mf Let every thought and work and word
 To thee be ever given:
 Then life shall be thy service, Lord,
 And death the gate of heaven.

[UNISON] 5

f All glory to the Father be,
 All glory to the Son,
 All glory, Holy Ghost, to thee,
 While endless ages run.

M. BRIDGES

618

Confirmation

A higher setting of this tune will be found at Hymn 333

O God, in this thine hour of grace,
With needy heart and empty hand,
Yet bidden of thee to seek thy face,
For blessing at thy feet we stand.

2
Ours are the vows, the frail desires,
The high resolve to dare and do;
Our flickering faith to thee aspires,
And passes like the morning dew.

3
Ours is the mighty need of thee—
How great, thy love alone can know;
Ours but the hunger and the plea
That strives and will not let thee go.

4
Thy word we clasp, thy touch we wait;
Our eyes, O God, are unto thee,
Whose lovingkindness makes us great,
Whose strength shall seal our victory.

BISHOP C. H. BOUTFLOWER

619

Confirmation

A higher setting of this tune will be found at Hymn 218

Strong Captain, in thy holy ranks
  We take our places now :
Give us the mood befitting those⌣
  Who make so great a vow.

2

For foolishness it were to come
  In hardihood of pride,
And cowardice it were to come
  And wish to be untried.

3

We'll not mistrust our want of strength
  Nor trust our strength of will ;
Our only confidence, that thou⌣
  Believest in us still.

4

Make, then, our task to match ou⸺
  strength,
  Our strength to match our task,
And make us unafraid to do
  Whatever thou wilt ask.

J. M. C. CRUM

Confirmation

After the Confirmation

Once pledged by the Cross, as children of God,
To tread in the steps your Captain has trod,
Now, sealed by the Spirit of wisdom and might,
Go forward, Christ's soldiers, go forward and fight!

2

Your weapons of war are sent from above:
The Spirit's good sword, the breastplate of love;
Your feet with the Gospel of peace be well shod;
Put on the whole armour, the armour of God.

3

Full well do ye know the foe must be met,
Full well do ye feel that Satan has set
His powèrs of darkness in battle array;
But those who are for you are stronger than they.

4

The fight may be long, but triumph is sure,
And rest comes at last to those who endure:
The rest that remaineth, the victory won,
And (dearer than all things) your Captain's 'Well done!'

5

Then, on to the fight 'gainst sin and the world!
Stand fast in his strength, his banner unfurled;
And, sealed by the Spirit of wisdom and might,
Go forward, Christ's soldiers, go forward and fight!

ALICE M. BODE

Alternative Tune, Hanover, 167

The following hymns are also suitable:

156 Come, thou Holy Spirit, come.
157 Come, Holy Ghost, our souls inspire.
232 Come, gracious Spirit, heavenly Dove.
303 Soldiers of Christ, arise.
307 Stand up, stand up for Jesus.
330 Thine for ever, God of Love.
331 O Jesus, I have promised.

HOLY MATRIMONY

HYMN **463**   Felix — 11 10 11 10   F. Mendelssohn-Bartholdy, 1809–47

mf O perfect Love, all human thought transcending,
Lowly we kneel in prayer before thy throne,
That theirs may be the love which knows no ending,
Whom thou for evermore dost join in one.

2

O perfect Life, be thou their full assurance
Of tender charity and steadfast faith,
Of patient hope, and quiet brave endurance,
With childlike trust that fears nor pain nor death.

3

Grant them the joy which brightens earthly sorrow,
p   Grant them the peace which calms all earthly strife;
mf And to life's day the glorious unknown morrow
That dawns upon eternal love and life.

Mrs. D. F. Gurney

Alternative Tune, Strength and Stay, 17

Holy Matrimony

HYMN **464**   Melcombe — L.M.   S. Webbe, 1740–1816

O thou who gavest power to love
   That we might fix our hearts on thee,
Preparing us for joys above
   By that which here on earth we see;

2
Thy Spirit trains our souls to know⌣
   The growing purpose of thy will,
And gives to love the power to show⌣
   That purpose growing larger still:

3
Larger, as love to reverent eyes
   Makes manifest another soul,
And shows to life a richer prize,
   A clearer course, a nobler goal.

4
Lord, grant thy servants who implore⌣
   Thy blessing on the hearts they blend,
That from that union evermore
   New joys may blossom to the end.

5
Make what is best in each combine
   To purge all earthly dross away,
To strengthen, purify, refine,
   To beautify each coming day.

6
So may they hand in hand advance
   Along life's paths from troubles free;
Brave to meet adverse circumstance
   Because their love points up to thee.

BISHOP MANDELL CREIGHTON

623

Holy Matrimony

Lower settings of this tune will be found at Hymns 502 and 582

O Father, by whose sovereign sway
The sun and stars in order move,
Yet who hast made us bold to say
Thy nature and thy name is love:

2

O royal Son, whose every deed
Showed love and love's divinity,
Yet didst not scorn the humblest need
At Cana's feast in Galilee:

3

O Holy Spirit, who dost speak
In saint and sage since time began,
Yet givest courage to the weak
And teachest love to selfish man:

4

Be present in our hearts to-day,
All powerful to bless, and give
To these thy children grace that they
May love, and through their loving live.

C. A. ALINGTON

The following hymns are also suitable:

182   Father, hear the prayer we offer.
231   O Holy Spirit, Lord of grace.
311   Lead us, heavenly Father, lead us.

THE DEPARTED

Dies irae, dies illa

1 Day of wrath! O day of mourn - ing! See ful - filled the
2 O what fear man's bo - som rend - eth When from heaven the
7 What shall I, frail man, be plead - ing, Who for me be
8 King of ma - jes - ty tre - mend - ous, Who dost free sal -

1 pro-phets' warn - ing! Heaven and earth to ash - es turn - ing!
2 Judge de - scend - eth, On whose sen - tence all de - pend - eth!
7 in - ter - ced - ing, When the just are mer - cy need - ing?
8 va - tion send us, Fount of pi - ty, then be-friend us.

3 Won-drous sound the trum-pet fling - eth, Through earth's sep - ul -
4 Death a - mazed and na - ture quak - ing See all creat - ures
9 Think, good Je - su, my sal - va - tion Caused thy won - drous
10 Faint and wea - ry thou hast sought me, On the Cross of

625

3 chres it ring - eth, All be - fore the throne it bring - eth.
4 now a - wak - ing, To the Judge their an - swer mak - ing.
9 In - car - na - tion; Leave me not to re - pro - ba - tion.
10 suff - ering bought me; Shall such grace be vain - ly brought me?

5 Lo, the book ex - act - ly word - ed, Where-in all hath
6 When the Judge his seat at - tain - eth, And each hid - den
11 Right-eous Judge! for sin's pol - lu - tion Grant thy gift of
12 Guil - ty, now I pour my moan-ing, All my shame with

5 been re - cord - ed: Thence shall judge-ment be a - ward - ed.
6 deed ar - raign - eth, Not a sin un-judged re - main - eth.
11 ab - so - lu - tion, Ere that day of re - tri - bu - tion.
12 an-guish own - ing; Spare, O God, thy sup - pliant groan-ing.

626

13 By the sin-ful wo-man shri - ven, By the dy - ing
14 Worth-less are my prayers and sigh - ing; Yet, thy mer-cy

13 thief for - giv - en, Thou to me a hope hast giv - en.
14 not de - ny - ing, Save me from the wrath un - dy - ing.

15 With the sheep vouch-safe to place me; Do not with the
16 While the wick - ed are con-found-ed, Doomed to grief and

15 goats a - base me; But to thy right hand up - raise me.
16 loss un - bound - ed, Call me with thy saints sur - round - ed.

17 Low I kneel, with heart - sub - mis - sion, Bowed to dust in

sore con - tri - tion: Shield me, dy - ing, from per - di - tion.

18 Ah, that day of tears and mourn-ing! From the dust of earth re-turn-ing

Man for judge-ment must pre-pare him: Spare, O God, in mer - cy spare him!

19 Lord, all pity-ing, Je - su blest, Grant them thine e - ter-nal rest.

THOMAS OF CELANO
Tr. W. J. Irons and Compilers

The Departed

* *If there is no accompaniment the small notes may be sung*

p Now the labourer's task is o'er,
   Now the battle day is past;
mf Now upon the farther shore
   Lands the voyager at last:
p Father, in thy gracious keeping
   Leave we now thy servant sleeping.

2
There the tears of earth are dried,
   There its hidden things are clear;
mf There the work of life is tried
   By a juster Judge than here:
p Father, in thy gracious keeping
   Leave we now thy servant sleeping.

3
There the sinful souls, that turn
   To the Cross their dying eyes,
mf All the love of Christ shall learn
   At his feet in Paradise:
p Father, in thy gracious keeping
   Leave we now thy servant sleeping.

4
mf There no more the powers of hell
   Can prevail to mar their peace;
Christ the Lord shall guard them well,
   He who died for their release:
p Father, in thy gracious keeping
   Leave we now thy servant sleeping.

5
'Earth to earth, and dust to dust,'
   Calmly now the words we say,
Leaving *him* to sleep in trust
   Till the resurrection-day:
Father, in thy gracious keeping
Leave we now thy servant sleeping.

J. ELLERTON

The Departed

p O Lord, to whom the spirits live
   Of all the faithful passed away,
mf Unto their path that brightness give
   Which shineth to the perfect day:
p   O Lamb of God, Redeemer
      blest,
   Grant them eternal light and
   rest.

2

mf Bless thou the dead that die in thee;
   As thou hast given them release,
   So quicken them thy face to see,
   And give them everlasting peace:
p   O Lamb of God, Redeemer
      blest,
   Grant them eternal light and
   rest.

3

mf Direct us with thine arm of might,
   And bring us, perfected with them,
f To dwell within thy city bright,
   The heavenly Jerusalem:
p   O Lamb of God, Redeemer blest,
   Grant them eternal light and rest.

R. F. LITTLEDALE and Compilers

631

The Departed

632

The Departed

Yesu Bin Mariamu

PART 1

mf Jesu, Son of Mary,
    Fount of life alone,
Here we hail thee present
    On thine altar-throne:
Humbly we adore thee,
    Lord of endless might,
In the mystic symbols
    Veiled from earthly sight.

PART 2

2

p Think, O Lord, in mercy
    On the souls of those
Who, in faith gone from us,
    Now in death repose.
Here 'mid stress and conflict
    Toils can never cease;
There, the warfare ended,
    Bid them rest in peace.

3

Often were they wounded
    In the deadly strife;
Heal them, Good Physician,
    With the balm of life.
Every taint of evil,
    Frailty, and decay,
Good and gracious Saviour,
    Cleanse and purge away.

4

Rest eternal grant them,
    After weary fight;
Shed on them the radiance
    Of thy heavenly light.
mf Lead them onward, upward,
    To the holy place,
Where thy saints made perfect
    Gaze upon thy face.

From the Swahili *Tr.* E. S. PALMER

The following hymns are also suitable:

140   Jesus lives! thy terrors now.
272   Let saints on earth in concert sing.
275   Brief life is here our portion.
285   There is a land of pure delight.

HYMN **470**   St. David — C.M.   T. Ravenscroft, *Psalms*, 1621

mf Christ is gone up; yet ere he passed⌣
From earth, in heaven to reign,
He formed one holy Church to last
Till he should come again.

2
His twelve apostles first he made
His ministers of grace;
And they their hands on others laid,
To fill in turn their place.

3
So age by age, and year by year,
His grace was handed on;
And still the holy Church is here,
Although her Lord is gone.

4
p   Let those find pardon, Lord, from thee,
Whose love to her is cold:
mf Bring wanderers in, and let there be
One Shepherd and one fold.

J. M. NEALE

634

Ember Days

mf   O thou who makest souls to shine
      With light from lighter worlds above,
    And droppest glistening dew divine
      On all who seek a Saviour's love;

2
Do thou thy benediction give
    On all who teach, on all who learn,
That so thy Church may holier live,
    And every lamp more brightly burn.

3
Give those who teach pure hearts and wise,
    Faith, hope, and love, all warmed by prayer:
Themselves first training for the skies,
    They best will raise their people there.

4
Give those who learn the willing ear,
    The spirit meek, the guileless mind:
Such gifts will make the lowliest here
    Far better than a kingdom find.

5
O bless the shepherd, bless the sheep,
    That guide and guided both be one:
One in the faithful watch they keep,
    Until this hurrying life be done.

6
f   If thus, good Lord, thy grace be given,
    In thee to live, in thee to die,
Before we upward pass to heaven
    We taste our immortality.

BISHOP J. ARMSTRONG

HYMN **472** Manchester New — C.M. R. Wainwright, 1748–82

A lower setting of this tune will be found at Hymn 619

The earth, O Lord, is one wide field
Of all thy chosen seed;
The crop prepared its fruit to yield,
The labourers few indeed.

2
We therefore come before thee now
With fasting and with prayer,
Beseeching of thy love that thou
Wouldst send more labourers there.

3
Not for our land alone we pray,
Though that above the rest;
The realms and islands far away,
O let them all be blest.

4
Endue the bishops of thy flock
With wisdom and with grace,
Against false doctrine like a rock
To set the heart and face.

5
To all thy priests thy truth reveal,
And make thy judgements clear;
Make thou thy deacons full of zeal,
And humble and sincere:

6
And give their flocks a lowly mind
To hear—and not in vain;
That each and all may mercy find
When thou shalt come again.

J. M. NEALE

Hymn **473** Ludborough — L.M. T. R. Matthews, 1826–1910

mf Lord, pour thy Spirit from on high,
  And thine ordainèd servants bless;
  Graces and gifts to each supply,
  And clothe thy priests with righteousness.

2
Within thy temple when they stand,
  To teach the truth as taught by thee,
Saviour, like stars in thy right hand
  Let all thy Church's pastors be.

3
Wisdom and zeal and faith impart,
  Firmness with meekness, from above,
To bear thy people in their heart,
  And love the souls whom thou dost love;

4
p To watch and pray and never faint,
  By day and night their guard to keep,
To warn the sinner, cheer the saint,
  To feed thy lambs and tend thy sheep.

5
mf So, when their work is finished here,
  May they in hope their charge resign;
f When the Chief Shepherd shall appear,
  O God, may they and we be thine.

J. MONTGOMERY‡

637

DEDICATION OF A CHURCH

Urbs beata — 8 7. 8 7. 8 7   Mode ii

Urbs beata Jerusalem

1 Bless-èd ci - ty, heaven-ly Sa - lem, Vi - sion dear of peace and love,
2 Christ is made the sure Foun-da - tion, Christ the Head and Cor-ner-stone,
3 To this tem - ple, where we call thee, Come, O Lord of hosts, to - day;
4 *Here vouch-safe to all thy ser - vants What they ask of thee to gain,

1 Who of liv - ing stones art build - ed In the height of heaven a-bove,
2 Cho-sen of the Lord, and pre - cious, Bind-ing all the Church in one,
3 With thy wont-ed lov - ing-kind - ness Hear thy ser-vants as they pray;
4 What they gain from thee for ev - er With the bless-èd to re - tain,

1 And by an - gel hosts en - cir-cled As a bride dost earth-ward move!
2 Ho - ly Si - on's help for ev - er, And her con - fi - dence a - lone.
3 And thy full-est ben - e - dic-tion Shed with - in its walls al - way.
4 And here-af - ter in thy glo - ry Ev - er - more with thee to reign.

HYMN **474**   SECOND TUNE

Oriel — 8 7. 8 7. 8 7   C. Ett, *Cantica Sacra*, 1840

A lower setting of this tune with a descant will be found at Hymn 190

Urbs beata Jerusalem

Blessèd city, heavenly Salem,
 Vision dear of peace and love,
Who of living stones art builded
 In the height of heaven above,
And by angel hosts encircled
 As a bride dost earthward move!

2

Christ is made the sure Foundation,
 Christ the Head and Corner-stone,
Chosen of the Lord, and precious,
 Binding all the Church in one,
Holy Sion's help for ever,
 And her confidence alone.

3

To this temple, where we call thee,
 Come, O Lord of hosts, to-day;
With thy wonted loving-kindness
 Hear thy servants as they pray;
And thy fullest benediction
 Shed within its walls alway.

4*

Here vouchsafe to all thy servants
 What they ask of thee to gain,
What they gain from thee for ever
 With the blessèd to retain,
And hereafter in thy glory
 Evermore with thee to reign.

Tr. J. M. NEALE

Alternative Tune, Westminster Abbey, 620

NOTE. *The complete version of the above hymn (the several parts of which may be ~ng separately) will be found in the 'Processional' section (*620*)*

HYMN **475**   St. Helena (Mount Ephraim) — S.M.   Adapted from
B. Milgrove, 1731-1810

A lower setting of this tune will be found at Hymn 531

Patris aeterni Suboles coaeva

f   O word of God above,
     Who fillest all in all,
   Hallow this house with thy sure love,
     And bless our festival.

2

mf   Here from the font is poured⌣
     The grace to cleanse from sin;
   Here the anointing of the Lord
     Confirms the soul within.

3

   Here Christ to faithful hearts
     His Body gives for food;
   The Lamb of God himself imparts⌣
     The chalice of his Blood.

4

   Here guilty souls that pine
     May health and pardon win;

The Judge acquits, and grace divine⌣
  Restores the dead in sin.

5

Yea, God enthroned on high
  Here also dwells to bless;
Here trains adoring souls that sigh⌣
  His mansions to possess.

6

f   Against this holy home
     Rude tempests harmless beat,
   And Satan's angels fiercely come
     But to endure defeat.

[UNISON]   7

All might, all praise be thine,
  Father, co-equal Son,
And Spirit, bond of love divine,
  While endless ages run.

C. GUIET   *Tr.* I. Williams and Compiler

HYMN **476**   St. Catherine's Court — 12 11 12 11   R. Strutt, 1848-192

The Dedication of a Church

IN REMEMBRANCE OF PAST WORSHIPPERS

f   In our day of thanksgiving one psalm let us offer
      For the saints who before us have found their reward;
p When the shadow of death fell upon them, we sorrowed,
f   But now we rejoice that they rest in the Lord.

2

mf In the morning of life, and at noon, and at even,
      He called them away from our worship below;
      But not till his love, at the font and the altar,
      Had girt them with grace for the way they should go.

3

These stones that have echoed their praises are holy,
      And dear is the ground where their feet have once trod;
Yet here they confessed they were strangers and pilgrims,
      And still they were seeking the city of God.

4

f   Sing praise, then, for all who here sought and here found him,
      Whose journey is ended, whose perils are past:
They believed in the Light; and its glory is round them,
      Where the clouds of earth's sorrow are lifted at last.

W. H. DRAPER

HOSPITALS: THE SICK

HYMN 477 FIRST TUNE

Gott des Himmels — 8 7. 8 7. 7 7 H. Albert, 1604–51

SECOND TUNE

Requiem — 8 7. 8 7. 7 7 W. Schulthes, 1816–79

Hospitals: The Sick

mf Thou to whom the sick and dying
Ever came, nor came in vain,
Still with healing word replying
To the wearied cry of pain,
p   Hear us, Jesu, as we meet
Suppliants at thy mercy-seat.

2
Still the weary, sick, and dying
Need a brother's, sister's, care,
mf On thy higher help relying
May we now their burden share,
Bringing all our offerings meet
Suppliants at thy mercy-seat.

3
May each child of thine be willing,
Willing both in hand and heart,
All the law of love fulfilling,
Ever comfort to impart;
Ever bringing offerings meet
Suppliant to thy mercy-seat.

4
So may sickness, sin, and sadness
To thy healing virtue yield,
f Till the sick and sad, in gladness,
Rescued, ransomed, cleansèd, healed,
One in thee together meet,
Pardoned at thy judgement-seat.

G. THRING

643

HYMN **478** St. Matthew — D.C.M. W. Croft, 1678–1727

f Thine arm, O Lord, in days of old
  Was strong to heal and save;
  It triumphed o'er disease and death,
  O'er darkness and the grave:
p To thee they went, the blind, the
  The palsied and the lame, [dumb,
  The leper with his tainted life,
  The sick with fevered frame.

2

f And lo, thy touch brought life and
  health, [sight;
  Gave speech and strength and
  And youth renewed and frenzy
  calmed
  Owned thee, the Lord of light:

And now, O Lord, be near to bless,
  Almighty as of yore,
In crowded street, by restless couch,
  As by Gennesareth's shore.

3

mf Be thou our great deliverer still,
  Thou Lord of life and death;
Restore and quicken, soothe and bless
  With thine almighty breath:
To hands that work, and eyes that
  see,
Give wisdom's heavenly lore,
That whole and sick, and weak and
  strong,
May praise thee evermore.

E. H. PLUMPTRE

HYMN **479** Belgrave — C.M. W. Horsley, 1774–1858

  mf From thee all skill and science flow,
     All pity, care, and love,
     All calm and courage, faith and hope:
     O pour them from above!

2
And part them, Lord, to each and all,
  As each and all shall need,
To rise, like incense, each to thee,
  In noble thought and deed.

3
And hasten, Lord, that perfect day
  When pain and death shall cease,
f And thy just rule shall fill the earth
  With health and light and peace;

4
When ever blue the sky shall gleam,
  And ever green the sod,
And man's rude work deface no more
  The paradise of God.

CHARLES KINGSLEY

ALMSGIVING

                        J. B. Dykes, 1823–76

f O Lord of heaven and earth and sea,
    To thee all praise and glory be!
    How shall we show our love to thee,
          Who givest all?

2

mf The golden sunshine, vernal air,
    Sweet flowers and fruit, thy love
        declare;
    When harvests ripen, thou art there,
          Who givest all.

3

For peaceful homes, and healthful
    days,
For all the blessings earth displays,
We owe thee thankfulness and praise,
          Who givest all.

4

p Thou didst not spare thine only Son,
    But gav'st him for a world undone,
    And freely with that blessèd One
          Thou givest all.

5

mf Thou giv'st the Holy Spirit's dower,
    Spirit of life and love and power,
    And dost his sevenfold graces shower
          Upon us all.

6

For souls redeemed, for sins forgiven,
For means of grace and hopes of
    heaven,
Father, what can to thee be given,
          Who givest all?

7

    We lose what on ourselves we spend,
f We have as treasure without end
    Whatever, Lord, to thee we lend,
          Who givest all;

8

To thee, from whom we all derive⌣
Our life, our gifts, our power to give:
O may we ever with thee live,
          Who givest all.

BISHOP CHR. WORDSWORTH

Alternative Tune, Es ist kein Tag, 589

HARVEST

Hymn **481**   Monkland — 7 7 7 7   J. Wilkes, 1785-1869. Adapted from
J. Lee's *Hymn Tunes of the United Brethren*, 1824

Praise, O praise our God and King;
Hymns of adoration sing :
  For his mercies still endure
  Ever faithful, ever sure.

2
Praise him that he made the sun
Day by day his course to run:
  For his mercies, etc.

3
And the silver moon by night,
Shining with her gentle light :
  For his mercies, etc.

4
Praise him that he gave the rain
To mature the swelling grain :
  For his mercies, etc.

5
And hath bid the fruitful field
Crops of precious increase yield :
  For his mercies, etc.

6
Praise him for our harvest-store;
He hath filled the garner-floor :
  For his mercies, etc.

7
And for richer food than this,
Pledge of everlasting bliss :
  For his mercies, etc

[UNISON]   8
Glory to our bounteous King;
Glory let creation sing :
  Glory to the Father, Son,
  And blest Spirit, Three in One.

Sir H. W. Baker

647

Harvest

HYMN 482   St. George — 7 7 7 7. D   Sir G. J. Elvey, 1816–93

Harvest

f   Come, ye thankful people, come,
Raise the song of harvest-home :
All is safely gathered in,
Ere the winter storms begin ;
mf God, our Maker, doth provide⌣
For our wants to be supplied :
f   Come to God's own temple, come ;
Raise the song of harvest-home.

2

mf All this world is God's own field,
Fruit unto his praise to yield ;
Wheat and tares therein are sown,
Unto joy or sorrow grown ;
Ripening with a wondrous power
Till the final harvest-hour :
p   Grant, O Lord of life, that we⌣
Holy grain and pure may be.

3

mf For we know that thou wilt come,
And wilt take thy people home ;
From thy field wilt purge away
All that doth offend, that day ;
p   And thine angels charge at last
In the fire the tares to cast,
f   But the fruitful ears to store⌣
In thy garner evermore.

4

mf Come then, Lord of mercy, come,
Bid us sing thy harvest-home :
Let thy saints be gathered in,
Free from sorrow, free from sin ;
f   All upon the golden floor
Praising thee for evermore :
Come, with all thine angels come,
Bid us sing thy harvest-home.

H. ALFORD and Compilers

Harvest

Hymn **483**   Wir pflügen — 7 6 7 6. 7 6 7 6. 6 6 8 4   J. A. P. Schulz,
1747–1800

Harvest

Wir pflügen und wir streuen

mf We plough the fields, and scatter
  The good seed on the land,
 But it is fed and watered
  By God's almighty hand:
 He sends the snow in winter,
  The warmth to swell the grain,
 The breezes, and the sunshine,
  And soft, refreshing rain.
f   All good gifts around us
   Are sent from heaven above;
  Then thank the Lord, O thank the Lord,
   For all his love.

2

mf He only is the Maker
  Of all things near and far;
 He paints the wayside flower,
  He lights the evening star;
 The winds and waves obey him,
  By him the birds are fed;
 Much more to us, his children,
  He gives our daily bread.
f   All good gifts around us
   Are sent from heaven above;
  Then thank the Lord, O thank the Lord,
   For all his love.

3

mf We thank thee then, O Father,
  For all things bright and good,
 The seed-time and the harvest,
  Our life, our health, our food.
 Accept the gifts we offer
  For all thy love imparts,
 And, what thou most desirest,
  Our humble, thankful hearts.
f   All good gifts around us
   Are sent from heaven above;
  Then thank the Lord, O thank the Lord,
   For all his love.

M. CLAUDIUS
Tr. Jane M. Campbell

Hymn **484** Golden Sheaves — 8 7 8 7. D Sir A. Sullivan, 1842–1900

f To thee, O Lord, our hearts we raise
In hymns of adoration,
To thee bring sacrifice of praise
With shouts of exultation :
Bright robes of gold the fields adorn,
The hills with joy are ringing,
The valleys stand so thick with corn
That even they are singing.

2
mf And now, on this our festal day,
Thy bounteous hand confessing,
Upon thine altar, Lord, we lay
The first-fruits of thy blessing :
p By thee the souls of men are fed
With gifts of grace supernal ;
Thou who dost give us earthly
bread,
Give us the Bread eternal.

3
mf We bear the burden of the day,
And often toil seems dreary ;
But labour ends with sunset ray,
And rest comes for the weary :
May we, the angel-reaping o'er,
Stand at the last accepted,
Christ's golden sheaves for evermor
To garners bright elected.

4
f O blessèd is that land of God,
Where saints abide for ever ;
Where golden fields spread far an
broad,
Where flows the crystal river :
The strains of all its holy throng
With ours to-day are blending ;
Thrice blessèd is that harvest-song
Which never hath an ending.

W. CHATTERTON I

Harvest

Praise to God, immortal praise,
For the love that crowns our days!
Bounteous source of every joy,
Let thy praise our tongues employ:

2

For the blessings of the field,
For the stores the gardens yield,
Flocks that whiten all the plain,
Yellow sheaves of ripened grain:

3

All that spring with bounteous hand
Scatters o'er the smiling land;
All that liberal autumn pours
From her rich o'erflowing stores.

4

These to thee, my God, we owe,
Source whence all our blessings flow;
And for these my soul shall raise
Grateful vows and solemn praise.

Mrs. A. L. Barbauld

Alternative Tune, Culbach, 73

653

Harvest

Harvest

2

mf The sower went forth sowing,
    The seed in secret slept
  Through weeks of faith and patience,
    Till out the green blade crept;
  And warmed by golden sunshine
    And fed by silver rain,
  At last the fields were whitened
    To harvest once again.
f   O praise the heavenly Sower,
      Who gave the fruitful seed,
    And watched and watered duly,
      And ripened for our need.

mf Behold, the heavenly Sower
    Goes forth with better seed,
  The word of sure salvation,
    With feet and hands that bleed;
  Here in his Church 'tis scattered,
    Our spirits are the soil;
  Then let an ample fruitage
    Repay his pain and toil.
f   O beauteous is the harvest
      Wherein all goodness thrives!
    And this the true thanksgiving—
      The first-fruits of our lives.

3

p   Within a hallowed acre
      He sows yet other grain,
    When peaceful earth receiveth
      The dead he died to gain;
    For though the growth be hidden,
mf   We know that they shall rise;
    Yea, even now they ripen
      In sunny Paradise.
f   O summer land of harvest,
      O fields for ever white
    With souls that wear Christ's raiment,
      With crowns of golden light!

4

mf   One day the heavenly Sower
      Shall reap where he hath sown,
    And come again rejoicing,
      And with him bring his own;
p   And then the fan of judgement
      Shall winnow from his floor
    The chaff into the furnace
      That flameth evermore.
    O holy, aweful Reaper,
      Have mercy in the day
    Thou puttest in thy sickle,
      And cast us not away.

W. St. Hill Bourne

655

FOR THOSE AT SEA

Hymn **487**   Melita — 8 8. 8 8. 8 8   J. B. Dykes, 1823–76

3

Eternal Father, strong to save,
Whose arm hath bound the restless wave,
Who bidd'st the mighty ocean deep
Its own appointed limits keep :
 O hear us when we cry to thee
 For those in peril on the sea.

O Holy Spirit, who didst brood
Upon the waters dark and rude,
And bid their angry tumult cease,
And give, for wild confusion, peace :
 O hear us when we cry to thee
 For those in peril on the sea.

2

O Christ, whose voice the waters
       heard
And hushed their raging at thy word,
Who walkedst on the foaming deep,
And calm amid the storm didst sleep :
 O hear us when we cry to thee
 For those in peril on the sea.

4

O Trinity of love and power,
Our brethren shield in danger's hour ;
From rock and tempest, fire and foe,
Protect them wheresoe'er they go :
 Thus evermore shall rise to thee
 Glad hymns of praise from land and
  sea.

W. Whiting

656

FOR ABSENT FRIENDS

Hymn **488**   Cairnbrook — 8 5 8 3   E. Prout, 1835–1909

mf Holy Father, in thy mercy⌣
    Hear our anxious prayer:
    Keep our loved ones, now far distant,
        'Neath thy care.

2
Jesus, Saviour, let thy presence⌣
    Be their light and guide;
p Keep, O keep them, in their weakness,
        At thy side.

3
When in sorrow, when in danger,
    When in loneliness,
In thy love look down and comfort
        Their distress.

4
mf   May the joy of thy salvation⌣
    Be their strength and stay;
May they love and may they praise thee
        Day by day.

5
p   Holy Spirit, let thy teaching⌣
    Sanctify their life;
mf   Send thy grace, that they may conquer
        In the strife.

6
Father, Son, and Holy Spirit,
    God the One in Three,
Bless them, guide them, save them, keep them
        Near to thee.

ISABEL S. STEVENSON

FAREWELL SERVICES

HYMN **489** Dominus vobiscum — 9 8 8 9   Sir A. Somervell, 1863–1937

God be with you till we meet again ;
By his counsels guide, uphold you,
With his sheep securely fold you :
God be with you till we meet again.

2

God be with you till we meet again ;
'Neath his wings protecting hide you,
Daily manna still provide you :
God be with you till we meet again.

3

God be with you till we meet again ;
When life's perils thick confound you,
Put his arm unfailing round you :
God be with you till we meet again.

4

God be with you till we meet again ;
Keep love's banner floating o'er you,
Smite death's threatening wave before you :
God be with you till we meet again.

J. E. RANKIN

IN TIME OF WAR

Hymn **490** Rockingham — L.M.   Adapted by E. Miller, 1731–1807

A higher setting of this tune will be found at Hymn 108

mf O God of love, O King of peace,
    Make wars throughout the world to cease;
    The wrath of sinful man restrain :
p   Give peace, O God, give peace again.

2
mf Remember, Lord, thy works of old,
    The wonders that our fathers told;
    Remember not our sin's dark stain :
p   Give peace, O God, give peace again.

3
mf Whom shall we trust but thee, O Lord?
    Where rest but on thy faithful word?
    None ever called on thee in vain :
p   Give peace, O God, give peace again.

4
f   Where saints and angels dwell above,
    All hearts are knit in holy love;
    O bind us in that heavenly chain :
p   Give peace, O God, give peace again.

Sir H. W. Baker

659

In Time of War

f   God the all-terrible! King, who ordainest⌣
    Great winds thy clarions, the lightnings thy sword,
mf Show forth thy pity on high where thou reignest:
    Grant to us peace, O most merciful Lord.

2

p   God the omnipotent! mighty avenger,
    Watching invisible, judging unheard,
    Doom us not now in the day of our danger:
    Grant to us peace, O most merciful Lord.

3

God the all-merciful! earth has forsaken⌣
    Thy ways of blessedness, slighted thy word;
Bid not thy wrath in its terrors awaken:
    Grant to us peace, O most merciful Lord.

4

f   So shall thy children in thankful devotion
    Praise him who saved them from peril and sword,
Singing in chorus from ocean to ocean,
    'Peace to the nations, and praise to the Lord.'

H. F. CHORLEY

In Time of War

HYMN **492**   Ad Astra — 8 8. 8 8. 8 8   H. G. Ley

By permission of the S.P.C.K.

For Airmen

f Lord of the worlds, unseen or seen,
　　Whose eyes behold all things that
Who rulest earth and sea and air　[are,
　　And guid'st the course of every star,
Look pitying from thy throne, nor
　　cease⌣
To draw the nations to thy peace.

2

And if, at duty's trumpet call, [hence
　　Our manhood now be summoned
To battle for the right, the just,
　　O shield them by thy providence.
How confident are those that stand
Beneath the shelter of thy hand!

3

f To all who, spurning earthly joys,
　　Seek undismayed the trackless way
High in the wide expanse of heaven,
　　Be thou their help, by night and
　　　day;

Through fire, through cloud, o'er
　　land, o'er wave,
Still be thy presence strong to save.

4

p But should, O God, thy sovran will
　　Allow the final sacrifice,
To thee their lives are dedicate :
　　Not theirs to falter at the price.
O Lord of earth and sea and air,
For those in peril hear our prayer.

5

mf Not given in vain, these gallant lives!
　　The silent passing of the years⌣
Shall touch them not, who fought—
　　and fell :
They ask no tribute of our tears.
f O loyal hearts, from death set free!
　　Not lost, but living unto thee.

　　　　　　　　　　　　E. H. BLAKENEY

Alternative Tune, Melita, 487

661

SOCIETIES AND MEETINGS

Hymn **493**   Harewood — 6 6 6 6. 8 8   S. S. Wesley, 1810–76

CHOIRS

How joyful 'tis to sing
  To God enthroned on high,
To raise the ancient strain
  Of tuneful psalmody
    As choristers, who thus delight⏝
    To chant his praise by day and
      night!

2

mf Yet art is not enough,
  Nor voice that charms the ear,
Unless the heart be tuned
  And worship be sincere :
    Help us to fix our minds on thee,
    And lead us to simplicity.

3

Should we with wandering thoughts
  Our minds allow to stray,
Nor heed God's holy word,
  And, kneeling, fail to pray,
    Help us to serve with godly fear,
    Lest we forget thy presence near.

4

We seek to perfect praise⏝
  On earth, in hope that we⏝
Some glimpses here may gain
  Of heavenly harmony,   [tone
    Where discord ne'er shall mar the
    Of those that sing around the
      throne.

5

f   Then in the praise of God
    Let boys and men unite,
  And, mindful of our trust,
    Gird on our robes of white,
      As symbol of the purity
      That all must seek, who seek for thee.

Sir S. H. Nicholson

662

Societies and Meetings

SERVERS

Hands that have been handling⏝
  Holy things and high
Still, Lord, in thy service
  Bless and fortify.

2
Ears which heard the message
  Of the words of life
Keep thou closed and guarded
  From the noise of strife.

3
Eyes whose contemplation⏝
  Looked upon thy love,
Let them gaze expectant
  On the world above.

4
'Holy, Holy, Holy,'
  Thee our lips confessed :
On those lips for ever
  Let no falsehood rest.

5
Feet which trod the pavement
  Round about God's board,
Let them walk in glory
  Where God's light is poured.

6
Bodies that have tasted
  Of the living Bread,
Be they re-created
  In their living Head.

7*
Be we all one Body,
  All our members one,
Measured by the stature
  Of God's full-grown Son.

ADAM FOX
Based on *Liturgy of Malabar*

Societies and Meetings

By permission of J. Curwen & Sons, Ltd., from Curwen edition No. 80631

TEACHERS

Lord and Master, who hast called us
    All our days to follow thee,
We have heard thy clear commandment,
    'Bring the children unto me.'

2
So we come to thee, the Teacher,
    At thy feet we kneel to pray :
We can only lead the children
    When thyself shalt show the way.

3
Teach us thy most wondrous method,
    As of old in Galilee
Thou didst show thy chosen servants
    How to bring men unto thee.

4
Give us store of wit and wisdom,
    Give us love which never tires,
Give us thine abiding patience,
    Give us hope which ay inspires.

5
Mighty Wisdom of the Godhead,
    Thou the one eternal Word,
Thou the Counsellor, the Teacher,
    Fill us with thy fullness, Lord.

FLORENCE SMITH

HYMN **496** Belfry Praise — 7 6 7 6. D   J. H. Matthews

BELL-RINGERS

Unchanging God, who livest⌣
  Enthroned in realms on high,
To men the power thou givest
  Thy name to magnify.
We raise the bells for ringing
  With ready mind and will,
And come before thee, bringing⌣
  Our hearts, our strength, our skill.

3
By union free and willing
  The work of God is done;
Our Master's prayer fulfilling,
  We would in him be one:
One, as the Church our Mother
  Would have her children stand,
Befriending one another,
  A strong and steadfast band.

2
We call, from tower and steeple,
  Upon the day of days,
All faithful Christian people
  To worship, prayer, and praise;
We ring with joyous gladness
  When man and wife are blessed;
We peal in muffled sadness
  For loved ones laid to rest.

4
Our lives, like bells, while changing,
  An ordered course pursue;
Through joys and sorrows ranging,
  May all those lives ring true.
May we, through Christ forgiven,
  Our faults and failures past,
Attain our place in heaven,
  Called home to rest at last.

H. C. WILDER

HYMN **497**   Battle cry — 7 6 8 6. D   A. Gray, 1855–1935

UNISON   MEN'S SERVICES

1 Rise at the cry of bat - tle, Arm for the
2 Fie - ry and fierce the con - flict, Dar - ing and
3 Strive till the strife is o - ver, Fight till the

1 com - ing strife; By night and day you must
2 swift the foe; His hosts are found on the
3 fight is won; Though sore op - prest, seek

1 fight your way Till you pass through death to life;
2 bat - tle ground, Where they wait to lay you low.
3 not for rest Un - til the day is done.

666

1 Rea - dy to face the dan - ger, Rea - dy to
2 Sharp are his darts and dead - ly, Keen is the
3 Af - ter the well - fought bat - tle Join in the

1 right the wrong. There is ma - ny a foe on the
2 strife and long; Then arm for the fight in the
3 vic - tor's song; Your tro - phies bring to

1 way you go: Quit you like men, be strong!
2 ar - mour of light: Quit you like men, be strong!
3 Christ your King: Quit you like men, be strong!

ADA R. GREENAWAY

HYMN **498**   Alleluia, dulce carmen — 8 7. 8 7. 8 7   *Essay on the Church Plain Chant*, 1782

A higher setting of this tune will be found at Hymn 82

MOTHERS' SERVICES

1
Lord of life and King of Glory,
  Who didst deign a child to be,
Cradled on a mother's bosom,
  Throned upon a mother's knee;
For the children thou hast given
  We must answer unto thee.

2
Since the day the blessèd Mother
  Thee, the world's Redeemer, bore,
Thou hast crowned us with an honour
  Women never knew before;
And that we may bear it meetly
  We must seek thine aid the more.

3
Grant us then pure hearts and patient,
  That in all we do or say
Little souls our deeds may copy,
  And be never led astray;
Little feet our steps may follow
  In a safe and narrow way.

4
When our growing sons and daughters
  Look on life with eager eyes,
Grant us then a deeper insight
  And new powers of sacrifice;
Hope to trust them, faith to guide them,
  Love that nothing good denies.

5
May we keep our holy calling
  Stainless in its fair renown,
That, when all the work is over
  And we lay the burden down,
Then the children thou hast given
  Still may be our joy and crown.

CHRISTIAN BURKE

HYMN **499**   Palms of glory — 7 7 7 7   Archbishop W. D. Maclagan,
1826–1910

'Hail, O Mary, full of grace,
Daughter true of David's race!
Thou, of women first and best,
Art beyond all others blest.

2
Fear not, thou shalt bear a Son,
Aided by the Holy One;
Greater than the greatest, he
Son of God most high shall be.'

3
Thus the holy angel said.
Blessèd Mary bowed her head:
'Lo, the handmaid of the Lord;
With his word may all accord.'

4
So to hearts still undefiled
Comes the promise of a child,
Full of joy, akin to tears,
Full of hope, yet full of fears.

5
Happy she who answers still,
'Be it, Lord, at thy sweet will;
All I am to thee I owe,
All thy purpose thou dost know.

6
What thou givest to be mine,
May it ne'er be aught but thine:
Be it good or be it ill,
Still be all at thy sweet will.'

7
Holy Mary, taught by thee
Let us vain forebodings flee.
God is giving; fears must cease:
In his will is perfect peace.

BISHOP GILBERT WHITE

Societies and Meetings

In March Time

By permission of the Oxford University Press

YOUTH SERVICES

Go forth with God! the day is now⌣
  That thou must meet the test of youth:
Salvation's helm upon thy brow,
    Go, girded with the living truth.
      In ways thine elder brethren trod⌣
      Thy feet are set. Go forth with God!

2

Think fair of all, and all men love,
  And with the builder bear thy part:
Let every day and duty prove
    The humble witness of thy heart.
      Go forth! tis God bids thee increase⌣
      The bounds of love and joy and peace.

3

Behold with thine uplifted eyes
  Beauty through all that sorrow seems,
And make of earth a paradise,
    The substance of thy dearest dreams.
      Bring laughter to thy great employ:
      Go forth with God and find his joy.

4

Go forth with God! the world awaits⌣
  The coming of the pure and strong;
Strike for the faith and storm the gates
    That keep the citadel of wrong.
      Glory shall shine about thy road,
      Great heart, if thou go forth with God!

B. Baron

HYMN **501** Agincourt — L.M.   English Melody (15th cent.)

May be sung in Unison

(*National*)

O God, whose mighty works of old
Our fathers to their sons have told,
Be with us still from age to age,
Our children's children's heritage.

2
Thine are the kingdoms : at thy feet⌣
All peoples of the earth do meet
In equal lowliness of prayer
To find thine equal pity there.

3
Thy strength made strong our fathers'
A people great on seas and lands, [hands,
To win, till earth shall pass away,
Such honour as the earth can pay.

4
Be with their children : give us grace
To know, nor fear to hold, their place,
Nor meanly shrink, nor boast at ease—
A people great on lands and seas.

5
Keep thou our boyhood free and fair
And quick to help and brave to dare :
From greed and selfishness and shame
Guard thou, O Lord, the English name.

6
Keep thou our girlhood fair and free
In mirth and love and modesty :
From ugly thought and deed and word
Guard thou our English homes, O Lord.

7
O God, whose mighty works of old
Our fathers to their sons have told,
Be thou our strength from age to age,
Our children's children's heritage.

J. M. C. CRUM

Alternative Tune, Canon, 23

672

Societies and Meetings

Higher settings of this tune will be found at Hymns 245 (with descant) and 582

REUNION GATHERINGS

Thou gracious God, whose mercy lends⌣
The light of home, the smile of friends,
Our gathered flock thine arms enfold
As in the peaceful days of old.

2
Wilt thou not hear us while we raise
In sweet accord of solemn praise
The voices that have mingled long
In joyous flow of mirth and song?

3
For all the blessings life has brought,
For all its sorrowing hours have taught,
For all we mourn, for all we keep,
The hands we clasp, the loved that sleep,

4
The noon-tide sunshine of the past,
These brief, bright moments fading fast,
The stars that gild our darkening years,
The twilight ray from holier spheres,

5
We thank thee, Father; let thy grace⌣
Our loving circle still embrace,
Thy mercy shed its heavenly store,
Thy peace be with us evermore.

O. W. HOLMES

HYMN **503** FIRST TUNE

Aeterna Christi munera — L.M. Mode vii

Aeterna Christi munera

1 The e-ter-nal gifts of Christ the King, The a-pos-tles'
2 For they the Church-'s prin - ces are, Tri - umph-ant
3 Theirs is the stead-fast faith of saints, And hope that
4 In them the Fa-ther's glo - ry shone, In them the
5 To thee, Re-deem-er, now we cry, That thou wouldst

1 glo - ry, let us sing; And all, with hearts of glad -
2 lead-ers in the war, In heaven-ly courts a war -
3 nev-er yields nor faints, And love of Christ in per -
4 will of God the Son, In them ex - ults the Ho -
5 join to them on high Thy ser - vants, who this grace

1 ness, raise Due hymns of thank-ful love and praise.
2 rior band, True lights to light-en ev - ery land.
3 fect glow That lays the prince of this world low.
4 ly Ghost, Through them re-joice the heaven-ly host.
5 im - plore, For ev - er and for ev - er - more.

674

HYMN **503**   SECOND TUNE

Illsley (*or* Bishop) — L.M.   J. Bishop, 1665-1737

A lower setting of this tune will be found at Hymn 1

Aeterna Christi munera

f   The eternal gifts of Christ the King,
     The apostles' glory, let us sing;
     And all, with hearts of gladness, raise⌣
     Due hymns of thankful love and praise.

2

For they the Church's princes are,
Triumphant leaders in the war,
In heavenly courts a warrior band,
True lights to lighten every land.

3

mf Theirs is the steadfast faith of saints,
     And hope that never yields nor faints,
     And love of Christ in perfect glow
     That lays the prince of this world low.

4

f   In them the Father's glory shone,
     In them the will of God the Son,
     In them exults the Holy Ghost,
     Through them rejoice the heavenly host.

5

p   To thee, Redeemer, now we cry,
     That thou wouldst join to them on high
     Thy servants, who this grace implore,
mf For ever and for evermore.

                ? ST. AMBROSE
                Tr. J. M. Neale and Compilers

HYMN **504**　　　　　　FIRST TUNE

Exultet caelum laudibus — L.M.　　　　　　Mode iv

Exultet caelum laudibus

1 Let all on earth their voi - ces raise, Re - echo - ing
2 Thou at whose word they bore the light, Of Gos - pel
3 Thou at whose will to them was given To bind and
4 Thou in whose might they spake the word Which cured dis -
5 And when the thrones are set on high, And judge - ment's

1 heaven's tri - umph - ant praise, To him who gave the a -
2 truth o'er hea - then night, To us that heaven - ly
3 loose in earth and heaven, Our chains un - bind, our
4 ease and health re - stored, To us its heal - ing
5 awe - ful hour draws nigh, Then, Lord, with them pro -

1 pos - tles grace To run on earth their glo - rious race.
2 light im - part, To glad our eyes and cheer our heart.
3 sins un - do, And in our hearts thy grace re - new.
4 power pro - long, Sup - port the weak, con - firm the strong.
5 nounce us blest. And take us to thine end - less rest.

676

HYMN **504**   SECOND TUNE

Rex gloriose martyrum — L.M.   *Catholische Geistliche Gesänge*
(Andernach, 1608)

Exultet caelum laudibus

Let all on earth their voices raise,
Re-echoing heaven's triumphant praise,
To him who gave the apostles grace
To run on earth their glorious race.

2
Thou at whose word they bore the light
Of Gospel truth o'er heathen night,
To us that heavenly light impart,
To glad our eyes and cheer our heart.

3
Thou at whose will to them was given
To bind and loose in earth and heaven,
Our chains unbind, our sins undo,
And in our hearts thy grace renew.

4
Thou in whose might they spake the word
Which cured disease and health restored,
To us its healing power prolong,
Support the weak, confirm the strong.

5
And when the thrones are set on high,
And judgement's aweful hour draws nigh,
Then, Lord, with them pronounce us blest,
And take us to thine endless rest.

Tr. BISHOP R. MANT and Compilers

Festivals of Apostles

HYMN **505**   Annue Christe — 12 12 12 12   Melody from La Feillée,
Méthode, 1808

May be sung in Unison

Festivals of Apostles

Annue, Christe

O Christ, thou Lord of worlds, thine ear to hear us bow
On this the festival of thine apostle now,
Who taught to men thy power to free from sin's offence
The souls of those that tread the way of penitence.

2

Redeemer, save thy work, thy noble work of grace,
Sealed with the holy light that beameth from thy face;
Nor suffer them to fall to Satan's wiles a prey
For whom thou didst on earth death's costly ransom pay.

3

Pity thy flock, enthralled by sin's captivity,
Forgive each guilty soul and set the bondmen free;
And those thou hast redeemed by thine own Passion sore
Grant to rejoice with thee, O King, for evermore.

Tr. J. M. NEALE‡

Festivals of Apostles

Hymn **506**   Hanover — 10 10 11 11   *Supplement to the New Version,*
1708

Descant by Alan Gray, 1855–1935

The Descant may be sung by Trebles for verse 6, the main melody being sung in Unison

A higher setting of this tune will be found at Hymn 167

Festivals of Apostles

Supreme, quales, Arbiter

mf Disposer supreme, and Judge of the earth,
  Who choosest for thine the meek and the poor;
  To frail earthen vessels, and things of no worth,
  Entrusting thy riches which ay shall endure;

2

  Those vessels soon fail, though full of thy light,
  And at thy decree are broken and gone;
f Thence brightly appeareth thy truth in its might,
  As through the clouds riven the lightnings have shone.

3

  Like clouds are they borne to do thy great will,
  And swift as the winds about the world go:
  The Word with his wisdom their spirits doth fill;
  They thunder, they lighten, the waters o'erflow.

[UNISON]   4

  Their sound goeth forth, 'Christ Jesus the Lord!'
  Then Satan doth fear, his citadels fall;
  As when the dread trumpets went forth at thy word,
  And one long blast shattered the Canaanite's wall.

5

mf O loud be their trump, and stirring their sound,
  To rouse us, O Lord, from slumber of sin!
  The lights thou hast kindled in darkness around,
  O may they awaken our spirits within!

[UNISON]   6

f All honour and praise, dominion and might,
  To God, Three in One, eternally be,
  Who round us hath shed his own marvellous light,
  And called us from darkness his glory to see.

J. B. DE SANTEUIL
Tr. I. Williams‡

HYMN **507**　　　　　　FIRST TUNE

Corbeil — 7 7 7 7　　　　　Office of P. de Corbeil (*d.* 1222)

SECOND TUNE

University College — 7 7 7 7　　　　H. J. Gauntlett, 1805–76

Caelestis aulae principes

f　Captains of the saintly band,
　　Lights who lighten every land,
　　Princes who with Jesus dwell,
　　Judges of his Israel;

2

On the nations sunk in night
Ye have shed the Gospel light;
Sin and error flee away,
Truth reveals the promised day.

3

mf Not by warrior's spear and sword,
Not by art of human word,
Preaching but the Cross of shame,
Rebel hearts for Christ ye tame.

4

p Earth, that long in sin and pain
Groaned in Satan's deadly chain,
f Now to serve its God is free
In the law of liberty.

5

Distant lands with one acclaim
Tell the honour of your name,
Who, wherever man has trod,
Teach the mysteries of God.

[UNISON] **6**

Glory to the Three in One
While eternal ages run,
Who from deepest shades of night
Called us to his glorious light.

J. B. DE SANTEUIL
Tr. Sir H. W. Baker

See also hymn **529** *and accompanying note*

NOTE. *Hymn* 602, *parts* 2 *and* 3, *may be used on the Festivals of Apostles or Evangelists between Easter Day and Trinity Sunday*

HYMN **508**   Evangelists — 8 8 7. 8 8 7   Melody by J. B. König (?),
1691–1758
Harmony adapted from J. S. Bach, 1685–1750

mf Come, pure hearts, in sweetest measures
Sing of those who spread the treasures
In the holy gospels shrined :
Blessèd tidings of salvation,
Peace on earth, their proclamation,
Love from God to lost mankind.

2

Thou, by whom the words were given
For our light and guide to heaven,
Spirit, on our darkness shine ;
Graft them in our hearts, increasing
Faith, hope, love, and joy unceasing,
Till our hearts are wholly thine.

3

O that we, thy truth confessing
And thy holy word possessing,
Jesu, may thy love adore ;
f Unto thee our voices raising,
Thee with all thy ransomed praising
Ever and for evermore.

R. CAMPBELL and others
Based on Adam of St. Victor

HYMN **509**   Ach Gott vom Himmelreiche — 7 6 7 6. D   M. Praetorius,
1571–1621

Plausu chorus laetabundo

f Come sing, ye choirs exultant,
Those messengers of God,
Through whom the living gospels
Came sounding all abroad;
Whose voice proclaimed salvation,
That poured upon the night,
And drove away the shadows,
And flushed the world with light.

2
mf He chose them, our Good Shepherd,
And, tending evermore [quarters,
His flock through earth's four
In wisdom made them four:
In one harmonious witness
The chosen four combine,
While each his own commission
Fulfils in every line.

3
f   Four-square on this foundation
The Church of Christ remains,
A house to stand unshaken
By floods or winds or rains.
O glorious happy portion
In this safe home to be,
By God, true Man, united
With God eternally!

ADAM OF ST. VICTOR
Tr. Jackson Mason

Alternative Tune, Erfreut euch, 625

HYMN **510**   Venice — S.M.   W. Amps, 1824–1910

A lower setting of this tune will be found at Hymn 615

mf   How beauteous are their feet,
Who stand on Sion's hill,
Who bring salvation on their tongues
And words of peace instil!

2
How happy are our ears
That hear this happy sound,
Which kings and prophets waited for,
And sought, but never found!

3
How blessèd are our eyes
That see this heavenly light!
Prophets and kings desired it long,
But died without the sight.

4
f   The Lord makes bare his arm
Through all the earth abroad:
Let every nation now behold
Their Saviour and their God.

I. WATTS

HYMN **511**   Song 34 — L.M.   Orlando Gibbons, 1583–1625

Spirit of Jesus, who didst move
  The hearts and pens of men to write
  The story of the world's true Light,
His words of power and deeds of love;

2
We thank thee for those scribes of old
  Who, while apostles journeyed still
  Their worldwide witness to fulfil,
Set down the glorious tale they told;

3
We thank thee for the writers three,
  Who from such fleeting records wrought⌣
  The first three gospels, and so taught⌣
The truth for every age to see.

4
Then, as faith ripened, thou didst call⌣
  A fourth evangelist, to show⌣
  The Christ whom souls had come to know
As Way, as Truth, as Life, for all.

5
Spirit of Jesus, give thy grace
  To us who read, that so we may⌣
  Know him more fully day by day
Until we see him face to face.

C. S. PHILLIPS

FESTIVALS OF THE BLESSED
VIRGIN MARY

Quem terra, pontus, aethera — L.M.   Mode ii

Quem terra, pontus, aethera

1 The God whom earth and sea and sky⌣ A - dore and
2 O Mo - ther blest! the cho - sen shrine⌣ Where - in the
3 Blest in the mes - sage Ga - briel brought; Blest in the
4 O Lord, the Vir - gin - born, to thee E - ter - nal

1 laud and mag - ni - fy, Whose might they own, whose
2 Ar - chi - tect di - vine, Whose hand con - tains the
3 work the Spi - rit wrought; Most blest, to bring to
4 praise and glo - ry be, Whom with the Fa - ther

1 praise they tell, In Ma - ry's bo - dy deigned to dwell.
2 earth and sky, Vouch - safed in hid - den guise to lie:
3 hu - man birth The long De - sired of all the earth.
4 we a - dore And Ho - ly Ghost for ev - er - more.

Festivals of the Blessed Virgin Mary

St. Ambrose — L.M. La Feillée, *Méthode*, 1808

Quem terra, pontus, aethera

mf The God whom earth and sea and sky
Adore and laud and magnify,
Whose might they own, whose praise they tell,
p In Mary's body deigned to dwell.

2

mf O Mother blest! the chosen shrine
Wherein the Architect divine,
Whose hand contains the earth and sky,
p Vouchsafed in hidden guise to lie :

3

mf Blest in the message Gabriel brought;
Blest in the work the Spirit wrought;
f Most blest, to bring to human birth
The long Desired of all the earth.

[UNISON] 4

O Lord, the Virgin-born, to thee
Eternal praise and glory be,
Whom with the Father we adore
And Holy Ghost for evermore.

BISHOP VENANTIUS FORTUNATUS
Tr. J. M. Neale and Compilers

HYMN **513**   Farley Castle — 10 10 10 10   H. Lawes, 1596–1662

mf   Her Virgin eyes saw God incarnate born,
     When she to Bethlem came that happy morn:
     How high her raptures then began to swell,
     None but her own omniscient Son can tell.

2

p   As Eve, when she her fontal sin reviewed,
    Wept for herself and all she should include,
f   Blest Mary, with man's Saviour in embrace,
    Joyed for herself and for all human race.

3

mf   All saints are by her Son's dear influence blest;
     She kept the very fountain at her breast:
     The Son adored and nursed by the sweet Maid
     A thousandfold of love for love repaid.

4

f   Heaven with transcendent joys her entrance graced,
    Near to his throne her Son his Mother placed;
    And here below, now she's of heaven possest,
    All generations are to call her blest.

BISHOP T. KEN†

Festivals of the Blessed Virgin Mary

HYMN **514**   Genevan Psalm lxxxvi — 8 8 7 7. D   L. Bourgeois, *Genevan Psalter*, 1543

May be sung in Unison

1 Vir-gin-born, we bow be-fore thee: Bless-èd was the womb that bore thee;
3 Bless-èd she by all cre-a-tion, Who brought forth the world's Sal-va-tion, And

1 Ma-ry, Maid and Mo-ther mild, Bless-èd was she in her Child.
3 bless-èd they—for ev-er blest—Who love thee most and serve thee best.

2 Bless-èd was the breast that fed thee; Bless-èd was the hand that led thee;
4 Vir-gin-born, we bow be-fore thee: Bless-èd was the womb that bore thee;

2 Bless-èd was the par-ent's eye That watched thy slum-bering in-fan-cy.
4 Ma-ry, Maid and Mo-ther mild, Bless-èd was she in her Child.

BISHOP R. HEBER

Festivals of the Blessed Virgin Mary

FIRST TUNE

Belmont — C.M.   Adapted from W. Gardiner's *Sacred Melodies*, 1812

SECOND TUNE

St. Agnes — C.M.   J. B. Dykes, 1823–76

mf Shall we not love thee, Mother dear,
       Whom Jesus loves so well?
       And to his glory year by year
       Thy joy and honour tell?

692

2

p Bound with the curse of sin and shame
    We helpless sinners lay,
mf Until in tender love he came
    To bear the curse away.

3

mf And thee he chose from whom to take
    True flesh his flesh to be;
p In it to suffer for our sake,
f   By it to make us free.

4

p Thy Babe he lay upon thy breast,
    To thee he cried for food;
  Thy gentle nursing soothed to rest
    The incarnate Son of God.

5

mf O wondrous depth of grace divine
    That he should bend so low!
  And, Mary, O what joy 'twas thine
    In his dear love to know!

6

f Joy to be Mother of the Lord,
    And thine the truer bliss,
  In every thought and deed and word
    To be for ever his.

7

mf And as he loves thee, Mother dear,
    We too will love thee well;
  And to his glory year by year
    Thy joy and honour tell.

[UNISON] **8**

f Jesu, the Virgin's holy Son,
    We praise thee and adore,
  Who art with God the Father One
    And Spirit evermore.

SIR H. W. BAKER

HYMN **516**   FIRST TUNE

Deus, tuorum militum — L.M.   Mode viii

Deus, tuorum militum

1 O God, thy sol - diers' great re - ward, Their por - tion,
2 By wis - dom taught he learned to know The van - i -
3 Right man - ful - ly his cross he bore, And ran his
4 We there - fore pray thee, Lord of love, Re - gard us
5 All praise to God the Fa - ther be, All praise, e -

1 crown, and faith - ful Lord, From all trans - gres - sions set
2 ty of all be - low, The fleet - ing joys of earth
3 race of tor - ments sore; For thee he poured his life
4 from thy throne a - bove; On this thy mar - tyr's tri -
5 ter - nal Son, to thee, Whom with the Spi - rit we

1 us free Who sing thy mar - tyr's vic - to - ry.
2 dis - dained, And ev - er - last - ing glo - ry gained.
3 a - way, With thee he lives in end - less day.
4 umph - day Wash ev - ery stain of sin a - way.
5 a - dore For ev - er and for ev - er - more.

694

HYMN 516 SECOND TUNE

Agincourt — L.M. English Melody (15th cent.)

May be sung in Unison

FOR A MARTYR

Deus, tuorum militum

O God, thy soldiers' great reward,
Their portion, crown, and faithful Lord,
From all transgressions set us free
Who sing thy martyr's victory.

2

By wisdom taught he learned to know
The vanity of all below,
The fleeting joys of earth disdained,
And everlasting glory gained.

3

Right manfully his cross he bore,
And ran his race of torments sore;
For thee he poured his life away,
With thee he lives in endless day.

4

We therefore pray thee, Lord of love,
Regard us from thy throne above;
On this thy martyr's triumph-day
Wash every stain of sin away.

[UNISON] 5

All praise to God the Father be,
All praise, eternal Son, to thee,
Whom with the Spirit we adore
For ever and for evermore.

Tr. J. M. NEALE and Compilers

Alternative Tune, Grenoble, 129

HYMN **517**   Salus mortalium — 8 8 8 4 with Alleluias   *Gesangbuch*
(Erfurt, 1663)

f Al - le - lu - ia, Al - le - lu - ia.

FOR A MARTYR

Ex quo salus mortalium

mf Our Lord the path of suffering trod;
    And, since his Blood for man hath
        flowed,
    'Tis meet that man should yield to
        God
        The life he owed. Alleluia!

2

No shame to own the Crucified!
Nay, 'tis our immortality
That we confess our God who died,
    And for him die. Alleluia!

3

p Beholding his predestined crown,
    Into death's arms the martyr goes :
f Dying, he conquers death; o'er-
        thrown,
    O'erthrows his foes. Alleluia!

4

mf Lord, make us thine own soldiers
        true;
    Grant us brave faith, a spirit pure,
    That for thy name, thy Cross in view,
        We may endure. Alleluia!

[UNISON]   5
f   Eternal Father of the Word,
        Eternal Word, we thee adore,
    Eternal Spirit, God and Lord
        For evermore. Alleluia!

J. B. DE SANTEUIL
Tr. I. Williams†

696

HYMN **518**   Schwing dich — 7 6 7 6. D   Peter Franck (1657)
Harmonized by F. Layriz (1844)

FOR MARTYRS

τῶν ἱερῶν ἀθλοφόρων

Let our choir new anthems raise,
  Wake the song of gladness :
God himself to joy and praise
  Turns the martyrs' sadness.
Bright the day that won their crown,
  Opened heaven's bright portal,
As they laid the mortal down
  To put on the immortal.

2

Never flinched they from the flame,
  From the torture never ;
Vain the foeman's sharpest aim,
  Satan's best endeavour :
For by faith they saw the land
  Decked in all its glory,
Where triumphant now they stand
  With the victor's story.

3

Up and follow, Christian men !
Press through toil and sorrow ;
Spurn the night of fear, and then,
O the glorious morrow !
Who will venture on the strife ?
Blest who first begin it !
Who will grasp the land of life ?
Warriors, up and win it !

ST. JOSEPH THE HYMNOGRAPHER
Tr. J. M. Neale†

HYMN **519**   Diva servatrix — 11 11 11 5   French Melody

May be sung in Unison

FOR A CONFESSOR OR BISHOP

Iste confessor

He who to Jesus manfully bore witness,
He whom God's people join to-day to honour,
Now in the hidden mansions of the blessèd
Bideth for ever.

2

With store of virtues God adorned his spirit,
Guiding his willing feet in paths of goodness,
Through all the earthly years while in his body
Mortal breath tarried.

3

Wherefore with voices linked in happy chorus
Hymn we his praises on this holy feast-day,
Praying for grace to follow in his footsteps
Now and hereafter.

4

Glory and honour, powèr and salvation
Be unto him, who, thronèd in the highest,
Ordereth meetly earth and sky and ocean,
Triune, eternal.

Tr. COMPILERS

698

HYMN **520**   Diva servatrix — 11 11 11 5   French Melody

May be sung in Unison

FOR DOCTORS OF THE CHURCH

Stalwart as pillars bearing high their burden,
So do the Church's doctors stay the temple
Where truth abideth, on the one Foundation
    Grounded for ever.

2
O faithful stewards in God's holy household,
Out of your treasure new and old things bringing,
Still do your writings to the Light of ages
    Steadfastly witness.

3
Souls wise and loyal to the Spirit's leading,
Bravely ye battled for the faith delivered,
While of its ageless mysteries ye furnished
    New understanding.

4
Now with unclouded gaze ye are beholding
Him of whose face ye strained to catch the vision;
To whom be glory, Father, Son, and Spirit,
    Through endless ages.

C. S. PHILLIPS

699

HYMN **521**   Ealing — L.M.   Sir H. S. Oakeley, 1830–1903

FOR VIRGINS

Jesu, corona virginum

O Jesu, thou the virgins' crown,
Thy gracious ear to us bow down,
Born of that Virgin whom alone
The Mother and the Maid we own.

2

In thee, their Bridegroom and their Lord,
The virgins find their bright reward,
And wheresoe'er thy footsteps wend
With hymns and praises thee attend.

3

O gracious Lord, we thee implore
Thy grace into our minds to pour;
From all defilement keep us free,
And make us pure in heart for thee.

[UNISON]   4

All praise to God the Father be,
All praise, eternal Son, to thee,
Whom with the Spirit we adore,
For ever and for evermore.

                    ? ST. AMBROSE
                    Tr. Compilers† (1904)

Alternative Plainsong Tune, Deus, tuorum militum, 516

Festivals of Martyrs and Others

FOR MISSIONARY SAINTS

The saints who toiled from place to place,
Spreading the Gospel of God's grace,
Now in their heavenly homeland dwell
With Christ, whom here they served so well.

2

Alert at thy command to go,
And everywhere thy word to sow,
They went, O Master, far and wide,
Eager, but yet unsatisfied.

3

Thine was the task they took in hand,
Thine their good news for every land,
Thine was their power, and thine again
Their passion for the souls of men.

4

That task of thine, by them begun,
Must now by our weak hands be done:
Strengthen, O Lord, to work for thee
These hands, at home and over sea.

BISHOP W. H. FRERE†

701

FOR ANY SAINT'S DAY

HYMN **523**   Genevan Psalm xlii — 8787.7788   Melody by L. Bourgeois,
Genevan Psalter, 1551

702

For any Saint's Day

Supernae matris gaudia

Joy and triumph everlasting
  Hath the heavenly Church on high;
For that pure immortal gladness
  All our feast-days mourn and sigh;
Yet in death's dark desert wild
Doth the mother aid her child;
Guards celestial thence attend us,
Stand in combat to defend us.

2

Here the world's perpetual warfare
  Holds from heaven the soul apart;
Legioned foes in shadowy terror
  Vex the Sabbath of the heart.
O how happy that estate
Where delight doth not abate!
For that home the spirit yearneth,
Where none languisheth nor mourneth.

3

There the body hath no torment,
  There the mind is free from care,
There is every voice rejoicing,
  Every heart is loving there.
Angels in that city dwell;
Them their King delighteth well:
Still they joy and weary never,
More and more desiring ever.

4

There the seers and fathers holy,
  There the prophets glorified,
All their doubts and darkness ended,
  In the Light of Light abide.
There the saints, whose memories old
We in faithful hymns uphold,
Have forgot their bitter story
In the joy of Jesus' glory.

ADAM OF ST. VICTOR
Tr. Yattendon Hymnal

HYMN **524**   Orientis partibus — 7 7 7 7   Office of P. de Corbeil (*d.* 1222)

Pugnate, Christi milites

f   Soldiers, who are Christ's below,
Strong in faith resist the foe:
Boundless is the pledged reward
Unto them who serve the Lord.

2

mf   'Tis no palm of fading leaves
That the conqueror's hand receives;
Joys are his, serene and pure,
Light that ever shall endure.

3

For the souls that overcome
Waits the beauteous heavenly home,
Where the blessèd evermore
Tread on high the starry floor.

4

p   Passing soon and little worth
Are the things that tempt on earth;
mf   Heavenward lift thy soul's regard:
God himself is thy reward.

5

f   Father, who the crown dost give,
Saviour, by whose Death we live,
Spirit, who our hearts dost raise,
Three in One, thy name we praise.

18th cent. *Tr.* J. H. CLARK

HYMN **525**   Sandys Psalm viii — L.M.   Melody and bass by H. Lawes, 1596–1662

mf Lo, round the throne, a glorious band,
The saints in countless myriads stand,
Of every tongue redeemed to God,
Arrayed in garments washed in Blood.

2

p Through tribulation great they came;
They bore the cross, despised the shame;
From all their labours now they rest,
In God's eternal glory blest.

3

mf They see their Saviour face to face,
And sing the triumphs of his grace;
f Him day and night they ceaseless praise,
To him the loud thanksgiving raise:

4

'Worthy the Lamb, for sinners slain,
Through endless years to live and reign!
Thou hast redeemed us by thy Blood,
And made us kings and priests to God.'

5

mf O may we tread the sacred road
That saints and holy martyrs trod;
Wage to the end the glorious strife,
f And win, like them, a crown of life.

R. HILL and others

Alternative Tune, Old 100th, 166

705

For any Saint's Day

HYMN **526**   Deerhurst — 8 7 8 7. D   J. Langran, 1835-1909

f   Hark! the sound of holy voices,
   Chanting at the crystal sea
Alleluia, Alleluia,
   Alleluia, Lord, to thee:
Multitude, which none can number,
   Like the stars in glory stands,
Clothed in white apparel, holding⌣
   Palms of victory in their hands.

2

mf   Patriarch, and holy prophet,
   Who prepared the way of Christ,
King, apostle, saint, confessor,
   Martyr, and evangelist,
Saintly maiden, godly matron,
   Widows who have watched to prayer,
f   Joined in holy concert, singing⌣
   To the Lord of all, are there.

706

For any Saint's Day

3*

p They have come from tribulation,
    And have washed their robes in **Blood**,
    Washed them in the Blood of Jesus;
    Tried they were, and firm they stood:
    Mocked, imprisoned, stoned, tormented,
    Sawn asunder, slain with sword,
f They have conquered death and Satan
    By the might of Christ the Lord.

[UNISON]   **4**

Marching with thy Cross their banner,
    They have triumphed following⌣
Thee, the Captain of Salvation,
    Thee their Saviour and their King:
[HARMONY]
mf Gladly, Lord, with thee they suffered;
    Gladly, Lord, with thee they died,
f And by death to life immortal
    They were born, and glorified.

[UNISON]   **5**

Now they reign in heavenly glory,
    Now they walk in golden light,
Now they drink, as from a river,
    Holy bliss and infinite;
[HARMONY]
p Love and peace they taste for ever,
    And all truth and knowledge see
mf In the beatific vision
    Of the blessèd Trinity.

6

f God of God, the One-begotten,
    Light of Light, Emmanuel,
In whose Body joined together
    All the saints for ever dwell;
Pour upon us of thy fulness,
    That we may for evermore
God the Father, God the Son, and⌣
    God the Holy Ghost adore.

BISHOP CHR. WORDSWORTH

For any Saint's Day

FIRST TUNE

Engelberg — 10 10 10 4 Sir C. V. Stanford, 1852–1924

UNISON

1 For all the saints who from their la-bours rest,
2 Thou wast their rock, their fort-ress, and their might;
3 O may thy sol-diers, faith-ful, true, and bold,

1 Who thee by faith be-fore the world con-fessed,
2 Thou, Lord, their Cap-tain in the well-fought fight;
3 Fight as the saints who no-bly fought of old,

1 Thy name, O Je-su, be for ev-er blest.
2 Thou, in the dark-ness, still their one true Light.
3 And win, with them, the vic-tor's crown of gold.

708

For any Saint's Day

1 Al - le - lu - ia!
2 Al - le - lu - ia!
3 Al - le - lu - ia!

HARMONY

mf

4 O blest com - mun - ion! fel - low - ship di - vine!

We fee - bly strug - gle, they in glo - ry shine;

cres.

Yet all are one in thee, for all are thine.

HYMN **527** (first tune—*continued*)

Al - le - lu - ia!

UNISON

5 And when the strife is fierce, the war-fare long,

Steals on the ear the dis-tant tri-umph-song, And hearts are

brave a-gain and arms are strong. Al - le - lu - ia!

For any Saint's Day

6 The gold - en eve - ning bright - ens in the west;

Without Pedals

Soon, soon to faith - ful war - riors comes their rest:

Sweet is the calm of Par - a - dise the blest.

Ped.

Al - le - lu - ia!

711

For any Saint's Day

TENORS AND BASSES ONLY

7 But lo! there breaks a yet more glo-rious day;

The saints tri — umph-ant rise in bright ar-ray:

The King of Glo-ry pass-es on his way.

Al — le-lu — ia!

712

For any Saint's Day

UNISON

ff

8 From earth's wide bounds, from o - cean's far - thest coast,

Through gates of pearl streams in the count - less host,

Sing - ing to Fa - ther, Son, and Ho - ly Ghost

Al - le - lu - ia! HARMONY

A - men.

By permission of Stainer & Bell, Ltd.

For any Saint's Day

For all the Saints — 10 10 10 4   Sir J. Barnby, 1838–96

Al - le - lu - ia! Al - le - lu - ia!

[UNISON]

f For all the saints who from their labours rest,
Who thee by faith before the world confessed,
Thy name, O Jesu, be for ever blest.
                    Alleluia!

[HARMONY]   2
Thou wast their rock, their fortress, and their might;
Thou, Lord, their Captain in the well-fought fight;
Thou, in the darkness, still their one true Light.
                    Alleluia!

[HARMONY]   3
O may thy soldiers, faithful, true, and bold,
Fight as the saints who nobly fought of old,
And win, with them, the victor's crown of gold.
                    Alleluia!

For any Saint's Day

[UNISON] **4**

mf O blest communion, fellowship divine!
We feebly struggle, they in glory shine;
Yet all are one in thee, for all are thine.
Alleluia!

[HARMONY] **5**

p And when the strife is fierce, the warfare long,
Steals on the ear the distant triumph-song,
mf And hearts are brave again and arms are strong.
Alleluia!

[HARMONY] **6**

The golden evening brightens in the west;
Soon, soon to faithful warriors comes their rest:
p Sweet is the calm of Paradise the blest.
Alleluia!

[HARMONY] **7**

f But lo, there breaks a yet more glorious day;
The saints triumphant rise in bright array:
The King of Glory passes on his way.
Alleluia!

[UNISON] **8**

From earth's wide bounds, from ocean's farthest coast,
Through gates of pearl streams in the countless host,
Singing to Father, Son, and Holy Ghost
Alleluia!

BISHOP W. WALSHAM HOW

Alternative Tune, Woodchurch, 532

For any Saint's Day

FIRST TUNE

Sennen Cove — C.M.

W. H. Harris

VERSES 3 AND 4 SHOULD BEGIN THUS

SECOND TUNE

Beatitudo — C.M.

J. B. Dykes, 1823–76

For any Saint's Day

f   How bright these glorious spirits shine!
      Whence all their white array?
    How came they to the blissful seats
      Of everlasting day?

2

p   Lo, these are they from sufferings great
      Who came to realms of light;
    And in the Blood of Christ have washed
      Those robes that shine so bright.

3

f   Now with triumphal palms they stand
      Before the throne on high,
    And serve the God they love amidst
      The glories of the sky.

4

mf   Hunger and thirst are felt no more,
      Nor suns with scorching ray;
    God is their Sun, whose cheering beams
      Diffuse eternal day.

5

The Lamb, which dwells amidst the throne,
    Shall o'er them still preside,
Feed them with nourishment divine,
    And all their footsteps guide.

6

p   Midst pastures green he'll lead his flock,
      Where living streams appear;
mf   And God the Lord from every eye
      Shall wipe off every tear.

[UNISON]   7

f   To Father, Son, and Holy Ghost,
      The God whom we adore,
Be glory, as it was, is now,
    And shall be evermore.

                   I. Watts and others

For any Saint's Day

For any Saint's Day

f   The Son of God goes forth to war
     A kingly crown to gain;
His blood-red banner streams afar:
     Who follows in his train?
Who best can drink his cup of woe,
     Triumphant over pain,
Who patient bears his cross below,
     He follows in his train.

2

mf The martyr first, whose eagle eye
     Could pierce beyond the grave;
Who saw his Master in the sky,
     And called on him to save.
Like him, with pardon on his tongue
     In midst of mortal pain,
He prayed for them that did the wrong:
     Who follows in his train?

3

A glorious band, the chosen few
     On whom the Spirit came,
Twelve valiant saints, their hope they knew,
     And mocked the cross and flame.
They met the tyrant's brandished steel,
     The lion's gory mane;
They bowed their necks, the death to feel:
     Who follows in their train?

4

f   A noble army, men and boys,
     The matron and the maid,
Around the Saviour's throne rejoice
     In robes of light arrayed.
They climbed the steep ascent of heaven
     Through peril, toil, and pain:
O God, to us may grace be given
     To follow in their train.

BISHOP R. HEBER

Alternative Tune, St. Anne, 165

NOTE. *Verses 1 and 4 are suitable for any saint's day.
Verse 2 refers to St. Stephen, verse 3 to the apostles, and may
be used with verses 1 and 4 on the festivals for which they are
respectively appropriate. The whole hymn is suitable for All
Saints' Day*

For any Saint's Day

HYMN **530** Palms of glory — 7 7 7 7   Archbishop W. D. Maclagan, 1826–1910

f Palms of glory, raiment bright,
   Crowns that never fade away,
   Gird and deck the saints in light:
   Priests and kings and conquerors
   they.

2
mf Yet the conquerors bring their palms
   To the Lamb amidst the throne,
f And proclaim in joyful psalms
   Victory through his Cross alone.

3
mf Kings for harps their crowns resign,
   Crying, as they strike the chords,
f 'Take the Kingdom, it is thine,
   King of Kings and Lord of Lords.'

4
p Round the altar priests confess,
   If their robes are white as snow,
   'Twas the Saviour's righteousness,
   And his Blood, that made them so.

5
mf They were mortal too like us:
   O, when we like them must die,
f May our souls translated thus
   Triumph, reign, and shine on high.

J. MONTGOMERY

HYMN **531**   FIRST TUNE

Mount Ephraim — S.M.   B. Milgrove, 1731–1810
                            Harmonized by S. S. Wesley, 1810–76

For any Saint's Day

SECOND TUNE

St. Helena (Mount Ephraim) — S.M.   Adapted from B. Milgrove,
1731–1810

A higher setting of this tune will be found at Hymn 475

mf For all thy saints, O Lord,
    Who strove in thee to live,
Who followed thee, obeyed, adored,
    Our grateful hymn receive.

2
For all thy saints, O Lord,
    Who strove in thee to die,
And found in thee a full reward,
    Accept our thankful cry.

3
Thine earthly members fit
    To join thy saints above,
In one communion ever knit,
    One fellowship of love.

4
Jesu, thy name we bless,
    And humbly pray that we
May follow them in holiness,
    Who lived and died for thee.

[UNISON] 5
f All might, all praise, be thine,
    Father, co-equal Son,
And Spirit, bond of love divine,
    While endless ages run.

BISHOP R. MANT and Compilers

Alternative Tune, St. Michael, 539

HYMN **532**   Woodchurch — 10 10 10 4   Sir S. H. Nicholson, 1875–1947

Al - le - lu - ia, Al - le - lu - ia!

We praise thee, Lord, for all the martyred throng,
Those who by fire and sword or suffering long
Laid down their lives, but would not yield to wrong:
                                            Alleluia!

2
For those who fought to keep the faith secure,
For all whose hearts were selfless, strong and pure,
For those whose courage taught us to endure:
                                            Alleluia!

3
For fiery spirits, held and God-controlled,
For gentle natures by his power made bold,
For all whose gracious lives God's love retold.
                                            Alleluia!

4
Thanks be to thee, O Lord, for saints unknown,
Who by obedience to thy word have shown
That thou didst call and mark them for thine own.
                                            Alleluia!

BISHOP R. HEBER

ST. ANDREW THE APOSTLE

HYMN **533**   St. Andrew — 8 7 8 7   E. H. Thorne, 1834-1916

mf Jesus calls us! o'er the tumult
  Of our life's wild restless sea
Day by day his sweet voice soundeth,
  Saying, 'Christian, follow me;'

2
As of old Saint Andrew heard it
  By the Galilean lake,
Turned from home and toil and kindred,
  Leaving all for his dear sake.

3
p Jesus calls us from the worship
  Of the vain world's golden store,
From each idol that would keep us,
  Saying, 'Christian, love me more.'

4
mf In our joys and in our sorrows,
  Days of toil and hours of ease,
Still he calls, in cares and pleasures,
  That we love him more than these.

5
p Jesus calls us! by thy mercies,
  Saviour, make us hear thy call,
Give our hearts to thine obedience,
  Serve and love thee best of all.

MRS. C. F. ALEXANDER

Alternative Tune, Merton, 47

ST. THOMAS THE APOSTLE

HYMN **534** Elton — 6 5 6 5. 6 6 6 5

J. Dykes Bower

724

St. Thomas the Apostle

Who dreads, yet undismayed
  Dares face his terror;
Who errs, yet having strayed
  Avows his error—
Him let Saint Thomas guide,
Who stirred his fellows' pride
To move to death beside⌣
  Their Lord and Master.

2

Who longs for guidance clear
  When doubts assail him,
Nor dares to move for fear
  Lest faith should fail him—
For such let Christ's reply
To his disciple's cry,
'I am the Way,' supply⌣
  The light in darkness.

3

Who grieves that love lies dead
  On fate's wheel broken;
And stands uncomforted
  By any token.—
His faith shall be restored
By Christ's compelling word
When Thomas saw the Lord,
  And seeing worshipped.

ARCHBISHOP J. R. DARBYSHIRE

ST. STEPHEN

HYMN **535** Evangelists — 8 8 7. 8 8 7 Melody by J. B. König (?),
1691–1758
Harmony adapted from J. S. Bach, 1685–1750

Heri mundus exultavit

Yesterday with exultation
Joined the world in celebration
  Of her promised Saviour's birth;
Yesterday the angel-nation
Poured the strains of jubilation
  O'er the Monarch born on earth:

2
But to-day, O deacon glorious,
By thy faith and deeds victorious,
  Stephen, champion renowned,
Thee we hail who, triumph gaining,
Mid the faithless faith sustaining,
  First of martyr saints wast found.

3
For the crown that fadeth never
Bear thy murderers' brief endeavour;
  Victory waits to end the strife:
Death shall be thy life's beginning,
And life's losing be the winning
  Of the true and better life.

ADAM OF ST. VICTOR
Tr. J. M. Neale and Compilers

See also hymn **529** *and accompanying note*

726

ST. JOHN THE EVANGELIST

HYMN **536**   St. Thomas — 8 7. 8 7. 8 7   Traditional Melody (18th cent.)

A higher setting of this tune will be found at Hymn 388

mf Word supreme, before creation
Born of God eternally,
Who didst will for our salvation
To be born on earth, and die;
Well thy saints have kept their sta-
tion,
Watching till thine hour drew nigh.

2

Now 'tis come, and faith espies thee:
Like an eaglet in the morn,
One in steadfast worship eyes thee,
Thy beloved, thy latest born;
In thy glory he descries thee
Reigning from the Tree of scorn.

3

f Lo, heaven's doors lift up, revealing
How thy judgements earthward
move:
Scrolls unfolded, trumpets pealing,
Wine-cups from the wrath above;
p Yet o'er all a soft voice stealing,
'Little children, trust and love!'

4

f Thee, the almighty King eternal,
Father of the eternal Word,
Thee, the Father's Word supernal,
Thee, of Both, the Breath adored,
Heaven and earth and realms infernal
Own, one glorious God and Lord.

J. KEBLE

727

St. John the Evangelist

HYMN **537**   Golden Sheaves — 8 7 8 7. D   Sir A. Sullivan, 1842–1900

St. John the Evangelist

To you was given, O saint beloved,
  A vision of Christ's glory
Before he lived his earthly life
  Begun with Christmas story:
The glory of the Son of God
  Before the world's creation,
In whom all things that are were made
  And have their consummation.

2

In you he found his closest friend,
  A friend though frail and mortal,
Whose love so pure gave sight so sure
  It pierced beyond heaven's portal:
So to the world you witness gave,
  With prophet's eye descrying
The life of grace and fellowship,
  The life in God undying.

3

O love of God that overflowed
  In glories of creation!
O crowning glory of all life
  In wondrous Incarnation!
All praise to God whose saint and seer
  Declared the love excelling
Now shed abroad in faithful hearts,
  Abounding and indwelling.

                                F. B. MERRYWEATHER

HYMN **538**   Puer nobis — L.M.   Melody by M. Praetorius, 1571–1621

Salvete, flores martyrum

O Martyrs young and fresh as flowers,
Your day was in its morning hours
When Christ was sought and you were found
Like rain-strewn petals on the ground.

2

How weak to hurt you was the king!
You are Christ's morning offering,
His pretty lambs, his children, gay
With martyr-crowns and palms at play.

3

And you had cheated Herod's rage,
You little boys of Jesus' age;
For he whom Herod sought to slay,
Jesus, untouched escaped away.

[UNISON]   4

Glory, O Christ the Lord, to thee,
Child of the blessèd Virgin, be,
Whom with the Father we adore
And Holy Spirit evermore.

PRUDENTIUS
Tr. J. M. C. Crum

Alternative Tune, Alstone, 435

THE CIRCUMCISION

HYMN **539**   St. Michael — S.M.   *Anglo-Genevan Psalms*, 1561

A higher setting of this tune will be found at Hymn 142

Debilis cessent elementa legis

The ancient law departs,
And all its fears remove,
For Jesus makes with faithful hearts
A covenant of love.

2

The Light of Light divine,
True brightness undefiled,
He bears for us the pain of sin,
A holy spotless Child.

3

To-day the name is thine
At which we bend the knee;
They call thee Jesus, Child divine:
Our Jesus deign to be.

4

All praise, eternal Son,
For thy redeeming love,
With Father, Spirit, ever One,
In glorious might above.

S. BESNAULT
Tr. Compilers (1904)

The following hymns are also suitable:

190   To the name of our salvation.
191   Conquering kings their titles take.
192   How sweet the name of Jesus sounds.

731

THE CONVERSION OF ST. PAUL

Hymn **540** Woolmer's — L.M. Sir F. A. G. Ouseley, 1825–89

Paule, doctor egregie

From heaven's height Christ spake to
call
The Gentiles' great apostle, Paul,
Whose doctrine, like the thunder, sounds
To the wide world's remotest bounds.

2

O bliss of Paul, beyond all thought,
To Paradise, yet living, caught!
He hears the heavenly mysteries there,
Which mortal tongue cannot declare.

3

The word's good seed abroad he flings;
Straightway a mighty harvest springs,
And fruits of holy deeds supply
God's everlasting granary.

4

The lamp his burning faith displays
Has filled the world with glorious rays;
That darkness' realm may be o'er-
thrown,
And Christ may reign, and reign alone.

St. Peter Damiani
Tr. J. M. Neale‡

Alternative Tune, Agincourt, 501

Hymn **541** Ellacombe — 7 6 7 6. D *Würtemburg Gesangbuch*, 1784

The Conversion of St. Paul

We sing the glorious conquest
  Before Damascus' gate,
When Saul, the Church's spoiler,
  Came breathing threats and hate;
The ravening wolf rushed forward
  Full early to the prey;
But lo, the Shepherd met him,
  And bound him fast to-day.

2*

O glory most excelling
  That smote across his path!
O light that pierced and blinded
  The zealot in his wrath!
O voice that spake within him
  The calm reproving word!
O love that sought and held him
  The bondman of his Lord!

3

O Wisdom, ordering all things
  In order strong and sweet,
What nobler spoil was ever
  Cast at the Victor's feet?
What wiser master-builder
  E'er wrought at thine employ
Than he, till now so furious
  Thy building to destroy?

4

Lord, teach thy Church the lesson,
  Still in her darkest hour
Of weakness and of danger
  To trust thy hidden power:
Thy grace by ways mysterious
  The wrath of man can bind,
And in thy boldest foeman
  Thy chosen saint can find.

J. Ellerton

The Conversion of St. Paul

HYMN **542** Stuttgart — 8 7 8 7 C. F. Witt, 1660–1716

Paul the preacher, Paul the poet,
  Fearless fighter for the truth,
Mystic, pioneer, and prophet,
  Builder of the Church's youth;

2
Foremost of Gamaliel's pupils,
  Pharisee of Christian fame,
Great apostle of the Gentiles,
  We as Gentiles bless thy name.

3
Loyal Jew, yet born a Roman,
  Citizen, yet slave of Christ,
Wealth, position, kindred, freedom,
  To thy Lord were sacrificed.

4
Still to-day we need thy teaching,
  Stern yet loving, hard yet true:
Only those who share his Passion
  Can their lives in Christ renew.

5
Paul the fiery, Paul the saintly,
  Worship with us at thy feast;
May our love to Christ be strengthened,
  And our faith through thee increased;

6
Till, when faith no more is needed,
  There where faith and sight are one,
We in heaven shall praise the Father
  In the Spirit through the Son.

AMY SAYLE

Alternative Tune, St. Oswald, 292

734

PRESENTATION OF CHRIST IN THE TEMPLE

COMMONLY CALLED

THE PURIFICATION OF ST. MARY THE VIRGIN

HYMN **543**   Bristol — C.M.   T. Ravenscroft, *Psalms*, 1621

An Alternative Version of this tune with the melody in the tenor part will be found at Hymn 53

Templi sacratas pande, Sion, fores

1

O Sion, open wide thy gates,
   Let symbols disappear:
A Priest and Victim, both in one,
   The Truth himself is here.

2

No more the slaughtered beast must die:
   Behold, the Father's Son
His Temple enters, soon himself
   For sinners to atone.

3

Conscious of hidden Deity,
   The lowly Virgin brings
Her new-born Babe, with two young
   Her humble offerings.   [doves,

4

There waiting Simeon sees at last
   The Saviour long desired,
And Anna welcomes Israel's Hope,
   With holy rapture fired.

5

But silent stood the Mother blest
   Of the yet silent Word,
And, pondering in her steadfast heart,
   With speechless praise adored.

[UNISON]   6

All glory to the Father be,
   All glory to the Son,
All glory, Holy Ghost, to thee,
   While endless ages run.

J. B. DE SANTEUIL
Tr. E. Caswall and Compilers

735

The Purification of St. Mary the Virgin

Old 120th — 6 6. 6 6. 6 6   *Psalms*, 1570

A higher setting of this tune will be found at Hymn 259

SECOND TUNE

St. Veronica — 6 6. 6 6. 6 6   Sir F. Champneys, 1848–1930

* *For verses 2, 3 and 5*

The Purification of St. Mary the Virgin

f   Hail to the Lord who comes,
     Comes to his Temple gate!
mf Not with his angel host,
     Not in his kingly state:
    No shouts proclaim him nigh,
     No crowds his coming wait.

2

p   But borne upon the throne
     Of Mary's gentle breast,
    Watched by her duteous love,
     In her fond arms at rest;
mf Thus to his Father's house
     He comes, the heavenly guest.

3

There Joseph at her side
  In reverent wonder stands;
And, filled with holy joy,
  Old Simeon in his hands
Takes up the promised Child,
  The glory of all lands.

4

Hail to the great First-born,
  Whose ransom-price they pay!
The Son before all worlds;
  The Child of man to-day,
f   That he might ransom us
    Who still in bondage lay.

5

mf O Light of all the earth,
    Thy children wait for thee:
Come to thy temples here,
    That we, from sin set free,
Before thy Father's face
    May all presented be.

J. ELLERTON

737

ST. MATTHIAS THE APOSTLE

HYMN **545**   Tallis — C.M.   T. Tallis, *c.* 1505–85

A lower setting of this tune will be found at Hymn 231

The highest and the holiest place
  Guards not the heart from sin :
The Church that safest seems without
  May harbour foes within.

2

Thus in the small and chosen band
  Beloved above the rest,
One fell from his apostleship,
  A traitor soul unblest.

3

But not the great designs of God
  Man's sins shall overthrow;
Another witness to the truth
  Forth to the lands shall go.

4

The soul that sinneth, it shall die;
  Thy purpose shall not fail :
The word of grace no less shall sound,
  The truth no less prevail.

5

Righteous, O Lord, are all thy ways :
  Long as the worlds endure,
From foes without and foes within
  Thy Church shall stand secure.

H. ALFORD

738

THE ANNUNCIATION OF THE BLESSED VIRGIN MARY

Hymn **546**   Annunciation — S.M.   C. A. Barry, 1830–1915

Praise we the Lord this day,
This day so long foretold,
Whose promise shone with cheering ray
On waiting saints of old.

2
The prophet gave the sign
For faithful men to read :
A Virgin, born of David's line,
Shall bear the promised Seed.

3
Ask not how this should be,
But worship and adore ;
Like her, whom heaven's majesty
Came down to shadow o'er.

4
Meekly she bowed her head
To hear the gracious word,
Mary, the pure and lowly maid,
The favoured of the Lord.

5
Blessèd shall be her name
In all the Church on earth,
Through whom that wondrous mercy came,
The incarnate Saviour's birth.

6
Jesu, the Virgin's Son,
We praise thee and adore,
Who art with God the Father One
And Spirit evermore.

ANON. (1847)

Alternative Tune, St. George, 63

The Annunciation of the Blessed Virgin Mary

HYMN **547** Angelus ad Virginem — 7777.88.116.76 Medieval Melody
from *Dublin Troper* (c. 1360)

Harmonized by Sir S. H. Nicholson, 1875–1947

The Annunciation of the Blessed Virgin Mary

Angelus ad Virginem

Gabriel to Mary came,
   She saw him in her chamber;
Mary's heart stood still with fear,
   But gently did he greet her:
'Thou queen of maidens, hail!' he said,
'Thou shalt become a Mother-maid;
Thy Son shall be the Lord of earth and heaven:
   He comes to save mankind
That men, their sins forgiven,
   The gate of heaven may find.'

2

'How can I a mother be
   That am a maid unwedded?
How can I a mother be
   That am a maid betrothèd?'
He answered to her questioning:
'The Holy Ghost shall do this thing.
Be not afraid, nor let thy heart be careful:
   God guards thy purity;
His power shall make thee joyful,
   And blessèd shalt thou be.'

3

Unto whom our Lady then
   Returned her answer meekly:
'Here am I, the handmaiden
   Of God the Lord almighty;
O messenger of God most high,
Revealer of this mystery,
With all my heart I long to see fulfilment
   Of what I hear thee tell:
Behold his handmaid ready
   To do his holy will.'

4

Ah, thou Mother of my Lord,
   What peace through thee was given!
Thy dear Child, our Christ adored,
   Makes peace in earth and heaven.
Beseech thy Son for us, that he
Would look upon us graciously,
And, all our shame and misery relieving,
   Would give us grace to come
To comfort out of grieving
   And, out of exile, home.

14th cent. *Tr.* J. M. C. CRUM

The following hymns are also suitable:

512   The God whom earth and sea and sky.
513   Her Virgin eyes saw God incarnate born.
514   Virgin-born, we bow before thee.
515   Shall we not love thee, Mother dear.

ST. MARK THE EVANGELIST

HYMN **548**   Winchester New — L.M.   *Musikalisch Handbuch*
(Hamburg, 1690)

A higher setting of this tune will be found at Hymn 50

From out the cloud of fiery light,
  Borne on the whirlwind from the north,
Four living creatures winged and bright
  Before the prophet's eye came forth.

2
The voice of God was in the four
  Beneath that awful crystal mist,
And every wondrous form they wore
  Foreshadowed an Evangelist.

3
The lion-faced, he told abroad⌣
  The strength of love, the strength of faith;
He showed the almighty Son of God,
  The Man divine who won by death.

4
O Lion of the Royal Tribe,
  Strong Son of God, and strong to save,
All power and honour we ascribe
  To thee who only makest brave.

5
For strength to love, for will to speak,
  For fiery crowns by martyrs won,
For suffering patience, strong and meek,
  We praise thee, Lord, and thee alone.

MRS. C. F. ALEXANDER‡

742

SS. PHILIP AND JAMES THE APOSTLES

HYMN **549** Montgomery — L.M.   *Magdalen Hospital Hymns, c.* 1762

Caelestis aulae principes

Hail! princes of the host of heaven,
To whom by Christ your Chief 'tis given
On shining thrones to sit on high,
And judge the world with equity.

2

Through you was borne the Gospel light
To those who lay in sin's dark night;
That Christ, the Life, the Truth, the Way,
Might lead them to eternal day.

3

Not in the power of earthly sword
Or arts of speech ye preached the Lord:
The Cross, the Cross which men despise,
'Twas this achieved your victories.

4

And now to God, the Three in One,
Be highest praise and glory done,
Who calls us from the gloom of night
To share the glory of his light.

J. B. DE SANTEUIL
Tr. J. Chandler and Compilers

Hymn 199 is also suitable

743

ST. BARNABAS THE APOSTLE

Hymn **550** St. Osyth — 11 10 11 10 T. Wood

With vigour. UNISON

By permission of the Oxford University Press

O Son of God, our Captain of Salvation,
  Thyself by suffering schooled to human grief,
We bless thee for thy sons of consolation,
  Who follow in the steps of thee their chief:

2

For all true helpers, patient, kind, and skilful,
  Who shed thy light across our darkened earth,
Counsel the doubting, and restrain the wilful,
  Soothe the sick bed, and share the children's mirth.

3

Such was thy Levite, strong in self-oblation
  To cast his all at thine apostles' feet;
He whose new name, through every Christian nation,
  From age to age our thankful strains repeat.

J. ELLERTON

Alternative Tune, Genevan Psalm xii, 17

744

ST. JOHN BAPTIST

Ut queant laxis — 11 11 11 5   Mode ii

Ut queant laxis Resonare fibris

1 Sing we the prai - ses of the great fore - run - ner, Tell
2 Lo, God's high her - ald, swift from heaven de - scend - ing, Gives
3 Oft had the pro - phets in the time be - fore thee Spo -

1 forth the migh - ty won - ders of his sto - ry: So may his
2 to thy fa - ther ti - dings of thy com - ing, Tell - ing thy
3 ken in vi - sion of the Day - star's com - ing; But when he

1 Mas - ter cleanse our lips and make them Fit to ex - tol him.
2 name and all the tale of mar - vels That shall be - fall thee.
3 came, 'twas thou that didst pro - claim him Sa - viour of all men.

745

St. John Baptist

Lobet den Herren — 11 11 11 5　　　　　J. Crüger, 1598-1662
Harmonized by F. Layriz (1853)

May be sung in Unison

Ut queant laxis　Resonare fibris

Sing we the praises of the great forerunner,
Tell forth the mighty wonders of his story :
So may his Master cleanse our lips and make them
　　　Fit to extol him.

2

Lo, God's high herald, swift from heaven descending,
Gives to thy father tidings of thy coming,
Telling thy name and all the tale of marvels
　　　That shall befall thee.

3

Oft had the prophets in the time before thee
Spoken in vision of the Daystar's coming ;
But when he came, 'twas thou that didst proclaim him
　　　Saviour of all men.

　　　　　　PAUL THE DEACON
　　　　　　Tr. Compilers

Alternative Tune, Diva servatrix, 519

St. John Baptist

Croft's 148th — 6 6 6 6. 4 4 4 4   W. Croft, 1678–1727

A higher setting of this tune will be found at Hymn 248

Nunc suis tandem novus e latebris

mf Lo, from the desert homes,
　　Where he hath hid so long,
　The new Elijah comes,
　　In sternest wisdom strong:
f　　The voice that cries
　　　Of Christ from high,
　　　And judgement nigh
　　From opening skies.

2
mf Your God e'en now doth stand
　At heaven's opening door;
　His fan is in his hand,
　　And he will purge his floor;
f　　The wheat he claims
　　　And with him stows,
　　　The chaff he throws
　　To quenchless flames.

3
　Ye haughty mountains, bow‿
　　Your sky-aspiring heads;
mf Ye valleys, hiding low,
　　Lift up your gentle meads;

f　　Make his way plain
　　Your King before,
　　For evermore
　　He comes to reign.

4
mf May thy dread voice around,
　　Thou harbinger of Light,
　On our dull ears still sound,
　　Lest here we sleep in night,
　　　Till judgement come,
　　　And on our path
　　　The Lamb's dread wrath
　　Shall burst in doom.

5
　O God, with love's sweet might,
　　Who dost anoint and arm‿
　Christ's soldier for the fight
　　With grace that shields from harm:
f　　Thrice blessèd Three,
　　　Heaven's endless days
　　　Shall sing thy praise
　　Eternally.

C. Coffin *Tr.* I. Williams†

St. John Baptist

Darwall's 148th — 6 6 6 6. 4 4 4 4   J. Darwall, 1731–89

A higher setting of this tune with a descant will be found at Hymn 371

Nunc suis tandem novus e latebris

mf Lo, from the desert homes,
Where he hath hid so long,
The new Elijah comes,
In sternest wisdom strong :
f   The voice that cries
Of Christ from high,
And judgement nigh
From opening skies.

2

mf Your God e'en now doth stand
At heaven's opening door ;
His fan is in his hand,
And he will purge his floor ;
f   The wheat he claims
And with him stows,
p   The chaff he throws
To quenchless flames.

3

f Ye haughty mountains, bow‿
Your sky-aspiring heads ;
mf Ye valleys, hiding low,
Lift up your gentle meads ;

f   Make his way plain
Your King before,
For evermore
He comes to reign.

4

mf May thy dread voice around,
Thou harbinger of Light,
On our dull ears still sound,
Lest here we sleep in night,
Till judgement come,
And on our path
The Lamb's dread wrath
Shall burst in doom.

5

O God, with love's sweet might,
Who dost anoint and arm‿
Christ's soldier for the fight
With grace that shields from harm,
f   Thrice blessèd Three,
Heaven's endless days
Shall sing thy praise
Eternally.

C. COFFIN *Tr.* I. Williams

HYMN **553**   Sedulius — L.M.   *Nürnbergisches Gesangbuch,* 1676

Praecursor altus luminis

The great forerunner of the morn,
The herald of the Word, is born;
And faithful hearts shall never fail
With thanks and praise his light to hail.

2
With heavenly message Gabriel came,
That John should be that herald's name,
And with prophetic utterance told
His actions great and manifold.

3
John, still unborn, yet gave aright
His witness to the coming Light;
And Christ, the Sun of all the earth,
Fulfilled that witness at his birth.

4
Of woman-born shall never be
A greater prophet than was he,
Whose mighty deeds exalt his fame
To greater than a prophet's name.

[UNISON]   5
All praise to God the Father be,
All praise, eternal Son, to thee,
Whom with the Spirit we adore
For ever and for evermore.

THE VENERABLE BEDE
Tr. J. M. Neale†

Hymn 50 is also suitable

ST. PETER THE APOSTLE

HYMN **554**   Commandments — 9 8 9 8   L. Bourgeois, *c.* 1500–61

O Rock of ages, one Foundation
  On which the living Church doth rest—
The Church whose walls are strong salvation,
  Whose gates are praise—thy name be blest.

2
Son of the living God, O call us
  Once and again to follow thee;
And give us strength, whate'er befall us,
  Thy true disciples still to be.

3
When fears appal and faith is failing,
  Make thy voice heard o'er wind and wave;
And in thy perfect love prevailing
  Put forth thy hand to help and save.

4
And if our coward hearts deny thee
  In inmost thought, in deed or word,
Let not our hardness still defy thee,
  But with a look subdue us, Lord.

5
O strengthen thou our weak endeavour
  Thee in thy sheep to serve and tend,
To give ourselves to thee for ever,
  And find thee with us to the end.

                    H. A. MARTIN

St. Peter the Apostle

3
Thrice fallen, thrice restored!
  The bitter lesson learnt,
That heart for thee, O Lord,
  With triple ardour burnt.
The cross he took he laid not down
Until he grasped the martyr's crown.

'Thou art the Christ, O Lord,
  The Son of God most high!'
For ever be adored
  That name in earth and sky,
In which, though mortal strength may fail,
The saints of God at last prevail.

2
O surely he was blest
  With blessedness unpriced,
Who, taught of God, confessed
  The Godhead in the Christ!
For of thy Church, Lord, thou didst own
Thy saint a true foundation-stone.

4
O bright triumphant faith,
  O courage void of fears!
O love most strong in death,
  O penitential tears!
By these, Lord, keep us lest we fall,
And make us go where thou shalt call.

BISHOP W. WALSHAM HOW

Hymn 323 is also suitable

751

ST. MARY MAGDALENE

Hymn **556**   Rhuddlan — 8 7. 8 7. 8 7   Welsh Traditional Melody

Magdalene, thy grief and gladness
  Voice and heart in concert sing,
Telling how the risen Saviour
  Called thee from thy sorrowing,
Tidings of his Resurrection
  To his chosen flock to bring.

2

She beheld him, yet she knew not
  In the gardener's seeming guise
Christ, who in her heart was sowing
  Seed of heavenly mysteries,
Till his voice, her name pronouncing,
  Bade her see and recognize.

3

Weep not, Mary, weep no longer!
  Now thy seeking heart may rest;
Christ the heavenly gardener soweth
  Light and joy within thy breast:
In the glowing cry 'Rabboni!'
  Be thy gratitude confest.

C. S. Phillips
Based on *Collaudemus Magdalenae*,
Philippe de Grève

Alternative Tune, Lewes, 64

752

ST. JAMES THE APOSTLE

HYMN **557** St. James — C.M.   R. Courteville (1697)

A higher setting of this tune will be found at Hymn 439

For all thy saints, a noble throng,
  Who fell by fire and sword,
Who soon were called, or waited long,
  We praise thy name, O Lord;

2
For him who left his father's side,
  Nor lingered by the shore,
When, softer than the weltering tide,
  Thy summons glided o'er;

3
Who stood beside the maiden dead,
  Who climbed the mount with thee,
And saw the glory round thy head,
  One of thy chosen three;

4
Who knelt beneath the olive shade,
  Who drank thy cup of pain,
And passed from Herod's flashing blade
  To see thy face again.

5
Lord, give us grace, and give us love,
  Like him to leave behind
Earth's cares and joys, and look above
  With true and earnest mind.

6
So shall we learn to drink thy cup,
  So meek and firm be found,
When thou shalt come to take us up
  Where thine elect are crowned.

Mrs. C. F. Alexander

753

THE TRANSFIGURATION

FIRST TUNE

O nata Lux de Lumine — L.M.

Mode iv

Caelestis formam gloriae

1 O won - drous type, O vi - sion fair Of glo - ry
2 The law and pro - phets there have place, The cho - sen
3 With shi - ning face and bright ar - ray, Christ deigns to
4 And Chris - tian hearts are raised on high By that great

1 that the Church shall share, Which Christ up - on the
2 wit - ness - es of grace; The Fa - ther's voice from
3 man - i - fest to - day What glo - ry shall to
4 vi - sion's mys - ter - y, For which in thank - ful

1 moun - tain shows, Where bright - er than the sun he glows!
2 out the cloud Pro - claims his on - ly Son a - loud.
3 faith be given When we en - joy our God in heaven.
4 strains we raise On this glad day the voice of praise.

The Transfiguration

Sandys Psalm viii — L.M.   Melody and bass by H. Lawes, 1596–1662

Caelestis formam gloriae

O wondrous type, O vision fair
Of glory that the Church shall share,
Which Christ upon the mountain shows,
Where brighter than the sun he glows!

2

The law and prophets there have place,
The chosen witnesses of grace;
The Father's voice from out the cloud
Proclaims his only Son aloud.

3

With shining face and bright array,
Christ deigns to manifest to-day
What glory shall to faith be given
When we enjoy our God in heaven.

4

And Christian hearts are raised on high
By that great vision's mystery,
For which in thankful strains we raise
On this glad day the voice of praise.

15th century
Tr. COMPILERS (1904)

The Transfiguration

HYMN **559**   Aurelia — 7 6 7 6. D   S. S. Wesley, 1810–76

χορὸς ᾿Ισραήλ

In days of old on Sinai
  The Lord almighty came
In majesty of terror,
  In thunder-cloud and flame :
On Tabor, with the glory⌣
  Of sunniest light for vest,
The excellence of beauty
  In Jesus was exprest.

2

All light created paled there,
  And did him worship meet ;
The sun itself adored him,
  And bowed before his feet ;
While Moses and Elijah,
  Upon the holy mount,
The co-eternal glory
  Of Christ our God recount.

3

O holy, wondrous vision!
  But O when, this life past,
The beauty of mount Tabor
  Shall end in heaven at last!
But O when all the glory
  Of uncreated light
Shall be the promised guerdon
  Of them that win the fight!

ST. COSMAS
Tr. J. M. Neale†

756

The Transfiguration

HYMN **560**   Carlisle — S.M.   C. Lockhart, 1745-1815

A higher setting of this tune will be found at Hymn 374

mf   'Tis good, Lord, to be here!
Thy glory fills the night;
Thy face and garments, like the sun,
Shine with unborrowed light.

2
'Tis good, Lord, to be here,
Thy beauty to behold,
Where Moses and Elijah stand,
Thy messengers of old.

3
f   Fulfiller of the past!
Promise of things to be!
We hail thy body glorified,
And our redemption see.

4
mf   Before we taste of death,
We see thy Kingdom come;
We fain would hold the vision bright,
And make this hill our home.

5
'Tis good, Lord, to be here!
Yet we may not remain;
But since thou bidst us leave the mount
Come with us to the plain.

J. A. ROBINSON

Alternative Tune, St. George (Gauntlett), 63

The Transfiguration

G. Cooper, 1820–76

Not always on the mount may we
Rapt in the heavenly vision be;
The shores of thought and feeling know
The Spirit's tidal ebb and flow.

2

'Lord, it is good abiding here,'
We cry, the heavenly presence near:
The vision vanishes, our eyes
Are lifted into vacant skies.

3

Yet hath one such exalted hour
Upon the soul redeeming power,
And in its strength through after days
We travel our appointed ways;

4

Till all the lowly vale grows bright,
Transfigured in remembered light,
And in untiring souls we bear
The freshness of the upper air.

5

The mount for vision: but below
The paths of daily duty go,
And nobler life therein shall own
The pattern on the mountain shown.

F. L. HOSMER

This hymn is suitable for general use

ST. BARTHOLOMEW THE APOSTLE

Hymn **562** Valley — 7 6 8 6   G. H. Knight

Not by far-famed deeds alone
  God's Kingdom comes to birth;
The memory of countless saints
  Has perished from the earth.

2

John and Peter, James and Paul,
  Have left a mighty fame:
Another of their company
  Is nothing but a name.

3

Yet for him no less the call
  And gallant course to run;
His too to hear at journey's end
  The Master's glad 'Well done!'

C. S. Phillips

Hymn 549 may also be used

ST. MATTHEW THE APOSTLE

Hymn **563** Ely — L.M.   Bishop T. Turton, 1780–1864

He sat to watch o'er customs paid,
A man of scorned and hardening trade:
Alike the symbol and the tool
Of foreign masters' hated rule.

2
But grace within his breast had stirred;
There needed but the timely word:
It came, true Lord of souls, from thee,
That royal summons, 'Follow me.'

3
Enough, when thou wast passing by,
To hear thy voice, to meet thine eye:
He rose, responsive to the call,
And left his task, his gains, his all.

4
O wise exchange! with these to part,
And lay up treasure in thy heart;
With twofold crown of light to shine
Amid thy servants' foremost line.

5
Come, Saviour, as in days of old;
Pass where the world has strongest hold,
And faithless care and selfish greed
Are thorns that choke the holy seed.

6
Who keep thy gifts, O bid them claim
The steward's, not the owner's, name:
Who yield all up for thy dear sake,
Let them of Matthew's wealth partake.

W. Bright

Alternative Tune, Illsley, 1

ST. MICHAEL AND ALL ANGELS

HYMN **564**

FIRST TUNE

Christe, sanctorum decus angelorum — 11 11 11 5

Mode viii

Christe, sanctorum decus angelorum

1 Christ, the fair glo - ry of the ho - ly an - gels, Ru - ler of
2 Send thine arch-an - gel Mi-chael from thy pre - sence: Peace-mak - er
3 Send thine arch-an - gel, Ga - bri - el the migh-ty: On strong wings
4 Send thine arch-an - gel, Ra - pha - el the hea - ler: Through him with
5 Fa - ther al - migh-ty, Son, and Ho - ly Spi - rit, God - head e -

1 all men, au - thor of cre - a - tion, Grant us in mer -
2 bless - èd, may he ho - ver o'er us, Hal - low our dwell -
3 fly - ing, may he come from hea - ven, Drive from thy tem -
4 whole - some medi-cines of sal - va - tion Heal our back - slid -
5 ter - nal, grant us our pe - ti - tion; Thine be the glo -

1 cy grace to win by pa - tience Joys ev - er - last - ing.
2 ings, that for us thy chil - dren All things may pros - per.
3 ple Sa - tan the old foe - man, Suc - cour our weak - ness.
4 ing, and in paths of good - ness Guide our steps dai - ly.
5 ry through the whole cre - a - tion Now and for ev · er.

761

St. Michael and All Angels

Rouen — 11 11 11 5　　　　　　　　　French Melody

Christe, sanctorum decus angelorum

Christ, the fair glory of the holy angels,
Ruler of all men, author of creation,
Grant us in mercy grace to win by patience
　　　Joys everlasting.

2
Send thine archangel Michael from thy presence:
Peacemaker blessèd, may he hover o'er us,
Hallow our dwellings, that for us thy children
　　　All things may prosper.

3
Send thine archangel, Gabriel the mighty:
On strong wings flying, may he come from heaven,
Drive from thy temple Satan the old foeman,
　　　Succour our weakness.

4
Send thine archangel, Raphael the healer:
Through him with wholesome medicines of salvation
Heal our backsliding, and in paths of goodness
　　　Guide our steps daily.

5
Father almighty, Son, and Holy Spirit,
Godhead eternal, grant us our petition;
Thine be the glory through the whole creation
　　　Now and for ever.

Ascribed to ARCHBISHOP RABANUS MAURUS
Tr. Compilers

St. Michael and All Angels

HYMN **565**   Xavier — 7 7 7 7   Sir F. Champneys, 1848–1930

f Praise to God who reigns above,
Binding earth and heaven in love;
All the armies of the sky
Worship his dread sovereignty.

3
mf Speeds the Archangel from his face,
Bearing messages of grace;
Angel hosts his words fulfil,
Ruling nature by his will.

2
Seraphim his praises sing,
Cherubim on fourfold wing,
Thrones, Dominions, Princes, Powers,
Marshalled might that never cowers.

4
Yet on man they joy to wait,
All that bright celestial state,
For in Man their Lord they see,
Christ, the incarnate Deity.

5
On the throne their Lord who died
Sits in Manhood glorified;
Where his people faint below
Angels count it joy to go.

6
O the depths of joy divine
Thrilling through those orders nine,
When the lost are found again,
When the banished come to reign!

[UNISON]   **7**
f   Now in faith, in hope, in love,
We will join the choirs above,
Praising, with the heavenly host,
Father, Son, and Holy Ghost.

R. M. BENSON

763

St. Michael and All Angels

HYMN **566**   Spetisbury — 5 5 5 5. D   W. Knapp, 1698–1768

f All praise be to God,
    Whom all things obey,
From angels and men
    For ever and ay;
Who sendeth on earth
    The powers of his throne,
His providence good
    And love to make known.

2

His angels are they
    Of countenance fair,
The arm of his strength,
    His hand of kind care;
His message of peace
    To us they reveal,
His wisdom most high
    They seal or unseal.

St. Michael and All Angels

3

mf By martyrs of old
    They stood in the flame,
And bade them not flinch,
    But call on God's name.
Through torment, through shame,
    Through darkness of death,
They led without fear
    The sires of our faith.

4

f They stand with the few,
    They fight for the free,
God's reign to advance
    O'er land and o'er sea;
And when the brave die
    Or fall in the fight,
Their spirits they bear
    To rest in God's sight.

5*

mf For patience and toil
    A crown they prepare;
They found for the meek
    A kingdom full fair;
No famine nor plague
    'Gainst them doth prevail;
Their bread cannot lack,
    Their cruse cannot fail.

6

We pray thee, who art
    Thy angels' reward,
Thy flock to defend
    Forget not, O Lord;
But prosper their aid,
    That us they may bring
To see the true face
    Of Jesus, our King.

R. B. in *Yattendon Hymnal*

Alternative Tune, Hanover, 167

The following hymns are also suitable:

ST. LUKE THE EVANGELIST

Hymn **567** Grasmere — 7878.7888 J. A. Freylinghausen, 1670–1739
Simplified by J. B. König, 1691–1758

1. Saviour, who didst healing give,
    Still in power go before us;
Thou through death didst bid men live,
    Unto fuller life restore us:
Strength from thee the fainting found,
    Deaf men heard, the blind went see-
        ing;
At thy touch was banished sickness,
    And the leper felt new being.

2. Thou didst work thy deeds of old
    Through the loving hands of others:
Still thy mercies manifold
    Bless men by the hands of brothers;
Angels still before thy face
    Go, sweet health to brothers bringing;
Still, hearts glow to tell his praises
    With whose name the Church is ring-
        ing.

3. Loved physician! for his word,
    Lo, the gospel page burns brighter:
Mission servant of the Lord,
    Painter true and faithful writer:
Saviour, of thy bounty send
    Such as Luke of Gospel story,
Friends to all in body's prison
    Till the sufferer see thy glory.

H. D. Rawnsley†

SS. SIMON AND JUDE THE APOSTLES

HYMN **568**   Alleluia, dulce carmen — 8 7. 8 7. 8 7   *Essay on the Church Plain Chant,* 1782

A lower setting of this tune will be found at Hymn 82

Thou who sentest thine apostles
    Two and two before thy face,
Partners in the night of toiling,
    Heirs together of thy grace,
Throned at length, their labours ended,
    Each in his appointed place;

2

Praise to thee for those thy champions
    Whom our hymns to-day proclaim:
One, whose zeal by thee enlightened
    Burned anew with nobler flame;
One, the kinsman of thy childhood,
    Brought at last to know thy name.

3

Praise to thee! thy fire within them
    Spake in love, and wrought in power:
Seen in mighty signs and wonders
    In thy Church's morning hour;
Heard in tones of sternest warning
    When the storms began to lower.

4

God the Father, great and wondrous
    In thy works, to thee be praise;
King of saints, to thee be glory,
    Just and true in all thy ways;
Praise to thee, from Both proceeding,
    Holy Ghost, through endless days.

J. ELLERTON

Alternative Tune, Rhuddlan, 556

767

ALL SAINTS' DAY

HYMN **569**   FIRST TUNE

Hic breve vivitur — 7 6 7 6   A. Pettet, *c.* 1785–*c.* 1845

SECOND TUNE

St. Alphege — 7 6 7 6   H. J. Gauntlett, 1805–76

A higher setting of this tune will be found at Hymn 275

All Saints' Day

O Heavenly Jerusalem,
    Of everlasting halls,
Thrice blessèd are the people
    Thou storest in thy walls.

2

Thou art the golden mansion
    Where saints for ever sing,
The seat of God's own chosen,
    The palace of the King.

3

There God for ever sitteth,
    Himself of all the crown:
The Lamb, the Light that shineth
    And never goeth down.

4

Naught to this seat approacheth
    Their sweet peace to molest;
They sing their God for ever,
    Nor day nor night they rest.

5

Sure hope doth thither lead us;
    Our longings thither tend:
May short-lived toil ne'er daunt us
    For joys that cannot end.

6

To Christ the Sun that lightens
    His Church above, below,
To Father, and to Spirit,
    All things created bow.

18th cent. *Tr.* I. WILLIAMS

HYMN **570**   All Saints — 8 7. 8 7. 7 7   *Geistreiches Gesangbuch*
(Darmstadt, 1698)

Wer sind die vor Gottes Throne

Who are these like stars appearing,
　These, before God's throne who
Each a golden crown is wearing: [stand?
　Who are all this glorious band?
　　Alleluia, hark! they sing,
　　Praising loud their heavenly King.

2*

Who are these in dazzling brightness,
　Clothed in God's own righteousness,
These, whose robes of purest whiteness
　Shall their lustre still possess, [hand?
　　Still untouched by time's rude
　　Whence came all this glorious band?

3

These are they who have contended
　For their Saviour's honour long,
Wrestling on till life was ended,
　Following not the sinful throng;
　　These, who well the fight sustained,
　　Triumph by the Lamb have gained

4*

These are they whose hearts were riven,
　Sore with woe and anguish tried,
Who in prayer full oft have striven
　With the God they glorified;
　　Now, their painful conflict o'er,
　　God has bid them weep no more.

5

These, the Almighty contemplating,
　Did as priests before him stand,
Soul and body always waiting
　Day and night at his command:
　　Now in God's most holy place
　　Blest they stand before his face.

H. T. SCHENCK
Tr. Frances E. Cox‡

All Saints' Day

Hymn **571** Song 67 — C.M.   Melody from E. Prys, *Psalms*, 1621
Bass by Orlando Gibbons, 1583-1625

A higher setting of this tune will be found at Hymn 325

mf Give us the wings of faith to rise
  Within the veil, and see
 The saints above, how great their joys,
  How bright their glories be.

2

p Once they were mourning here below,
  Their couch was wet with tears;
 They wrestled hard, as we do now,
  With sins and doubts and fears.

3

mf We ask them whence their victory came:
f   They, with united breath,
 Ascribe the conquest to the Lamb,
  Their triumph to his Death.

4

p They marked the footsteps that he trod,
  His zeal inspired their breast,
 And, following their incarnate God,
  They reached the promised rest.

5

f Our glorious Leader claims our praise
  For his own pattern given;
 While the great cloud of witnesses
  Show the same path to heaven.

         I. Watts‡

All Saints' Day

HYMN **572**   Rest — 8 8. 8 8. 8 8   Sir J. Stainer, 1840–1901

VOICES IN UNISON   HARMONY

The saints of God! their conflict past
And life's long battle won at last,
No more they need the shield or sword,
They cast them down before their Lord:
   O happy saints! for ever blest,
   At Jesus' feet how safe your rest!

2
The saints of God! their wanderings done,
No more their weary course they run,
No more they faint, no more they fall,
No foes oppress, no fears appal:
   O happy saints! for ever blest,
   In that dear home how sweet your rest!

3
The saints of God! life's voyage o'er,
Safe landed on that blissful shore,
No stormy tempest now they dread,
No roaring billows lift their head:
   O happy saints! for ever blest,
   In that calm haven of your rest.

4
The saints of God their vigil keep
While yet their mortal bodies sleep,
Till from the dust they too shall rise
And soar triumphant to the skies:
   O happy saints! rejoice and sing:
   He quickly comes, your Lord and King.

5
O God of saints, to thee we cry;
O Saviour, plead for us on high;
O Holy Ghost, our guide and friend,
Grant us thy grace till life shall end;
   That with all saints our rest may be
   In that bright Paradise with thee.

ARCHBISHOP W. D. MACLAGAN

Alternative Tune, Colchester, 90

ST. GEORGE, PATRON OF ENGLAND

HYMN **573**   Regent Square — 8 7. 8 7. 8 7   H. Smart, 1813–79

A higher setting of this tune will be found at Hymn 279

Jesus, Lord of our salvation,
 For thy warrior, bold and true,
Now accept our thankful praises,
 And our strength do thou renew,
That, like George, with courage daunt-
We may all our foes subdue.   [less

2
Blazoned on our country's banner
 England bears the knightly sign:
Lord, our fatherland empower,
 That, endued with strength divine,
She may evermore with courage
 Bear the standard that is thine.

3
Fill her youth with manly spirit,
 Patient, self-restrained, and pure,
Of thy cause the ready champions,
 Never flinching to endure⌣
Hardness for the name of Jesus:
 So their triumph shall be sure.

4
Teach her manhood to confess thee
 As the Master, Lord, and King;
All their powers consecrated
 To thy service may men bring,
And of loyal speech and action
 Make to thee an offering.

5
Jesus, Lord, thou mighty Victor,
 Thy all-glorious name we praise:
Thou art with us, God almighty;
 'Midst our ranks thy shout we raise:
Where thy kingly war-cry soundeth,
 Lead us on through all our days.

F. W. NEWMAN

773

SAINTS, MARTYRS, AND DOCTORS
OF THE CHURCH OF ENGLAND

HYMN **574**   Westminster Abbey — 8 7. 8 7. 8 7   Adapted from an anthem
by H. Purcell, 1658-95

God, whose city's sure foundation
   Stands upon his holy hill,
By his mighty inspiration
   Chose of old and chooseth still
Men of every race and nation
   His good pleasure to fulfil.

2

Here in England through the ages,
   While the Christian years went by,
Saints, confessors, martyrs, sages,
   Strong to live and strong to die,
Wrote their names upon the pages
   Of God's blessèd company.

3

Some there were like lamps of learning
   Shining in a faithless night,
Some on fire with love, and burning
   With a flaming zeal for right,
Some by simple goodness turning
   Souls from darkness unto light.

4

As we now with high thanksgiving
   Their triumphant names record,
Grant that we, like them, believing
   In the promise of thy word,
May, like them, in all good living
   Praise and magnify the Lord.

C. A. ALINGTON

774

ST. DAVID, PATRON OF WALES

HYMN **575**   Claudius — D.C.M.   Adapted from a song by G. W. Fink
(1783–1846)

By permission of the Royal School of Church Music

We praise thy name, all holy Lord,
　For him, the beacon-light
That shone beside our western sea
　Through mists of ancient night;
Who sent to Ireland's fainting Church
　New tidings of thy word:
For David, prince of Cambrian saints,
　We praise thee, holy Lord.

2
For all the saintly band whose prayers
　Still gird our land about,
Of whom, lest men disdain their praise,
　The voiceless stones cry out;

Our hills and vales on every hand
　Their names and deeds record:
For these, thy ancient hero-host,
　We praise thee, holy Lord.

3
Grant us but half their burning zeal,
　But half their iron faith,
But half their charity of heart,
　And fortitude to death;
That we with them and all thy saints
　May in thy truth accord,
And ever in thy holy Church
　May praise thee, holy Lord.

E. J. NEWELL

For ST. PATRICK, PATRON OF IRELAND, *see:*

　162   I bind unto myself to-day.

ST. NICOLAS, PATRON OF CHILDREN
AND SAILORS

Hymn **576**   St. Nicolas — L.M.   Sir S. H. Nicholson, 1875–1947

Far-shining names from age to age
Enrich the Church's heritage,
The loyal liegemen of the Lord,
Who found in thee their great reward

3
Who, far away in eastern land,
With gentle heart and open hand
Loved all things living, shared his store
With homeless men who sought his door.

2
One name from that immortal throng
Inspires to-day our festal song:
In loving memory we hold⌣
The bishop and the saint of old,

4
Friend of the poor, no less was he
The guardian saint of those at sea;
O'er wave-swept rock and sheltered bay
God's churches bear his name to-day.

5
And his the skill, the tender art
That wins the trustful, child-like heart:
His dearest title to the end
'Saint Nicolas, the children's friend.'

6
To thee, O Lord, the praise be given
For this true citizen of heaven:
A star above the stormy sea
To lead the wanderer home to thee.

W. H. Savile

For St. Cecilia, Patroness of Music, *see:*

246   Angel-voices, ever singing.

776

NATIONAL

mf   God save our gracious Queen,
Long live our noble Queen,
   God save the Queen.
Send her victorious,
Happy and glorious,
Long to reign over us :
   God save the Queen.

2*
O Lord our God, arise,
Scatter our enemies,
   And make them fall ;
Confound their politics,
Frustrate their knavish tricks ;
On thee our hopes we fix :
   God save us all.

3
f   Thy choicest gifts in store
On her be pleased to pour,
   Long may she reign.
May she defend our laws,
And ever give us cause
To sing with heart and voice,
   God save the Queen.

ANON.

HYMN **578** Jerusalem — D.L.M.

Sir C. H. H. Parry, 1848–1918
Arranged by G. T. Thalben-Ball

PREPARE: Sw. 8 & 4 with Reeds
Gt. to Princ.
Ped. 16, 8 Coup. to Gt.
Sw. to Gt.

Slow but with animation

MANUAL

PEDAL

VOICES IN UNISON

And did those feet   in an - cient time   Walk up - on

(Reduce Sw. & Gt.)

National

Bring me my bow of burn - ing gold! Bring me my ar - rows of de - sire! Bring me my spear! O clouds, un -

Hymn **578** (*continued*)

lem   In   Eng - land's   green   and   plea - sant

land.

By permission of the Executors of the late Sir C. H. H. Parry

WILLIAM BLAKE

National

National

I vow to thee, my country, all earthly things above,
Entire and whole and perfect, the service of my love :
The love that asks no question, the love that stands the test,
That lays upon the altar the dearest and the best;
The love that never falters, the love that pays the price,
The love that makes undaunted the final sacrifice.

2

And there's another country, I've heard of long ago,
Most dear to them that love her, most great to them that know;
We may not count her armies, we may not see her King;
Her fortress is a faithful heart, her pride is suffering;
And soul by soul and silently her shining bounds increase,
And her ways are ways of gentleness and all her paths are peace.

SIR CECIL SPRING-RICE

HYMN **580**   Genevan Psalm xii — 11 10 11 10   L. Bourgeois, *c.* 1500–61

PART 1

The Queen, O God, her heart to thee upraiseth;
  With her the nation bows before thy face;
With high thanksgiving thee thy glad Church praiseth,
  Our strength thy spirit, our trust and hope thy grace.

2

Unto great honour, glory undeservèd,
  Hast thou exalted us, and drawn thee nigh;
Nor, from thy judgements when our feet had swervèd,
  Didst thou forsake, nor leave us, Lord most high.

PART 2

3

In thee our fathers trusted and were savèd,
  In thee destroyèd thrones of tyrants proud;
From ancient bondage freed the poor enslavèd;
  To sow thy truth poured out their saintly blood.

4

Unto our minds give freedom and uprightness;
  Let strength and courage lead o'er land and wave;
To our souls' armour grant celestial brightness,
  Joy to our hearts, and faith beyond the grave.

5

Our plenteous nation still in power extending,
  Increase our joy, uphold us by thy word;
Beauty and wisdom all our ways attending,
  Good will to man and peace through Christ our Lord.

Yattendon Hymnal
Based on F. R. TAILOUR (1615)

Alternative Tune, St. Osyth, 550

National

Melody in *Chalmers' Collection* (Aberdeen, *c.* 1749)

Lord, while for all mankind we pray
Of every clime and coast,
O hear us for our native land,
The land we love the most.

2
O guard our shores from every foe,
With peace our borders bless;
With prosperous times our cities crown,
Our fields with plenteousness.

3
Unite us in the sacred love
Of knowledge, truth, and thee;
And let our hills and valleys shout
The songs of liberty.

4
Lord of the nations, thus to thee
Our country we commend;
Be thou her refuge and her trust,
Her everlasting friend.

J. R. WREFORD

National

Hymn **582** Wareham — L.M.　　　　　　　　　W. Knapp, 1698–1768

A higher setting of this tune with a descant will be found at Hymn 245, and a lower setting at Hymn 502

Rejoice, O land, in God thy might;
His will obey, him serve aright;
For thee the saints uplift their voice:
Fear not, O land, in God rejoice.

2

Glad shalt thou be, with blessing crowned,
With joy and peace thou shalt abound;
Yea, love with thee shall make his home
Until thou see God's Kingdom come.

3

He shall forgive thy sins untold:
Remember thou his love of old;
Walk in his way, his word adore,
And keep his truth for evermore.

Yattendon Hymnal

788

National

K. G. Finlay

Almighty Father, who dost give
The gift of life to all who live,
Look down on all earth's sin and strife
And lift us to a nobler life.

2

Lift up our hearts, O King of Kings,
To brighter hopes and kindlier things,
To visions of a larger good,
And holier dreams of brotherhood.

3

The world is weary of its pain,
Of selfish greed and fruitless gain,
Of tarnished honour, falsely strong,
And all its ancient deeds of wrong.

4

Hear thou the prayer thy servants pray,
Uprising from all lands to-day,
And, o'er the vanquished powers of sin,
O bring thy great salvation in!

BISHOP J. H. B. MASTERMAN

National

HYMN **584**　　　FIRST TUNE

Julius — 10 10 10 10　　　Martin Shaw

By permission of the Royal School of Church Music

SECOND TUNE

Ellers — 10 10 10 10　　　E. J. Hopkins, 1818–1901

790

National

FOR THE FALLEN

mf O valiant hearts, who to your glory came
Through dust of conflict and through battle flame;
Tranquil you lie, your knightly virtue proved,
Your memory hallowed in the land you loved.

2*

f Proudly you gathered, rank on rank, to war,
As who had heard God's message from afar;
mf All you had hoped for, all you had, you gave
To save mankind—yourselves you scorned to save.

3*

f Splendid you passed, the great surrender made,
Into the light that never more shall fade;
mf Deep your contentment in that blest abode,
Who wait the last clear trumpet-call of God.

4

Long years ago, as earth lay dark and still,
Rose a loud cry upon a lonely hill,
While in the frailty of our human clay
Christ, our Redeemer, passed the self-same way.

5

p Still stands his Cross from that dread hour to this,
Like some bright star above the dark abyss;
Still, through the veil, the Victor's pitying eyes
Look down to bless our lesser Calvaries.

6

These were his servants, in his steps they trod,
Following through death the martyred Son of God:
f Victor he rose; victorious too shall rise
They who have drunk his cup of sacrifice.

7

O risen Lord, O Shepherd of our dead,
Whose Cross has bought them and whose staff has led,
In glorious hope their proud and sorrowing land
mf Commits her children to thy gracious hand.

SIR JOHN S. ARKWRIGHT

National

FOR THE FALLEN

O Lord of Life, whose power sustains
    The world unseen no less than this—
One family in him who reigns,
    Triumphant over death, in bliss;
To thee with thankfulness we pray
For all our valiant dead to-day.

2

As nature's healing through the years
    Reclothes the stricken battle-fields;
So mercy gives us joy for tears,
    And grief to proud remembrance yields,
And mindful hearts are glad to keep
A tryst of love with them that sleep.

3

Not names engraved in marble make
    The best memorials of the dead,
But burdens shouldered for their sake
    And tasks completed in their stead;
A braver faith and stronger prayers,
Devouter worship, nobler cares.

4

O help us in the silence, Lord,
    To hear the whispered call of love,
And day by day thy strength afford
    Our work to do, our faith to prove.
So be thy blessing richly shed
On our communion with our dead.

ARCHBISHOP J. R. DARBYSHIRE

Alternative Tune, Wrestling Jacob, 343

LITANIES
LITANY FOR LENT

Hymn **586** Attende, Domine — 10 8. 11 11 11   Mode v

Attende, Domine

Chorus (this refrain may be sung in Harmony)   *Fine*

Hear-ken, O Lord, have mer-cy up-on us,   for we have sin-ned a-gainst thee.

1 To thee, Re-deem-er, King of high-est hea-ven, Lift we our eyes in
2 Head of the Cor - ner, right hand of the Fa-ther, Way of   sal - va - tion,
3 Lord, we be-seech thee, from thy throne of glo - ry Bow down thine ear to
4 All our mis - do - ings now we lay be - fore thee, Un - veil with con - trite
5 Guilt-less, a cap - tive tak - en un - re - sis - ting, By false ac - cus - ers

Repeat the refrain

1 grief and deep a - base-ment: Lis - ten, O Sa-viour, to our sup - pli - ca - tions.
2 gate of life e - ter - nal, Wash thou a - way the stain of our of - fen - ces.
3 hear our cry of sor - row, Look down in mer - cy on our sore trans - gres-sions.
4 heart each guil-ty se - cret: Sa - viour, in pi - ty grant us thy for - give-ness.
5 brought to con-dem-na - tion, Save, Lord, and help the souls thou hast re - deem-èd.

Tr. Compilers

794

LITANY OF THE PASSION

HYMN **587**   Litany of the Passion — 7 7 7 6   Sir S. H. Nicholson,
1875–1947

6

mf God the Father, God the Son,
   God the Spirit, Three in One,
   Hear us from thy heavenly throne;
      Spare us, holy Trinity.

2

Jesu, who for us didst bear
Scorn and sorrow, toil and care,
Hearken to our lowly prayer,
   We beseech thee, Jesu.

3

p By the hour of agony
Spent while thine apostles three
Slumbered in Gethsemane,
   Hear us, holy Jesu.

4

Jesu, by thy friend betrayed,
Jesu, sport for sinners made,
Jesu, in mock-robes arrayed,
   Hear us, holy Jesu.

5

By the scourging meekly borne,
By the reed and crown of thorn,
By the malice and the scorn,
   Hear us, holy Jesu.

mf By the outcry of the Jews,
   When a murderer they would choose
   And the Prince of Life refuse,
      Hear us, holy Jesu.

7

By the horror of that cry,
'Crucify him, crucify!'
By thy going forth to die,
   Hear us, holy Jesu.

8

p By thy nailing to the Tree,
By the title over thee,
By the gloom of Calvary,
   Hear us, holy Jesu.

9

By thy seven words then said,
By the bowing of thy head,
By thy numbering with the dead,
   Hear us, holy Jesu.

10

mf Jesu, who for us hast died
   And, for ever glorified,
   Reignest at the Father's side,
      Hear us, holy Jesu.

COMPILERS and others

795

Litanies

FOR ROGATION OR OTHER OCCASIONS

HYMN **588**   Ach Gott und Herr — 8 8 8 7   *Neu-Leipziger Gesangbuch*, 1682
Harmony from J. S. Bach, 1685–1750

ὑπὲρ τῆς ἄνωθεν εἰρήνης

THE GREAT COLLECT

Lord, to our humble prayers attend,
Let thou thy peace from heaven descend,
And to our souls salvation send:
 Have mercy, Lord, upon us.

2
Rule in our hearts, thou Prince of Peace,
The welfare of thy Church increase,
And bid all strife and discord cease:
 Have mercy, Lord, upon us.

3
To all who meet for worship here
Do thou in faithfulness draw near;
Inspire with faith and godly fear:
 Have mercy, Lord, upon us.

4
O let thy priests be clothed with might,
To rule within thy Church aright,
That they may serve as in thy sight:
 Have mercy, Lord, upon us.

5
The sovereign ruler of our land
Protect by thine almighty hand,
And all around the throne who stand:
 Have mercy, Lord, upon us.

6
Let clouds and sunshine bless the earth,
Give flowers and fruits a timely birth,
Our harvests crown with peaceful mirth:
 Have mercy, Lord, upon us.

7
Let voyagers by land and sea
In danger's hour in safety be;
The suffering and the captive free:
 Have mercy, Lord, upon us.

8
Around us let thine arm be cast,
Till wrath and danger are o'erpast
And tribulation's bitter blast:
 Have mercy, Lord, upon us.

Tr. J. BROWNLIE

Litanies

AN EVENING LITANY

HYMN 589   Es ist kein Tag — 8 8 8 4

Melody in J. Meyer's
Seelenfreud, 1692

By permission of the English Hymnal Co., Ltd.

ἀντιλαβοῦ, σῶσον, ἐλέησον

LITANY OF THE DEACON

O God of grace, thy mercy send;
Let thy protecting arm defend;
Save us and keep us to the end:
    Have mercy, Lord.

2
And through the coming hours of night
Fill us, we pray, with holy light;
Keep us all sinless in thy sight:
    Grant this, O Lord.

3
May some bright messenger abide
For ever by thy servants' side,
A faithful guardian and our guide:
    Grant this, O Lord.

4
From every sin in mercy free;
Let heart and conscience stainless be,
That we may live henceforth for thee:
    Grant this, O Lord.

5
We would not be by care opprest,
But in thy love and wisdom rest;
Give what thou seest to be best:
    Grant this, O Lord.

6
While we of every sin repent,
Let our remaining years be spent
In holiness and sweet content:
    Grant this, O Lord.

7
And when the end of life is near,
May we, unshamed and void of fear,
Wait for the judgement to appear:
    Grant this, O Lord.

Tr. J. BROWNLIE

797

Litanies

LITANY FOR CHILDREN

HYMN **590**   Antiphoner — 7 7 7 6

Melody from the *Rheims-Cambrai Antiphoner*, 1871

PART I

1
God the Father, God the Son,
God the Spirit, Three in One,
Hear us from thy heavenly throne;
    Spare us, holy Trinity.

2
Jesu, Saviour meek and mild,
Once for us a little Child
Born of Mary undefiled,
    Hear us, holy Jesu.

3
Jesu, by that blessèd Maid
In thy swaddling-clothes arrayed,
And within a manger laid,
    Hear us, holy Jesu.

4
Jesu, at whose infant feet,
Bending low in worship meet,
Shepherds knelt their Lord to greet,
    Hear us, holy Jesu.

5
Jesu, to thy Temple brought,
Whom the ancient Simeon sought
By thy Holy Spirit taught,
    Hear us, holy Jesu.

6
Jesu, unto whom of yore
Wise men, hasting to adore,
Gold and myrrh and incense bore,
    Hear us, holy Jesu.

7
Jesu, who wast driven to flee
From king Herod's cruelty,
When he sought to murder thee,
    Hear us, holy Jesu.

8
Jesu, whom thy Mother found
'Mid the doctors sitting round,
Marvelling at thy words profound,
    Hear us, holy Jesu.

798

Litanies

PART 2

9

From all pride and vain conceit,
From all spite and angry heat,
From all lying and deceit,
  Save us, holy Jesu.

10

From all sloth and idleness,
From hard hearts and selfishness,
From all lust and greediness,
  Save us, holy Jesu.

11

From refusing to obey,
From the love of our own way,
From forgetfulness to pray,
  Save us, holy Jesu.

PART 3

12

By thy birth and early years,
By thine infant wants and fears,
By thy sorrows and thy tears,
  Save us, holy Jesu.

13

By thy pattern bright and pure,
By the pains thou didst endure
Our salvation to procure,
  Save us, holy Jesu.

14

By thy wounds and thorn-crowned head,
By thy Blood for sinners shed,
By thy rising from the dead,
  Save us, holy Jesu.

15

By thy mercies infinite,
By thine all-surpassing might,
By thy glory in the height,
  Save us, holy Jesu.

    Compilers and others

PROCESSIONAL

CHRISTMAS

Hymn **591**   Divinum mysterium — 8787.877   P. Nyland, *Piae Cantiones,*
1582

Processional—Christmas

Corde natus ex Parentis

4

Of the Father's love begotten
  Ere the worlds began to be,
He is Alpha and Omega,
  He the source, the ending he,
Of the things that are, that have been,
  And that future years shall see,
    Evermore and evermore.

O ye heights of heaven, adore him;
  Angel-hosts, his praises sing;
Powers, dominions, bow before him,
  And extol our God and King:
Let no tongue on earth be silent,
  Every voice in concert ring,
    Evermore and evermore.

2*

5

At his word they were created;
  He commanded; it was done:
Heaven and earth and depths of ocean
  In their threefold order one;
All that grows beneath the shining
  Of the light of moon and sun,
    Evermore and evermore.

This is he whom seers and sages
  Sang of old with one accord;
Whom the writings of the Prophets
  Promised in their faithful word;
Now he shines, the long-expected:
  Let creation praise its Lord,
    Evermore and evermore.

3

6*

O that birth for ever blessèd!
  When the Virgin, full of grace,
By the Holy Ghost conceiving,
  Bare the Saviour of our race,
And the Babe, the world's Redeemer,
  First revealed his sacred face,
    Evermore and evermore.

Hail, thou Judge of souls departed!
  Hail, thou King of them that live!
On the Father's throne exalted
  None in might with thee may strive;
Who at last in judgement coming
  Sinners from thy face shalt drive,
    Evermore and evermore.

7

Now let old and young men's voices
  Join with boys' thy name to sing,
Matrons, virgins, little maidens
  In glad chorus answering;
Let their guileless songs re-echo,
  And the heart its praises bring,
    Evermore and evermore.

8

Christ, to thee, with God the Father,
  And, O Holy Ghost, to thee,
Hymn and chant and high thanksgiving
  And unwearied praises be,
Honour, glory, and dominion,
  And eternal victory,
    Evermore and evermore.

PRUDENTIUS *Tr.* J. M. Neale,
Sir H. W. Baker, and others

An optional Alternative Version for verses 4 and 7 will be found on page 802

HYMN 591 (*continued*)

ALTERNATIVE VERSION

FOR VERSES 4 AND 7

4 O ye heights of heaven, a - dore him; An - gel -
7 Now let old and young men's voi - ces Join with

4 hosts, his prais - es sing; Powers, do - min -ions, bow be -
7 boys' thy name to sing, Ma - trons, vir - gins, lit - tle

4 fore him, And ex - tol our God and King: Let no
7 maid - ens In glad chor - us an - swer - ing; Let their

4 tongue on earth be si - lent, Ev - ery voice in
7 guile - less songs re - ech - o, And the heart its

4 con - cert ring, Ev - er -more and ev - er - more.
7 prais - es bring, Ev - er -more and ev - er - more.

Processional—Christmas

At the entrance into the Chancel :

℣. Blessed is he that cometh in the name of   the   Lord.

℟. God is the Lord who hath shewed   us   light.

HYMN 592   Oxford New — C.M.   Isaac Smith's *Collection, c.* 1770

High let us swell our tuneful notes,
    And join the angelic throng,
For angels no such love have known
    To wake a cheerful song.

2

Good will to sinful men is shown,
    And peace on earth is given :
For, lo, the incarnate Saviour comes
    With grace and truth from heaven.

3

Justice and peace with sweet accord
    His rising beams adorn ;
Let heaven and earth in concert join :
    To us a Child is born !

P. DODDRIDGE

HYMN **593**   Adeste fideles — Irregular   Probably by J. F. Wade, *c.* 1711–86

Adeste fideles

1 O come, all ye faith - ful, Joy - ful and tri - um - phant, O
2 God of . . . God, . . . Light . . . of . . . Light, . . .
3 See how the shep - herds Sum - moned to his cra - dle,
4 Lo, star - led chief - tains, Ma - gi, Christ a - dor - ing,

1 come ye, O come ye to Beth - le - hem; Come and be -
2 Lo, he ab - hors not the Vir - gin's womb; Ve - ry . . .
3 Leav - ing their flocks, draw . . . nigh to gaze; We too will
4 Of - fer him in - cense, . . . gold, and myrrh : We to the

1 hold him Born, the King of an - gels:
2 God, Be - got - ten, not cre - a - ted: O come, let us a - dore him, O
3 thi - ther Bend our joy - ful foot-steps:
4 Christ-child Bring our hearts' ob - la - tions:

come, let us a - dore him, O come, let us a - dore him, Christ the Lord!

A higher setting of this tune will be found at Hymn 59

Processional—Christmas

DESCANT

5 Child, for us sin - ners Poor and in the man - ger,
6 Sing, choirs of an - gels, Sing in ex - ul - ta - tion,
7 Yea, Lord, we greet thee, Born this hap - py morn - ing;

5 Fain we em - brace .. thee with love and awe; Who would not
6 Sing, all ye ci - ti - zens of heaven a - bove: 'Glo - ry to
7 Je - su, to thee .. be ... glo - ry given: Word of the

O come,
O
cresc.

5 love thee, Lov - ing us so dear - ly? O come, let us a - dore him, O
6 God ... In ... the ... high - est:' O come, let us a - dore him, O
7 Fa - ther, Now in flesh ap - pear - ing:

come,
O come, let us a - dore him, Christ the Lord!

come, let us a - dore him, O come, let us a - dore him, Christ the Lord!

18th cent. *Tr.* F. OAKELEY,
W. T. BROOKE, and others

Processional—Christmas

At the entrance into the Chancel:

℣. Blessed is he that cometh in the name of the Lord.

℟. God is the Lord who hath shewed us light.

HYMN **594** Shepherds in the field — 8 7 8 7. 9 French or Flemish Melody
Harmonized by Charles Wood

Glo - - - - - - ri - a in ex - cel - sis De - o,

806

Glo - - - - - - - ri - a in ex - cel - sis De - - o.

By permission of A. R. Mowbray & Co., Ltd.

Shepherds, in the field abiding,
  Tell us, when the seraph bright
Greeted you with wondrous tiding,
  What ye saw and heard that night:
    Gloria in excelsis Deo.

2

We beheld (it is no fable)
  God incarnate, King of bliss,
Swathed and cradled in a stable,
  And the angel-strain was this:
    Gloria in excelsis Deo.

3

Quiristers on high were singing
  Jesus and his Virgin-birth;
Heavenly bells the while a-ringing
  'Peace, goodwill to men on earth:'
    Gloria in excelsis Deo.

4

Thanks, good herdmen; true your story;
  Have with you to Bethlehem:
Angels hymn the King of Glory;
  Carol we with you and them:
    Gloria in excelsis Deo.

G. R. WOODWARD

807

Processional

EPIPHANY

Hʏᴍɴ **595**   Evelyns — 6 5 6 5. D   W. H. Monk, 1823–89

2

From the eastern mountains
    Pressing on they come,
Wise men in their wisdom,
    To his humble home;
Stirred by deep devotion,
    Hasting from afar,
Ever journeying onward,
    Guided by a star.

There their Lord and Saviour
    Meek and lowly lay,
Wondrous Light that led them
    Onward on their way,
Ever now to lighten
    Nations from afar,
As they journey homeward
    By that guiding star.

808

Processional—Epiphany

3

Thou who in a manger
　Once hast lowly lain,
Who dost now in glory
　O'er all kingdoms reign,
Gather in the heathen,
　Who in lands afar
Ne'er have seen the brightness
　Of thy guiding star.

4★

Gather in the outcasts,
　All who've gone astray;
Throw thy radiance o'er them,
　Guide them on their way:
Those who never knew thee,
　Those who've wandered far,
Guide them by the brightness
　Of thy guiding star.

5

Onward through the darkness
　Of the lonely night,
Shining still before them
　With thy kindly light,
Guide them, Jew and Gentile,
　Homeward from afar,
Young and old together,
　By thy guiding star.

6★

Until every nation,
　Whether bond or free,
'Neath thy star-lit banner,
　Jesu, follow thee
O'er the distant mountains
　To that heavenly home,
Where nor sin nor sorrow
　Evermore shall come.

G. THRING

At the entrance into the Chancel:

℣. All nations whom thou　　　hast　　made.

℟. Shall come and worship thee,　　O　　Lord.

HYMN **596**   Quem pastores — 8 8 8 7   German Medieval Melody

Quem pastores laudavere

Thou whom shepherds worshipped, hear-
Angels tell their tidings cheering, [ing
'Sirs, away with doubt and fearing!
  Christ the King is born for all;'

2
Thou to whom came wise men faring,
Gold and myrrh and incense bearing,
Heartfelt homage thus declaring
  To the King that's born for all:

3
Bending low in adoration
Thee we greet, for our salvation
Given by wondrous Incarnation,
  King of Glory born for all.

Tr. C. S. PHILLIPS

PALM SUNDAY

HYMN **597**   St. Theodulph — 7 6 7 6. D   M. Teschner (1615)

Processional—Palm Sunday

Gloria, laus et honor

All glory, laud, and honour
To thee, Redeemer, King,
To whom the lips of children
Made sweet Hosannas ring.

2
Thou art the King of Israel,
Thou David's royal Son,
Who in the Lord's name comest,
The King and blessèd one.
All glory, etc.

3
The company of angels
Are praising thee on high,
And mortal men and all things⏝
Created make reply.
All glory, etc.

4
The people of the Hebrews
With palms before thee went:
Our praise and prayer and anthems
Before thee we present.
All glory, etc.

5
To thee before thy Passion
They sang their hymns of praise:
To thee now high exalted
Our melody we raise.
All glory, etc.

6
Thou didst accept their praises,
Accept the prayers we bring,
Who in all good delightest,
Thou good and gracious King.
All glory, etc.

7*
Thy sorrow and thy triumph
Grant us, O Christ, to share,
That to the holy city
Together we may fare.
All glory, etc.

8*
For homage may we bring thee
Our victory o'er the foe,
That in the Conqueror's triumph
This strain may ever flow:
All glory, etc.

ST. THEODULPH OF ORLEANS
Tr. J. M. Neale

811

Processional—Palm Sunday

Gloria, laus et honor

The refrain is first sung by solo voices, then repeated by chorus

1 Glo - ry and hon-our and laud   be to thee, Christ, King and Re-deem-er,

1 As when the   chil - dren   of   old   sang their Ho-san - nas of praise.

SOLO VOICES

2   Is - ra - el's Mon - arch art   thou,   the   glo - ri - ous off - spring of Da - vid,
3   'Glo - ry   to thee   in the height,' the   hea - ven-ly arm - ies are sing-ing;
4   Bear-ing their branch-es of   palm,   the   He - brews crowd-ed   to greet thee;
5   They came to ut - ter thy praise   as thou went-est thy way   to   thy Pas - sion;
6   Thou didst re - joice   in their praise: may   ours too by thee be   ac-cept - ed,

812

Processational—Palm Sunday

2	Thou that ap - proach - est as	King,	blest in	the	name of	the Lord.
3	'Glo - ry to thee up - on	earth,'	men and	cre -	a - tion	re - ply.
4	We with our prayers and our	hymns	now to	thy	pre - sence	draw nigh.
5	We to the King on his	throne	lift up	our	ju - bi -	lant hymn.
6	Gra-cious and mer - ci - ful	King,	who in	all	good-ness	art pleased.

St. Theodulph of Orleans
Tr. J. M. Neale and Compilers

At the entrance into the Chancel:

℣. O Saviour of the world, who by thy Cross and precious Blood hast redeem - ed us.

℟. Save us and help us, we humbly beseech thee,   O Lord.

HYMN **599**   Farley Castle — 10 10 10 10   H. Lawes, 1596–1662

Ride on triumphantly! Behold, we lay
Our lusts and sins and proud wills in thy way:
Thy road is ready, and thy paths made straight
With longing expectation seem to wait.

2

Hosanna! Welcome to our hearts! for here
Thou hast a temple too, as Sion dear:
Enter, O Lord, and cleanse that holy place
Where thou dost choose to set thy beauteous face.

Adapted from BISHOP JEREMY TAYLOR

EASTER DAY

HYMN **600**   Salve, festa dies — 16 14 with refrain   Mode iv

Salve, festa dies

This refrain is first sung by solo voices, then repeated by chorus

1 Wel-come, morn-ing of joy, glad feast that all a - ges shall hal - low,

Processional—Easter Day

1 Day where-in, van-quish-ing hell, God com-eth forth from the grave.

SOLO VOICES

2 Lo, the fresh beau - ty of spring, re - born from the womb of the win - ter,
4 Now, Lord of mer - cy and might, of thy pro-mise vouch-safe the ful-fil-ment:
6*Shame that in dur-ance should lie, close girt in the tomb's rock-y fast-ness,
8 Meek-ly thou stoop'st to the grave, who art Au-thor of life and cre-a - tion,
10 Out of the pri - son of death thou art res - cu - ing souls with-out num-ber;

Repeat the refrain

2 Tells how, to greet his re - turn, na - ture it - self is re-newed.
4 Rise, bur-ied Love, from the tomb; has - ten, the third day is here.
6* He who sus - tains the whole world, held in the grasp of his hand.
8 Tread-est the path-way of death, win-ning sal - va - tion for men.
10 Free - ly they press to the goal whi-ther their Ma - ker leads on.

Processional—Easter Day

SOLO VOICES

3 He who was nailed to the Cross   is   reign-ing as God o-ver all things,
5 Shame would it be that thy limbs   with   earth's sor-ry mould should be cov-ered,
7*Fling off the clothes of the grave, leave them there in the sep-ul-chre ly-ing;
9 Give back thy face   to the world, with its sun-shine to glad-den the a - ges;
11 Hell's gloom-y cas-tle is stormed, un-loosed are the chains of its cap-tives;

Repeat the refrain

3 While the Cre-a-tor   of all   all things cre-a-ted a-dore.
5 Or   that base rock should im-mure him who hath ran-somed the world.
7* For thou art all   that we need, and with-out thee we have naught.
9 Give back the light of the day, fled from our eyes at thy Death.
11 Cha-os and Death flee a-way, cowed at the face of the Light.

BISHOP VENANTIUS FORTUNATUS
Tr. C. S. Phillips

At the entrance into the Chancel:

℣. The Lord is risen from   the grave.

℟. Who for our sakes hung on the Tree. Al-le-lu - ia.

HYMN 601   Christ ist erstanden — 6 7 7 7 with Alleluias   Proper melody of
12th century hymn

Al - le - lu - ia! Al - le - lu - ia! Al - le - lu - ia! Al - le - lu - ia!

Christ ist erstanden

Christ is now risen again
From his death and all his pain;
Therefore will we merry be,
And rejoice with him gladly. Alleluia!

2

Since he is risen indeed
Let us love him with all speed;
Therefore glad now will we be,
And rejoice in him only. Alleluia!

Tr. BISHOP MILES COVERDALE†

HYMN **602**   FIRST TUNE

Easter Song — 8 8 8. 8 8 6. 12   *Catholische Kirchengesänge*
(Cologne, 1623)

Al - le - lu - ia! Al - le - lu - ia!

Al - le - lu - ia! Al - le -
lu - ia! Al - le - lu - ia! Al - le - lu - ia! Al - le - lu - ia!

Aurora lucis rutilat

PART I

Light's glittering morn bedecks the sky;
Heaven thunders forth its victor-cry:
            [Alleluia!]
The glad earth shouts her triumph high,
And groaning hell makes wild reply:
            [Alleluia!]

2

While he, the King, the mighty King,
Despoiling death of all its sting,
And trampling down the powers of night,
Brings forth his ransomed saints to light.

3

His tomb of late the threefold guard
Of watch and stone and seal had barred;
But now, in pomp and triumph high,
He comes from death to victory.

4

The pains of hell are loosed at last,
The days of mourning now are past;
An angel robed in light hath said,
'The Lord is risen from the dead.'

Processional—Easter Day

PART 2

5

O bitter the apostles' pain
For their dear Lord so lately slain,
By rebel servants doomed to die
A death of cruel agony!

6

With gentle voice the angel gave⌣
The women tidings at the grave:
'Fear not, your Master shall ye see;
He goes before to Galilee.'

7

Then, hastening on their eager way
The joyful tidings to convey,
Their Lord they met, their living Lord,
And falling at his feet adored.

8

His faithful followers with speed
To Galilee forthwith proceed,
That there once more they may behold
The Lord's dear face, as he foretold.

PART 3

9

That Eastertide with joy was bright,
The sun shone out with fairer light,
When, to their longing eyes restored,
The glad apostles saw their Lord.

10

He bade them see his hands, his side,
Where yet the glorious wounds abide;
The tokens true which made it plain
Their Lord indeed was risen again.

11

Jesu, the King of gentleness,
Do thou thyself our hearts possess,
That we may give thee all our days
The tribute of our grateful praise.

The following Doxology may be sung at the end of any Part,
or of the whole hymn:

12

O Lord of all, with us abide
In this our joyful Eastertide;
From every weapon death can wield
Thine own redeemed for ever shield.

13

All praise be thine, O risen Lord,
From death to endless life restored;
All praise to God the Father be
And Holy Ghost eternally.

Tr. J. M. NEALE and Compilers

An Alternative Version for verses 4, 8 and 11 will be found on page 820

SECOND TUNE

Devonshire — L.M.   J. F. Lampe, 1703-51

Processional—Easter Day

ALTERNATIVE VERSION (FIRST TUNE) FOR VERSES 4, 8 AND 11

4 The pains of hell are loosed at last, The days of mourn-ing now are
8 His faith-ful fol-low-ers with speed To Ga-li-lee forth-with pro-
11 Je-su, the King of gen-tle-ness, Do thou thy-self our hearts pos-

4 past; Al-le-lu-ia! Al-le-lu-ia! An an-gel robed in
8 ceed, That there once more they
11 sess, That we may give thee

4 light hath said, 'The Lord is ris-en from the dead.'
8 may be-hold The Lord's dear face, as he fore-told.
11 all our days The tri-bute of our grate-ful praise. Al-le-lu-

Al-le-lu-ia! Al-le-lu-ia!

Al-le-lu-ia! Al-le-lu-ia! Al-le-lu-ia!
Al-le-lu-ia! Al-le-lu-ia! Al-le-lu-ia!
-ia! Al-le-lu-ia! Al-le-lu-ia! Al-le-lu-ia!
lu-ia! Al-le-lu-ia! Al-le-lu-ia!

820

At the entrance into the Chancel:

℣. The Lord is risen from the grave.

℟. Who for our sakes hung on the Tree. Al - le - lu - ia.

HYMN **603**   Gelobt sei Gott — 8 8 8 with Alleluias   M. Vulpius,
Gesangbuch, 1609
Harmonized by F. Layriz (1844)

Al - le - lu - ia! . . . .   Al - le - lu - ia! . . . .   Al - le - lu - ia!

Good Christian men, rejoice and sing!
Now is the triumph of our King!
To all the world glad news we bring:
    Alleluia!

2
The Lord of Life is risen for ay:
Bring flowers of song to strew his way;
Let all mankind rejoice and say
    Alleluia!

3
Praise we in songs of victory
That Love, that Life, which cannot die,
And sing with hearts uplifted high
    Alleluia!

4
Thy name we bless, O risen Lord,
And sing to-day with one accord
The life laid down, the life restored:
    Alleluia!

C. A. ALINGTON

HYMN **604**   Scientia Salutis — 11 11 11 5. D   Sir J. Stainer, 1840–1901

In slow march time. MEN ONLY

Day - star on high, bright har - bin - ger of glad - ness,

Pier - cing the clouds of ig - nor - ance and er - ror, Thou hast dis-persed our

night of sin and sad - ness; Death has no ter - ror.

HARMONY

Dark-ness is past, joy com-eth in the morn-ing; Hope springs a-new for

sin-ners with-out num-ber: Sleep-ers, a-wake! a bright-er day is dawn-ing;

Shake off your slum - ber. Al - le - lu - ia,

Al - le - lu - ia, Al - le - lu - ia, Al - le - lu - ia,

Processional—Easter Day

Al - le - lu - ia, Al - le - lu - ia, Al - le - lu - ia.

[MEN] Daystar on high, bright harbinger of gladness,
Piercing the clouds of ignorance and error,
Thou hast dispersed our night of sin and sadness;
Death has no terror.

[HARMONY] Darkness is past, joy cometh in the morning;
Hope springs anew for sinners without number:
Sleepers, awake! a brighter day is dawning;
Shake off your slumber.

[FULL] Alleluia!

2

[MEN] Prophets of old spake darkly of this wonder,
Psalmist and saints have handed on the story;
Now he is risen, bursting bonds asunder,
Risen to glory.

[HARMONY] Earth's tyrants quail; the mighty make obeisance:
He hath preferred the innocent and lowly:
Mercy and truth shine round about his presence:
His name is Holy.

[FULL] Alleluia!

3

[MEN] Victor he comes in majesty, revealing
Promise of life and liberty to mortals:
Heaven and earth, with hymns of triumph pealing,
Throw wide their portals.

[HARMONY] Praise him, ye nations, hearts and voices blending:
Raise high your song; the Conqueror advances:
Praise him with cymbals, lute and harp attending,
Praise him with dances.

[FULL] Alleluia!

4

[MEN] Hail him the Monarch, Ruler of creation;
Princes and powers, bow your heads before him;
This is the Lord, the God of our salvation;
Let us adore him.

[HARMONY] Lord God of Hosts, great Deity supernal,
Be thou our strength, by thee our steps be guided,
Father and Son and Spirit co-eternal,
One undivided.

[FULL] Alleluia!

J. R. L. STAINER

Processional—Easter Day

At the entrance into the Chancel:

℣. The Lord is risen from the grave.
℟. Who for our sakes hung on the Tree. Al - le - lu - ia.

HYMN 605   Exodus — 8 8 7 7. 8 8 7   J. F. Rötscher (1790)

Cedant justi signa luctus

Jesus Christ from death hath risen!
Lo, his Godhead bursts the prison,
    While his Manhood passes free,
    Vanquishing our misery:
Risen with him to salvation
Through his self-humiliation,
    We may share his victory.

2

Far be sorrow, tears and sadness!
See the dayspring of our gladness!
    Satan's slaves no more are we,
    Children by the Son set free:
Rise, for Life with death hath striven,
All the snares of hell are riven;
    Rise and claim the victory.

H. LINDENBORN (1741)
Tr. Compilers

Processional

ROGATIONTIDE

HYMN 606　　　　　　　FIRST TUNE

Croft's 148th — 6 6 6 6. 8 8　　　　　　W. Croft, 1678–1727

O Lord, stretch forth thy migh-ty hand, And guard and bless our fa - ther - land.

A lower setting of this tune will be found at Hymn 552

To thee our God we fly
　For mercy and for grace;
O hear our lowly cry,
　And hide not thou thy face.
O Lord, stretch forth thy mighty hand,
And guard and bless our fatherland.

2
Arise, O Lord of Hosts!
　Be jealous for thy name,
And drive from out our coasts
　The sins that put to shame.
O Lord, stretch forth, etc.

3
Thy best gifts from on high
　In rich abundance pour,
That we may magnify
　And praise thee more and more.
O Lord, stretch forth, etc.

4
The powers ordained by thee
　With heavenly wisdom bless;
May they thy servants be,
　And rule in righteousness.
O Lord, stretch forth, etc.

5
The Church of thy dear Son
　Inflame with love's pure fire,

Bind her once more in one,
　And life and truth inspire.
O Lord, stretch forth, etc.

6*
The pastors of thy fold
　With grace and power endue,
That faithful, pure, and bold,
　They may be pastors true.
O Lord, stretch forth, etc.

7
O let us love thy house,
　And sanctify thy day,
Bring unto thee our vows,
　And loyal homage pay.
O Lord, stretch forth, etc.

8
Give peace, Lord, in our time;
　O let no foe draw nigh,
Nor lawless deed of crime
　Insult thy majesty.
O Lord, stretch forth, etc.

9*
Though vile and worthless, still‿
　Thy people, Lord, are we;
And for our God we will‿
　None other have but thee.
O Lord, stretch forth, etc.

BISHOP W. WALSHAM HOW

Processional—Rogationtide

HYMN **606**　　　　　SECOND TUNE

Pro Patria — 6 6 6 6. 8 8　　　　　J. Armistead, 1877-1935

VERSES I, 2, 4, 5, 7, 9 IN UNISON

1　To thee our God　we　fly　For mer - cy　and　for grace;
2　A - rise, O Lord　of Hosts! Be jeal - ous　for　thy name,
4　The powers or-dained　by　thee With heaven - ly　wis - dom bless;
5　The Church of thy　dear Son　In - flame with love's　pure fire,
7　O　let　us love　thy house, And sanc - ti - fy　thy day,
9*　Though vile and worth - less, still‿ Thy　peo - ple, Lord, are we;

ORGAN *f*

1 O　hear　our low - ly　cry, And hide　not　thou　thy　face.
2 And drive from out our　coasts The sins　that　put　to　shame.
4 May they　thy ser - vants　be, And rule　in　right - eous - ness.
5 Bind her　once more in　one, And life　and　truth　in - spire.
7 Bring un - to thee our　vows, And loy - al　hom - age　pay.
9*And　for　our God we　will‿ None o - ther　have　but　thee.

ff　　O Lord, stretch forth thy migh-ty hand, And guard and bless our fa-ther-land.

ff

Processional—Rogationtide

VERSES 3, 6 8 IN HARMONY

3 Thy best gifts from on high In rich a - bund - ance pour,
6★ The past - ors of thy fold With grace and power en - due,
8 Give peace, Lord, in our time; O let no foe draw nigh,

3 That we may mag - ni - fy And praise thee more and more.
6★ That faith - ful, pure, and bold, They may be pas - tors true.
8 Nor law - less deed of crime In - sult thy ma - jes - ty.

O Lord, stretch forth thy migh - ty hand,

And guard and bless our fa - ther - land.

BISHOP W. WALSHAM HOW

Processional—Rogationtide

℣. The eyes of all wait upon thee,   O   Lord.

℟. And thou givest them their meat in due sea   son.

Hymn **607** Northampton — 7 7 7 7   C. J. King, 1859–1934

Kindly spring again is here,
Trees and fields in bloom appear;
Hark! the birds with artless lays
Warble their Creator's praise.

2
Where in winter all was snow,
Now the flowers in clusters grow;
And the corn, in green array,
Promises a harvest-day.

3
On thy garden deign to smile,
Raise the plants, enrich the soil;
Soon thy presence will restore
Life to what seemed dead before.

J. Newton†

ASCENSIONTIDE

Hymn **608**   Salve, festa dies — 16 14 with refrain   Mode iv

Salve, festa dies

This refrain is first sung by solo voices then repeated by chorus

1 Wel - come, morn - ing of joy, glad feast that all

a - ges shall hal - low, Day where - in,

van - quish - ing hell, God to high hea - ven as - cends.

829

SOLO VOICES

2 Calm is   the breath   of   the spring   that   wa - kens the
4 Tramp-ling the pow - ers of   hell   he   mounts on his
6* Out of   the pri - son of   death   thou art res - cu - ing
8 Two are   the crowns   that for thee   the   Fa - ther hath
10 E - qual, co - e - val art thou,   and in fel - low - ship

2 glo - ry   of   blos - som,   Bright - er the
4 jour - ney to   hea - ven: Hea - ven's light
6* souls with - out num - ber;   Free - ly   they
8 laid up   in   hea - ven: One   shalt thou
10 one with the   Fa - ther;   Thine was   the

Repeat the refrain

2 sun - light that streams forth from the gates of the sky.
4 hails him   as God;   field, sky and sea tell his praise.
6* press to   the goal   whi - ther their Ma - ker leads on.
8 wear for   thine own,   one for a   peo - ple re - deemed.
10 word of   com - mand   when all cre - a - tion be - gan.

830

SOLO VOICES

3 Christ hath trod un - der his feet the king - dom of
5 Strike off the fet - ters that bind the spi - rits that
7* Now may'st thou nurse in thine arms a peo - ple that
9 Je - su, thou Sa - viour of all, Cre - a - tor of
11 Thou too, be - hold - ing in love the depth of hu -

3 tor - ment and sad - ness; Decked is the
5 hell hath im - pris - oned, Call back and
7* knows no de - file - ment, Bear them a -
9 men and Re - deem - er, On - ly - be -
11 man - i - ty's ru - in, Man to de -

Repeat the refrain

3 wood-land with leaves, earth strews her flowers at his feet.
5 lift to the light souls rush - ing down to the pit.
7* loft to be given for a pure host - age to God.
9 got - ten of God, sprung from the De - i - ty's fount;
11 liv - er from death, Man didst vouch-safe to be - come.

BISHOP VENANTIUS FORTUNATUS
Tr. C. S. Phillips

831

Processional—Ascensiontide

At the entrance into the Chancel:

℣. God is gone up with a mer - ry noise.

℟. And the Lord with the sound of a trumpet. Al-le-lu-ia.

Hymn 609 Erschienen ist — L.M. with Alleluia

N. Hermann,
c. 1485–1561

Harmony from J. S. Bach, 1685–1750

Al - le - lu - ia!

832

Our Lord is risen from the dead;
  Our Jesus is gone up on high;
The powers of hell are captive led,
  Dragged to the portals of the sky.
                    Alleluia!

2

There his triumphant chariot waits,
  And angels chant the solemn lay:
Lift up your heads, ye heavenly gates;
  Ye everlasting doors, give way.
                    Alleluia!

3

Loose all your bars of massy light,
  And wide unfold the ethereal scene:
He claims these mansions as his right;
  Receive the King of Glory in.
                    Alleluia!

4

Who is this King of Glory? Who?
  The Lord that all our foes o'ercame,
The world, sin, death and hell o'erthrew:
  And Jesus is the Conqueror's name.
                    Alleluia!

C. WESLEY

HYMN **610** Chislehurst — 7 7 7 7 with Alleluias Sir S. H. Nicholson,
1875–1947

Hail the day that sees him rise,   Alleluia!
To his throne above the skies;   Alleluia!
Christ, the Lamb for sinners given, [Alleluia!]
Enters now the highest heaven.   Alleluia!

2

There for him high triumph waits;	Alleluia!
Lift your heads, eternal gates!	Alleluia!
He hath conquered death and sin;	[Alleluia!]
Take the King of Glory in!	Alleluia!

3*

Circled round with angel-powers,	Alleluia!
Their triumphant Lord and ours:	Alleluia!
Wide unfold the radiant scene,	[Alleluia!]
Take the King of Glory in!	Alleluia!

4

Lo, the heaven its Lord receives,	Alleluia!
Yet he loves the earth he leaves;	Alleluia!
Though returning to his throne,	[Alleluia!]
Still he calls mankind his own.	Alleluia!

5

See! he lifts his hands above;	Alleluia!
See! he shows the prints of love;	Alleluia!
Hark! his gracious lips bestow	[Alleluia!]
Blessings on his Church below.	Alleluia!

6

Still for us he intercedes,	Alleluia!
His prevailing Death he pleads;	Alleluia!
Near himself prepares our place,	[Alleluia!]
He the first-fruits of our race.	Alleluia!

7

Lord, though parted from our sight,	Alleluia!
Far above the starry height,	Alleluia!
Grant our hearts may thither rise,	[Alleluia!]
Seeking thee above the skies.	Alleluia!

8*

Ever upward let us move,	Alleluia!
Wafted on the wings of love;	Alleluia!
Looking when our Lord shall come,	[Alleluia!]
Longing, sighing after home.	Alleluia!

9*

There we shall with thee remain,	Alleluia!
Partners of thine endless reign;	Alleluia!
There thy face unclouded see,	[Alleluia!]
Find our heaven of heavens in thee.	Alleluia!

C. WESLEY, T. COTTERILL, and others

Alternative Tunes, Ascension, Llanfair, 147

At the entrance into the Chancel:

℣. God is gone up with a mer   ry noise

℟. And the Lord with the sound of a trumpet. Al - le - lu - ia.

HYMN **611**   Allgütiger, mein Preisgesang — 8 8 6. 8 8 6   G. P. Weimar,
1734-1800

Processional—Ascensiontide

Tu, Christe, nostrum gaudium

O Christ our joy, gone up on high
To fill thy throne above the sky,
   How glorious dost thou shine!
Thy sovereign rule the worlds obey,
And earthly joys all fade away
   In that pure light of thine.

2

Ascended up from mortal sight,
Jesu, we praise thee in the height,
   Our joy, our great reward;
Whom with the Father we confess,
And with the Holy Spirit bless,
   One ever-glorious Lord.

Tr. D. T. MORGAN

WHITSUNDAY

HYMN **612**   Salve, festa dies — 16 14 with refrain   Mode iv

Salve, festa dies

This refrain is first sung by solo voices, then repeated by chorus

1 Wel - come, morn - ing of joy, glad feast that all a - ges shall hal - low, Day when to earth out of hea - ven flashed a new glo - ry of grace.

Processional—Whitsunday

2 Fling-ing his tor-rents of fire, the sun rides
4 Blue is the sky by day, with cry-stal-line
6 Flow-ers be-spang-le the field with ri-ot and

2 high in the hea - ven; Forth from the
4 ra - di - ance glow - ing; Night is a
6 glit - ter of col - our; White are the

Repeat the refrain

2 o - cean he comes, sinks to the o - cean at eve.
4 glo - ry of stars, sing - ing to - ge - ther for joy.
6 hedge - rows with may, green grows the grass in the meads.

839

HYMN **612** (*continued*)

SOLO VOICES

3 Dart-ing his rays as he goes through the li-quid
5 Now doth the coun-try re-joice in all the gay
7 One by one o-pen their buds the blos-soms of

3 air of the sum - mer, Now doth he
5 store of its boun - ty; Sum - mer re -
7 tu - lip and li - ly; Shy - ly

Repeat the refrain

3 short-en the nights, draw out the length of the days.
5 turns to the earth bear-ing her wealth in her hand.
7 smile from the grass dai-sies with my-ri-ad eyes.

BISHOP VENANTIUS FORTUNATUS
Tr. C. S. Phillips

840

At the entrance into the Chancel:

℣. The Spirit of the Lord filleth the world.

℟. And that which containeth all things hath knowledge of the voice. Al - le - lu - ia.

HYMN 613 Whitsun — 8 8 6 B. Luard Selby, 1853–1919

To thee, O Comforter divine,
For all thy grace and power benign,
　　Sing we Alleluia!

2

To thee, whose faithful love had place
In God's great covenant of grace,
　　Sing we Alleluia!

3

To thee, whose faithful power doth heal,
Enlighten, sanctify, and seal,
　　Sing we Alleluia!

4

To thee, our teacher and our friend,
Our faithful leader to the end,
　　Sing we Alleluia!

5

To thee, by Jesus Christ sent down,
Of all his gifts the sum and crown,
　　Sing we Alleluia!

FRANCES R. HAVERGAL

Processional—Whitsunday

HYMN **614**   Kybald Twychen — 7 7 7 7. 5 7 7 7   W. H. Harris

Holy Spirit, gently come,
  Raise us from our fallen state,
Fix thy everlasting home
  In the hearts thou didst create,
    Gift of God most high!
Visit every troubled breast,
Light and life and love supply,
  Give our spirits perfect rest.

2

Heavenly unction from above,
  Comforter of hearts that faint,
Fountain, life, and fire of love,
  Hear and answer our complaint:

Thee we humbly pray,
  Finger of the living God,
Now thy sevenfold gift display,
  Shed our Saviour's love abroad.

3

Now thy quickening influence bring,
  On our spirits sweetly move,
Open every mouth to sing
  Jesus' everlasting love:
    Lighten every heart;
Drive our enemies away,
Joy and peace to us impart,
  Lead us in the heavenly way.

842

4

Take the things of Christ and show
What our Lord for us hath done;
May we God the Father know
Only in and through the Son:
Nothing will we fear,
Though to wilds and deserts driven,
While we feel thy presence near,
Witnessing our sins forgiven.

5

Glory be to God alone,
God whose hand created all!
Glory be to God the Son,
Who redeemed us from our fall!
To the Holy Ghost
Equal praise and glory be,
When the course of time is lost,
Lost in wide eternity!

W. HAMMOND†
Based on *Veni, creator Spiritus*

At the entrance into the Chancel:

℣. The Spirit of the Lord filleth   the world.

℟. And that which containeth all things hath knowledge of the
voice. Al - le - lu - ia.

HYMN **615**   Venice — S.M.   W. Amps, 1824–1910

A higher setting of this tune will be found at Hymn 510

Lord God the Holy Ghost,
In this accepted hour,
As on the day of Pentecost,
Descend in all thy power.

2

The young, the old, inspire
With wisdom from above;
And give us hearts and tongues of fire,
To pray and praise and love.

3

Spirit of truth, be thou‿
In life and death our guide;
O Spirit of adoption, now‿
May we be sanctified.

J. MONTGOMERY

Processional

TRINITY SUNDAY

HYMN **616**   Dolberrow — 8 7 8 7. 8 8 7   W. K. Stanton

Sound aloud Jehovah's praises,
Tell abroad the aweful Name!
Heaven the ceaseless anthem raises;
Let the earth her God proclaim,
God, the hope of every nation,
God, the source of consolation,
Holy, blessèd Trinity.

844

Processional—Trinity Sunday

2

This the Name from ancient ages
　Hidden in its dazzling light;
This the Name that kings and sages
　Prayed and strove to know aright,
Through God's wondrous Incarnation
Now revealed the world's salvation,
　　Ever blessèd Trinity.

3

Into this great Name and holy
　We all tribes and tongues baptize;
Thus the Highest owns the lowly,
　Homeward, heavenward, bids them rise,
Gathers them from every nation,
Bids them join in adoration
　　Of the blessèd Trinity.

4

In this Name the heart rejoices,
　Pouring forth its secret prayer;
In this Name we lift our voices,
　And our common faith declare,
Offering praise and supplication
And the thankful life's oblation
　　To the blessèd Trinity.

5

Still thy Name o'er earth and ocean
　Shall be carried, 'God is Love,'
Whispered by the heart's devotion,
　Echoed by the choirs above,
Hallowed through all worlds for ever,
Lord, of life the only giver,
　　Blessèd, glorious Trinity.

H. A. MARTIN

At the entrance into the Chancel:

℣. Let us bless the Father and the Son and the Ho　-　ly Ghost.

℟. Let us praise and exalt him for ev　-　er.

Hymn **617**   Sharon — L.M.   Sir F. A. G. Ouseley, 1825–89

Ave, colenda Trinitas

All hail, adorèd Trinity!
All hail, eternal Unity!
O God the Father, God the Son,
And God the Spirit, ever One.

2

To thee upon this festal day
We offer here our thankful lay:
O let our work accepted be,
That blessèd work of praising thee.

3

Three Persons praise we evermore,
One only God our hearts adore:
In thy sure mercy ever kind
May we our strong protection find.

4

O Trinity! O Unity!
Be present as we worship thee;
And with the songs that angels sing
Unite the hymns of praise we bring.

Tr. J. D. Chambers and Compilers

DEDICATION FESTIVAL

Hymn 618 Salve, festa dies — 16 14 with refrain   Mode iv

Salve, festa dies

The refrain is first sung by solo voices, then repeated by chorus

1 Wel - come, morn - ing of joy, glad feast that all

a - ges shall hal - low, Day when the Bride

of the Lamb joy - ful - ly wed - deth her Spouse.

Processional—Dedication Festival

SOLO VOICES

3 True Son of Da-vid is he who hath knit us up
5 New-made from hea-ven des-cends Je - ru - sa-lem's
7 Here Da-vid's Tower stand-eth sure: on hast - ing feet
9 Lad-der of Ja-cob is here, the lad - der that

3 in - to his Bo - dy; Here in your
5 mys - ti - cal ci - ty, Decked with a
7 run to its strong - hold; Stored up with-
9 bring-eth to hea - ven Those who with

Repeat the refrain

3 mo - ther - home, hail him as God and as Man.
5 glo - ry that flows straight from the foun - tain of light.
7 in ye shall find pled - ges of hea - ven - ly bliss.
9 faith for their guide fol - low the path of the just.

c. 13th *cent.* (YORK PROCESSIONAL)
Tr. C. S. Phillips

849

℣. Blessed are they that dwell in   thy   house.

℟. They will be always prais - ing   thee.

HYMN **619**   Manchester New — C.M.   R. Wainwright, 1748–82

A higher setting of this tune will be found at Hymn 472

The heaven of heavens cannot contain
   The universal Lord;
Yet he in humble hearts will deign⌣
   To dwell and be adored.

2

Where'er ascends the sacrifice
   Of fervent praise and prayer,
Or in the earth or in the skies,
   The heaven of God is there.

3

His presence there is spread abroad
   Through realms, through worlds unknown;
Who seeks the mercies of his God
   Is ever near his throne.

W. DRENNAN

HYMN **620** Westminster Abbey — 8 7. 8 7. 8 7 Adapted from an anthem
by H. Purcell, 1658–95

Urbs beata

PART I

Blessèd city, heavenly Salem,
  Vision dear of peace and love,
Who of living stones art builded
  In the height of heaven above,
And, with angel hosts encircled,
  As a bride dost earthward move!

2
From celestial realms descending,
  Bridal glory round thee shed,
Meet for him whose love espoused thee,
  To thy Lord shalt thou be led;
All thy streets and all thy bulwarks
  Of pure gold are fashionèd.

3
Bright thy gates of pearl are shining,
  They are open evermore;
And by virtue of his merits
  Thither faithful souls do soar,
Who for Christ's dear name in this world
  Pain and tribulation bore.

4
Many a blow and biting sculpture
  Polished well those stones elect,
In their places now compacted
  By the heavenly Architect,
Who therewith hath willed for ever
  This his palace should be decked.

The following Doxology may be sung at the end of this Part:

Laud and honour to the Father,
Laud and honour to the Son,
Laud and honour to the Spirit,
Ever Three, and ever One,
Consubstantial, co-eternal,
While unending ages run.

Tr. J. M. NEALE and Compilers

851

PART 2

5

Christ is made the sure Foundation,
  Christ the Head and Corner-stone,
Chosen of the Lord, and precious,
  Binding all the Church in one,
Holy Sion's help for ever,
  And her confidence alone.

6

All that dedicated city,
  Dearly loved of God on high,
In exultant jubilation
  Pours perpetual melody,
God the One in Three adoring
  In glad hymns eternally.

PART 3

7

To this temple, where we call thee,
  Come, O Lord of Hosts, to-day;
With thy wonted loving-kindness
  Hear thy servants as they pray,
And thy fullest benediction
  Shed within its walls alway.

8

Here vouchsafe to all thy servants
  What they ask of thee to gain,
What they gain from thee for ever
  With the blessèd to retain,
And hereafter in thy glory
  Evermore with thee to reign.

*The following Doxology may be sung at the end of any
Part, or of the whole hymn:*

Laud and honour to the Father,
Laud and honour to the Son,
Laud and honour to the Spirit,
  Ever Three, and ever One,
Consubstantial, co-eternal,
  While unending ages run.

Tr. J. M. Neale and Compilers

Processional—Dedication Festival

At the entrance into the Chancel:

℣. Blessed are they that dwell in   thy   house.

℟. They will be always prais - ing   thee.

HYMN 621   Old 100th — L.M.   L. Bourgeois, *c.* 1500–61

A higher setting of this tune will be found at Hymn 166

Eternal Power, whose high abode
Becomes the grandeur of a God,
Infinite lengths beyond the bounds
Where stars revolve their little rounds;

2

Thee while the first Archangel sings,
He hides his face behind his wings,
And ranks of shining Thrones around
Fall worshipping and spread the ground.

3

Lord, what shall earth and ashes do?
We would adore our Maker too:
From sin and dust to thee we cry,
The great, the holy, and the high!

I. WATTS and J. WESLEY

853

THANKSGIVING FOR THE INSTITUTION OF HOLY COMMUNION

HYMN **622**   Cumulus — Irregular   Sir S. H. Nicholson, 1875-1947

HARMONIZED VERSION

Processional—Thanksgiving for Holy Communion

PART I

Lauda, Sion, Salvatorem

1

Praise, O Sion, praise thy Master,
Praise thy Saviour, praise thy Pastor,
  In a joyous melody :
Put forth all thy strength to sing him,
For the best that thou canst bring him
  Cannot ever worthy be.

2

Tell, O tell in praises glowing
How the living, life-bestowing⏝
  Bread from heaven is given to thee :
Bread which Christ, before he suffered,
At the sacred banquet proffered
  To the Twelve in company.

3*

Lift thy voice in tuneful chorus,
Joyfully in strain sonorous
  Be thy heart's delight outpoured ;
While this solemn day we celebrate
How the Saviour first did consecrate
  For his guests the mystic board.

4*

Here, our new King's table gracing,
This new Passover's new blessing
  Hath fulfilled the older rite :
Here is new to old succeeding,
Truth its shadow superseding,
  Darkness swallowed up in light.

5

What he did at supper seated
Christ ordained to be repeated
  In his memory divine ;
Wherefore we, his precept heeding,
And his saving Offering pleading,
  Consecrate the bread and wine.

6

'Tis the truth to Christians given,
Bread becomes his Flesh from heaven,
  Wine becomes his holy Blood :
Here, where sight is unavailing,
Faith may seize with grasp unfailing
  What can ne'er be understood.

7

'Neath these diverse signs are hidden
Priceless things to sense forbidden,
  Outward signs are all we see :
Bread for eating, wine for drinking,
Yet, in ways beyond all thinking,
  Christ in each doth deign to be.

8*

Whoso of this feast partaketh,
Christ divideth not nor breaketh—
  He is whole to all that taste :
Whether one this bread receiveth
Or a thousand, still he giveth
  One same food that cannot waste.

9*

Good and bad alike are sharing⏝
One repast, a doom preparing
  All unlike—'tis life or death :
Each a destiny is making—
See ye of the one partaking
  How the issue differeth !

10* When this Sa-cra-ment is bro-ken, Doubt not in each sev-ered to-ken,

Hal-lowed by the bless-ing spo-ken, What is veiled doth whole a-bide:

Though the sign is bro-ken du-ly, Christ him-self re-main-eth tru-ly

All un-bro-ken; pre-sent ful-ly Here a-bides the Sig-ni-fied.

Processional—Thanksgiving for Holy Communion

PART 2

Ecce, Panis angelorum

11 Lo, the an-gels' food is gi-ven   To the pil-grim who hath stri-ven;

See the chil-dren's Bread from hea-ven, Which on dogs may ne'er be spent:

Christ the old types is ful-fill-ing, I-saac bound, a Vic-tim will-ing,

Pas-chal Lamb its life-blood spill-ing, Man-na to the fa-thers sent.

At the entrance into the Chancel:

℣. I am the true Bread   of Life.

℟. He that cometh to me shall never hun - ger.

PART 3

Bone Pastor, Panis vere

12 O true Bread, Good Shep-herd, tend us, Je - su, of thy

love be-friend us, Thou re - fresh us, thou de - fend us,

Let thy good-ness here at - tend us Till the land of

life we see; Thou who all things canst and know - est,

Processional—Thanksgiving for Holy Communion

12 Who such food on earth be-stow-est, Make us, where thy

face thou show-est, 'Mid thy saints, though least and low-est,

Guests and fel-low heirs with thee. A - men.

St. Thomas Aquinas
Tr. C. S. Phillips and others

NOTE. *This hymn in its several parts (but omitting the starred verses) is suitable for general use at Holy Communion*

859

SAINTS' DAYS

Hymn **623**   Claudius — D.C.M.   Adapted from a song by G. W. Fink,
1783–1846

By permission of the Royal School of Church Music

Jerusalem, my happy home,
  When shall I come to thee?
When shall my sorrows have an end?
  Thy joys when shall I see?
O happy harbour of the saints!
  O sweet and pleasant soil!
In thee no sorrow may be found,
  No grief, no care, no toil.

2
There lust and lucre cannot dwell;
  There envy bears no sway;
There is no hunger, heat, nor cold,
  But pleasure every way:
Thy walls are made of precious stones,
  Thy bulwarks diamonds square;
Thy gates are of right orient pearl,
  Exceeding rich and rare.

3
Ah, my sweet home, Jerusalem,
  Would God I were in thee!
Would God my woes were at an end,
  Thy joys that I might see!

Thy saints are crowned with glory great,
  They see God face to face;
They triumph still, they still rejoice:
  Most happy is their case.

4
Thy vineyards and thy orchards are
  Most beautiful and fair,
Full furnishèd with trees and fruits
  Most wonderful and rare;
Thy gardens and thy gallant walks
  Continually are green;
There grow such sweet and pleasant
  As nowhere else are seen.   [flowers

5
Quite through the streets with silver
  The flood of life doth flow,   [sound
Upon whose banks on every side
  The wood of life doth grow:
There trees for evermore bear fruit,
  And evermore do spring;
There evermore the angels sit,
  And evermore do sing.

6*

There David stands with harp in hand
  As master of the choir;
Ten thousand times that man were blest
  That might this music hear:
Our Lady sings Magnificat
  With tune surpassing sweet,
And all the virgins bear their parts,
  Sitting about her feet.

7*

Te Deum doth Saint Ambrose sing,
  Saint Austin doth the like;
Old Simeon and Zachary
  Have not their songs to seek:

There Magdalene hath left her moan,
  And cheerfully doth sing
With blessèd saints, whose harmony
  In every street doth ring.

8

Jerusalem, my happy home,
  Would God I were in thee!
Would God my woes were at an end,
  Thy joys that I might see!
Jerusalem, Jerusalem,
  God grant I once may see
Thy endless joys, and of the same
  Partaker ay to be!

  'F. B. P.' (c. 1600)

At the entrance into the Chancel:

℣. Be glad, O ye righteous, and rejoice in   the   Lord.
℟. And be joyful, all ye that are true   of   heart.

HYMN **624** Eatington — C.M.   W. Croft, 1678-1727

The Church triumphant in thy love,
  Their mighty joys we know;
They sing the Lamb in hymns above,
  And we in hymns below.

2

Thee in thy glorious realm they praise,
  And bow before thy throne;
We in the kingdom of thy grace:
  The kingdoms are but one.

3

The holy to the Holiest leads:
  From hence our spirits rise,
And he that in thy statutes treads
  Shall meet thee in the skies.

  C. WESLEY

HYMN **625**   Erfreut euch — 7 6 7 6. D   German Melody (1536)

In domo Patris

Our Father's home eternal,
　O Christ, thou dost prepare
With many divers mansions,
　And each one passing fair :
They are the victors' guerdon
　Who, through the hard-won fight,
Have followed in thy footsteps
　And reign with thee in light.

2
Amid the happy number
　The virgins' crown and queen,
The ever-Virgin Mother,
　Is first and foremost seen :
Her one and only gladness,
　That undefilèd one,
To gaze in adoration,
　The Mother, on the Son.

3*

There Adam leads the chorus,
  And tunes the joyous strain
Of all his myriad children
  That follow in thy train:
Victorious over sorrow,
  The countless band to see,
Destroyed through his transgression,
  But raised to life through thee.

4

The patriarchs in their triumph
  Thy praises nobly sing,
Of old their promised offspring.
  And now their Victor-King:
The prophets harp their gladness
  That, whom their strains foretold,
In manifested glory
  They evermore behold.

5

And David calls to memory
  His own especial grace
In such clear prophet-vision
  To see thee face to face:
The apostolic cohort,
  Thy valiant and thine own,
As royal co-assessors
  Are nearest to thy throne.

6

Thy martyrs reign in glory
  Who triumphed as they fell,
And by a thousand tortures
  Defeated death and hell;
And every patient sufferer,
  Who sorrow dared contemn,
For each especial anguish
  Hath one especial gem.

7*

The valiant-souled confessors
  Put on their meet array,
Who bare the heat and burden
  Of many a weary day:
The scorners of life's pleasures,
  Their self-denial ceased,
Sit down with thee and banquet
  At thy eternal feast.

8*

The virgins walk in beauty
  Amidst their lily-bowers,
The coronals assuming
  Of never-fading flowers;
And innocents sport gaily
  Through all the courts of light,
To whom thou gav'st the guerdon
  Before they fought the fight.

9

The soldiers of thine army,
  Their earthly struggles o'er,
With joy put off the armour
  That they shall need no more:
For these, and all that battled
  Beneath their Monarch's eyes,
The harder was the conflict
  The brighter is the prize.

10

The penitent, attaining
  Full pardon in thy sight,
Leave off the vest of sackcloth
  And don the robe of white:
The bondsman and the noble,
  The peasant and the king,
All gird one glorious Monarch
  In one eternal ring.

Ascribed to THOMAS À KEMPIS
Tr. J. M. Neale†

At the entrance into the Chancel:

℣. Be glad, O ye righteous, and rejoice in   the   Lord.

℟. And be joyful, all ye that are true   of   heart.

HYMN **626** St. Magnus — C.M. J. Clarke, *c.* 1659–1707

A higher setting of this tune will be found at Hymn 218

2

Hail, glorious spirits, heirs of light,
  The high-born sons of fire,
Whose souls burn clear, whose flames
  All joy, yet all desire.   [shine bright:

Hail, all you happy souls above,
  Who make that glorious ring
About the sparkling throne of love,
  And there forever sing.

J. AUSTIN†

HYMN **627** Tenbury — 7 7 7 7. 8 5 8 5 Sir S. H. Nicholson, 1875–1947

In slow march time

Processional—Saints' Days

1
Let love arise and praise him
  Who came as Light from heaven,
And shines as light reflected
  In souls of men forgiven: [dows,
    Through the dimness of our sha-
    Through the mist he came;
    For the souls of them that see him
    Blessèd be his name.

2
He cometh as the morning,
  The light of day arisen,
To them that sit in darkness,
  The souls of men in prison:
    Blessèd Light that deigns to visit
    Man in his distress!
    Welcome with thy wings of healing,
    Sun of Righteousness!

3
Behold the sky at evening,
  When day on earth is ending,
What clouds are seen at sunset
  Upon the sun attending:
    Where our sun is sinking from us
    Into skies unknown,
    All the clouds aflame with glory
    Where he passes on.

4
So, where our Christ advances,
  The Lord of Life undying,
He goes with flashing trumpets
  And pomp of banners flying;
    Not in unattended glory,
    Nor in lonely might:
    Multitudes that none can number
    Answer back his light.

5
A burning mist around him,
  A flock of souls unending,
A cloud of flying spirits,
  Ascending and descending,
    Swimming on in light below him,
    Soaring on above,
    Who are these that move in rapture
    Round about his love?

6
O these are souls that pitied,
  Because they knew his pity,
And found him in their neighbour
  And met him in their city;
    These are they whose life among us
    Won the weak from vice;
    These are they who, little knowing,
    Shared his sacrifice.

7
Through them he healed our wounded,
  Through them he led our blindness,
Redeemed our unbelieving,
  Atoned for our unkindness,
    Therefore in the light they follow
    Where the Lamb doth go; [ment
    Therefore shines their dazzling rai-
    White as glistening snow.

8
So Christ his temple enters,
  The Priest that was so wounded,
And makes a new atonement
  As Love by love surrounded:
    Love amazing that transfigures
    Where its light has shone,
    Love that burns upon the altar,
    Love that mounts the throne.

J. M. C. CRUM

At the entrance into the Chancel:

  ℣. Be glad, O ye righteous, and rejoice in   the   Lord.
  ℟. And be joyful, all ye that are true   of   heart.

Processional—Saints' Days

HYMN **628**   Dundee — C.M.   *Psalms* (Edinburgh, 1615)

Come, let us join our friends above
That have obtained the prize,
And on the eagle wings of love
To joy celestial rise.

2
E'en now by faith we join our hands
With those that went before,
And greet our Captain's ransomed bands
On the eternal shore.

C. WESLEY†

GENERAL

HYMN **629**   St. Gertrude — 6 5 6 5. 6 5 6 5. 6 5 6 5   Sir A. Sullivan, 1842–1900

Processional—General

On - ward Chris - tian sol - diers, March-ing as to war,
war, With the

With the Cross of Je - sus Go - ing on be - fore.
Cross of Je - sus

With the Cross of Je - sus

Onward Christian soldiers!
  Marching as to war,
With the Cross of Jesus
  Going on before.
Christ the royal Master
  Leads against the foe;
Forward into battle,
  See, his banners go!
    Onward, Christian soldiers!
    Marching as to war,
    With the Cross of Jesus
    Going on before.

2
At the sign of triumph
  Satan's host doth flee;
On then, Christian soldiers,
  On to victory!
Hell's foundations quiver
  At the shout of praise;
Brothers, lift your voices,
  Loud your anthems raise. Onward,
                              [etc.

3
Like a mighty army
  Moves the Church of God;

Brothers, we are treading
  Where the saints have trod:
We are not divided,
  All one body we,
One in hope and doctrine,
  One in charity. Onward, etc.

4
Crowns and thrones may perish,
  Kingdoms rise and wane,
But the Church of Jesus
  Constant will remain:
Gates of hell can never
  'Gainst that Church prevail;
We have Christ's own promise,
  And that cannot fail. Onward, etc.

5
Onward, then, ye people,
  Join our happy throng,
Blend with ours your voices
  In the triumph song:
Glory, laud, and honour
  Unto Christ the King,
This through countless ages
  Men and angels sing. Onward, etc.

S. BARING-GOULD

867

Processional—General

At the entrance into the Chancel:

℣. Be strong and of a good cour - age.
℟. And the Lord, he it is that doth go be - fore thee.

HYMN 630 Illsley (*or* Bishop) — L.M.   J. Bishop, 1665-1737

From all that dwell below the skies
Let the Creator's praise arise :
Let the Redeemer's name be sung
Through every land by every tongue.

2

Eternal are thy mercies, Lord ;
Eternal truth attends thy word :
Thy praise shall sound from shore to shore,
Till suns shall rise and set no more.

I. WATTS

HYMN 631 Leoni — 6 6 8 4. D   Traditional Hebrew Melody

The God of Abraham praise
Who reigns enthroned above,
Ancient of everlasting Days,
    And God of love:
Jehovah, great I AM,
    By earth and heaven confest;
We bow and bless the sacred name
    For ever blest.

2*
The God of Abraham praise,
    At whose supreme command
From earth we rise, and seek the joys
    At his right hand:
We all on earth forsake,
    Its wisdom, fame, and power;
And him our only portion make,
    Our Shield and Tower.

3
Though nature's strength decay,
    And earth and hell withstand,
To Canaan's bounds we urge our way
    At his command:
The watery deep we pass,
    With Jesus in our view;
And through the howling wilderness
    Our way pursue.

4
The goodly land we see,
    With peace and plenty blest:
A land of sacred liberty
    And endless rest;
There milk and honey flow,
    And oil and wine abound,
And trees of life for ever grow,
    With mercy crowned.

5
There dwells the Lord our King,
    The Lord our Righteousness,
Triumphant o'er the world of sin,
    The Prince of Peace:
On Sion's sacred height
    His Kingdom he maintains,
And glorious with his saints in light
    For ever reigns.

6*
He keeps his own secure,
    He guards them by his side,
Arrays in garment white and pure
    His spotless Bride:
With streams of sacred bliss,
    Beneath serener skies,
With all the fruits of Paradise,
    He still supplies.

For the remaining verses see overleaf

7*
Before the great Three-One
They all exulting stand,
And tell the wonders he hath done
 Through all their land :
The listening spheres attend,
 And swell the growing fame,
And sing in songs which never end
 The wondrous name.

8*
The God who reigns on high
The great archangels sing,
And 'Holy, Holy, Holy,' cry,
 'Almighty King!
Who was, and is the same,
 And evermore shall be :
Jehovah, Father, great I AM,
 We worship thee.'

9
Before the Saviour's face
The ransomed nations bow,
O'erwhelmed at his almighty grace
 For ever new ;
He shows his prints of love—
 They kindle to a flame,
And sound through all the worlds above
 The slaughtered Lamb.

10
The whole triumphant host
Give thanks to God on high ;
'Hail! Father, Son, and Holy Ghost,'
 They ever cry :
Hail! Abraham's God, and mine!
 (I join the heavenly lays)
All might and majesty are thine,
 And endless praise.

T. OLIVERS
Based on the Hebrew Yigdal

At the entrance into the Chancel:

℣. They will go from strength   to strength.

℟. And unto the God of gods appeareth every one of them in Zi - on.

HYMN 632 Austria — 8 7 8 7. D   F. J. Haydn, 1732–1809

Worship, honour, glory, blessing,
 Lord, we offer to thy name;
Young and old, thy praise expressing,
 Join their Saviour to proclaim.
As the saints in heaven adore thee,
 We would bow before thy throne;
As thine angels serve before thee,
 So on earth thy will be done.

E. OSLER

HYMN **633**   Crucifer — 10 10 with refrain   Sir S. H. Nicholson,
1875–1947

UNISON

Lift   high   the   Cross,   the   love   of Christ   pro - claim

Till   all   the   world   a - dore   his   sa - cred   name.

Fine.

HARMONY

D.C.

Org.

Processional—General

Lift high the Cross, the love of Christ proclaim
Till all the world adore his sacred name.

2
Come, brethren, follow where our Captain trod,
Our King victorious, Christ the Son of God.
Lift high the Cross, etc.

3
Led on their way by this triumphant sign,
The hosts of God in conquering ranks combine.
Lift high the Cross, etc.

4
Each new-born soldier of the Crucified
Bears on his brow the seal of him who died.
Lift high the Cross, etc.

5
This is the sign which Satan's legions fear
And angels veil their faces to revere.
Lift high the Cross, etc.

6
Saved by this Cross whereon their Lord was slain,
The sons of Adam their lost home regain.
Lift high the Cross, etc.

7
From north and south, from east and west they raise
In growing unison their song of praise.
Lift high the Cross, etc.

8
O Lord, once lifted on the glorious Tree,
As thou hast promised, draw men unto thee.
Lift high the Cross, etc.

9
Let every race and every language tell
Of him who saves our souls from death and hell.
Lift high the Cross, etc.

10
From farthest regions let them homage bring,
And on his Cross adore their Saviour King.
Lift high the Cross, etc.

11
Set up thy throne, that earth's despair may cease
Beneath the shadow of its healing peace.
Lift high the Cross, etc.

12
For thy blest Cross which doth for all atone
Creation's praises rise before thy throne.
Lift high the Cross, etc.

G. W. KITCHIN and M. R. NEWBOLT

At the entrance into the Chancel:

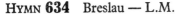

℣. God forbid that I should glo - ry.
℟. Save in the Cross of our Lord Je - sus Christ.

HYMN **634** Breslau — L.M.   *Geistliche Gesänge* (Leipzig, 1625)

'Twas by thy Blood, immortal Lamb,
Thine armies trod the tempter down;
'Twas by thy word and powerful name
They gained the battle and renown.

2

Rejoice, ye heavens! let every star
Shine with new glories round the sky;
Saints, while ye sing the heavenly war,
Raise your Deliverer's name on high.

I. WATTS

HYMN **635** Ich halte treulich still — D.S.M.   Attributed to J. S. Bach,
1685-1750

Processional—General

Rejoice, ye pure in heart!
Rejoice, give thanks, and sing;
Your festal banner wave on high,
The Cross of Christ your King:
Still lift your standard high,
Still march in firm array,
As warriors through the darkness toil
Till dawns the golden day.

2
Yes onward, onward still,
With hymn and chant and song, [aisle
Through gate and porch and columned
The hallowed pathways throng:
With all the angel choirs,
With all the saints on earth,
Pour out the strains of joy and bliss,
True rapture, noblest mirth.

3
Your clear Hosannas raise,
And Alleluias loud;
Whilst answering echoes upward float,
Like wreaths of incense cloud:
With voice as full and strong
As ocean's surging praise,
Send forth the hymns our fathers loved,
The psalms of ancient days.

4
Yes on, through life's long path,
Still chanting as ye go,
From youth to age, by night and day,
In gladness and in woe:
At last the march shall end,
The wearied ones shall rest,
The pilgrims find their Father's house,
Jerusalem the blest.

5
Then on, ye pure in heart!
Rejoice, give thanks, and sing;
Your festal banner wave on high,
The Cross of Christ your King.
Praise him who reigns on high,
The Lord whom we adore,
The Father, Son, and Holy Ghost,
One God for evermore.

E. H. PLUMPTRE

At the entrance into the Chancel:

℣. Let thy priests be clothed with right - eous - ness.

℟. And thy saints sing with joy . ful - ness.

HYMN **636**   Waltham — 8 7 8 7   H. Albert, 1604-51

Harmony from J. S. Bach, 1685-1750

May the grace of Christ our Saviour,
And the Father's boundless love,
With the Holy Spirit's favour,
Rest upon us from above.

2

Thus may we abide in union
With each other and the Lord,
And possess, in sweet communion,
Joys which earth cannot afford.

J. NEWTON